WITNESS TO COVID 2020

WITNESS TO COVID 2020

THE DIARY OF A GLOBAL PANDEMIC

PROFESSOR
JUSTIN STEBBING

AMBERLEY

Images on Inside Back Cover

Upper: Professor Justin Stebbings and the CEO of BenevolentAI, Baroness Joanna Shields, at No. 10 to meet Boris Johnson and others in government such as Dominic Cummings, 11 March 2020.

Middle: Super-resolution microscopy of viral particles before and after baricitinib. They are infecting our hepatic organoids, little livers in dishes, and baricitinib seems to stop this happening. Incredibly, the virus and its cytokine storm leads to upregulation of the ACE2 receptor that the virus uses, in part, to get into cells. Quite simply, the virus attacks the castle and secreted factors help it lower the drawbridge.

Lower: A three-dimensional structural prediction of a protein inside cells that is blocked by the drug we found to treat Covid-19, baricitinib.

First published 2021

Amberley Publishing
The Hill, Stroud
Gloucestershire, GL5 4EP

www.amberley-books.com

British Library Cataloguing in Publication Data.
A catalogue record for this book is available from the British Library.

ISBN 978 1 3981 1267 4 (hardback)
ISBN 978 1 3981 1268 1 (ebook)

1 2 3 4 5 6 7 8 9 10

Typeset in 10.5pt on 12.5pt Sabon.
Typesetting by SJmagic DESIGN SERVICES, India.
Printed in the UK.

For my darling boys, Teddy and Daniel, and Sofiya,
who put up with me during lockdown

Contents

Foreword

How will we remember the Covid-19 pandemic, and 2020 in particular, in years and decades to come? So many of our worlds were inverted and everything we knew changed. This book is not just a diary of the pandemic in 2020, but a scientific, economic and global narrative history, tracking the intertwined stories that the pandemic spun. There are two lessons here: first, the stupidest virus is cleverer than the cleverest immunologist; second, to paraphrase the statistician W. Edwards Deming, in God we trust, all the rest need data.

The reality here is that if we understand Covid-19 and SARS-CoV-2, we can understand all of medicine, and perhaps geopolitics now. It teaches us about virology, of course, but also of molecular and cellular biology, epidemiology and statistics, trial design and drug development and the roles of regulators, healthcare systems, journals and communication between scientists, politicians and the public. It teaches us a story of collaboration, speed and humility. This book intersects these themes, in a personal diary of the pandemic, including the unique discovery of a drug to treat patients, reducing the fatality rate. The breakneck speed that occurred at was unprecedented, reflective of human spirit coming together at times of adversity, bringing down barriers between biopharmaceutical companies, individuals, academic institutions and teams endeavouring to cut through red tape to 'get things done'.

I am sure in future the Covid story will be remembered as the event that paralysed the whole world for most of 2020. What this book does is not just look at the events in Dr Stebbing's home country of Britain or the most powerful nation on the planet at this time, America, it looks at the world as a whole. Sub-Saharan Africa, all too often forgotten by Western media, at times takes centre stage, reminding us that these nations had to deal with an outbreak not just of Covid but Ebola too. There are insights into the mental health of women in Bangladesh and healthcare campaigns in Japan. I hope that this will be read in fifty years' time as it genuinely gives a global view of this terrible pandemic. It is a chronicle that will forever remind us that in times of such global catastrophe, we are all part of one intertwined, connected planet, upon which humans have drawn lines and borders called nations. It took a minuscule piece of RNA wrapped in an envelope to remind us of how capricious, arbitrary and ultimately porous these human lines are.

Siddhartha Mukherjee
Physician and author of *The Emperor of All Maladies:*
A Biography of Cancer (Pulitzer Prize winner) and
Gene: An Intimate History

Acknowledgements

There are so many to thank here, but I am going to start with Jem Duducu, who has somehow reduced the 3 million words I wrote on Covid-19 in 2020 into 100,000 words without losing the meaning, depth or his own sense of humour. I am hugely grateful to Nick Hayward and Steven Tucker at Amberley Publishing for proceeding with this work. Thank you to those who tried to read the 3 million. You have the patience of many saints.

I am indebted to the team at BenevolentAI for simply working with me, and for their speed and clarity of purpose and teamwork throughout. Under Joanna Shields' immense leadership, Ivan Griffin and Peter Richardson were thoughtful and considered every step of the way. I hadn't previously realised one could be so patient, yet so very fast. I have worked with some remarkable doctors and scientists globally here: Mario Corbellino and Giacamo Casalini in Milan, who started trialling baricitinib in sick patients; Silvia Ottaviani, who helped me collate data at Imperial; and Anabela Cardoso, Jonathan Sims and the legendary Gary Krishnan at Eli Lilly, without whom much of this work would simply not have occurred. Somehow they kept their laboratories open, testing samples, generating and confirming hypotheses while many slept. Thank you to editors at *The Lancet* and *EMBO Molecular Medicine* for immediately supporting our AI/computer-laboratory-bedside approach, and for believing in us. Others that deserve mention include Ray Schinazi and Vincent Marconi at Emory, Joel Blankson at Johns Hopkins, Marco Falcone in Pisa, Fabrizio Cantini in Prato, Pedro Abizanda in Albacete and the outstanding team at the Karolinska Institute led by Volker Lauschke, one of the most diligent, conscientious and smartest scientists I have ever worked with. Remarkably, due to Covid-19, we've never met in person. So many people helped me in my discussions throughout the pandemic. Peter Davies, Greg Boggis, Patrick Degorce, Steven Hoge,

Acknowledgements

Stéphane Bancel, Tom Friend, Freddie Boiardi, Paul Ettlinger, George Dranitsaris, Sam Waksal, Garo Armen, Siddhartha Mukherjee, Eyck Freymann and Niall Ferguson stand out as being wise beyond words in the face of uncertainty. They all have the remarkable ability to make a baffling and complex situation simple, or at least definable, and ask the right questions, at times a much more delicate art than finding the answers. Continuously, they taught me about the science, the delicate balance of mixing it with art, and, importantly, a different way of looking at data.

Finally, I am indebted to the patients who participated in studies and trials here. They are the unsung heroes, and all make Newton's poetic comments regarding 'standing on the shoulders of giants' very true.

Glossary of Acronyms

ACA	Affordable Care Act
ACE	Angiotensin-Converting Enzyme
ACTT	Adaptive Covid-19 Treatment Trial
AdCom	Advisory Committee, a meeting mostly of doctors and experts that advises the FDA whether to approve a drug or not based on the evidence
ADE	Adverse Drug Effect, also Antibody-Dependent Enhancement
AfD	Alternative for Germany
AI	Artificial Intelligence
AIDS	Acquired Immune Deficiency Syndrome
API	Application Programming Interface or Active Pharmaceutical Ingredient
APT29	Advanced Persistent Threat
ARDS	Acute Respiratory Distress Syndrome
AZN	AstraZeneca
BAME	Black, Asian and Minority Ethnic
BARDA	Biomedical Advanced Research and Development Authority
BMA	British Medical Association
BMI	Body Mass Index
BMJ	British Medical Journal
BRI	Belt and Road Initiative
CARES Act	Coronavirus Aid, Relief and Economic Security Act
CDC	Centers for Disease Control and Prevention
CEPI	Coalition for Epidemic Preparedness Innovations
CFR	Case Fatality Rate
COPE	Covid-19 in Older People
COVAX	Covid-19 Vaccines Global Access

Covid-19	Coronavirus Disease 2019
CoV	Coronavirus
CPS	Child Protection Services
CVS	CVS Pharmacy
DACA	Deferred Action for Childhood Arrivals
DM	Developed Market
DNA	Deoxyribonucleic acid
DNAR/DNR	Do Not Attempt Resuscitation/Do Not Resuscitate
DRC	Democratic Republic of Congo
DTP	Diptheria, Typhoid, Polio
ECDC	European Centre for Disease Prevention and Control
ED	Emergency Department
EM	Emerging Market
EMA	European Medicines Agency
EMEA	Europe, Middle East and Africa
EUA	Emergency Use Authorisation
FDA	Food and Drug Administration
FT	Financial Times
GSK	GlaxoSmithKline
GDP	Gross Domestic Product
HCQ	Hydroxychloroquine
HCP	Healthcare Professional
HCW	Healthcare Worker
HCQ	Hydroxychloroquine
HHS	Health and Human Services
HIV	Human Immunodeficiency Virus
IAVI	International AIDS Vaccine Initiative
ICU	Intensive Care Unit
ICER	Institute for Cost-Effectiveness Research
ID	Infectious Disease
IFR	Infection Fatality Rate
IHME	Institute for Health Metrics and Evaluation
IHR	International Health Regulations
IL	Interleukin
IOC	International Olympic Committee
ISI	International Sensitivity Index
ITU	Intensive Therapy Unit
JAMA	Journal of the American Medical Association
J&J	Johnson & Johnson
LMIC	Low- and Middle-Income Countries
LTCF	Long-Term Care Facilities
MERS	Middle Eastern Respiratory Syndrome
MHRA	Medicines and Healthcare Products Regulatory Agency
ML	Machine Learning
MMR	Measles, Mumps, Rubella

MOMO	Mortality Monitoring
MRK	Merck & Co.
MRNA	Moderna, Inc.
mRNA	Messenger RNA
NBA	National Basketball Association
NERVTAG	New and Emerging Respiratory Virus Threats Advisory Group
NEJM	New England Journal of Medicine
NHP	Non-Human Primate
NIA	National Institute of Aging
NIAID	National Institute of Allergy and Infectious Diseases
NICE	National Institute for Health and Care Excellence
NIH	National Institutes of Health
NPI	Non-Pharmaceutical Intervention
NVAX	Novavax, Inc.
NYT	New York Times
OECD	Organisation for Economic Cooperation and Development
ONS	Office of National Statistics
OWS	Operation Warp Speed
PBM	Pharmacy Benefit Manager
PCR (test)	Polymerase Chain Reaction (test for Covid)
PETA	People for the Ethical Treatment of Animals
PHE	Public Health England
PHEIC	Public Health Emergency of International Concern
PPE	Personal Protective Equipment
PPV	Positive Predictive Value
PRM	Predictive Risk Modelling
PSCN	Pandemic Supply Chain Network
QALY	Quality Adjusted Life Year
R&D	Research & Development
RBC	Red Blood Cell
RCT	Randomised Controlled Trial
RKI	Robert Koch Institute
RNA	Ribonucleic Acid
RR	Relative Risk
SAGE	Scientific Advisory Group for Emergencies
SARS	Severe Acute Respiratory Syndrome
SARS-CoV-2	Severe Acute Respiratory Syndrome Coronavirus-2
TTTI	Test Track Trace Isolate
USDA	US Department of Agriculture
VRBPAC	Vaccines and Related Biological Products Advisory Committee
WEF	World Economic Forum
WHO	World Health Organisation
WSJ	Wall Street Journal

Introduction

In late 2019, a woman goes to a wet market in Wuhan. She's never quite sure what the traders will have … pangolin or maybe bat, but they never disappoint. It is an expedition into the delights of the culinary diversity of China. She's there because she wants to treat her husband. He is about to go on his first overseas business trip where he will be meeting senior executives from a number of South Korean companies. If the trip goes well, he will bring major accounts to his employer and be heaped with praise and honour. So, to calm her nervous husband and give him a good send-off, she has decided to prepare a feast fit for an emperor. It will be his last meal before he gets up early and heads to the airport.

As she wanders through the market and browses the stalls, a trader calls her over and points proudly to his display. He stifles a cough but follows it up with a smile and a promise of the finest delicacies in all of Wuhan. His hustle is interrupted by another coughing fit, but his smile is warm and his pitch is persuasive, despite a little shortness of breath. He wins her over, and she buys from him.

Her husband comes home after a hard day's work and last-minute briefings with his boss. He is distracted, tired and stressed – nothing out of the ordinary. However, his worries melt away as he opens the door to the apartment to find his nose overwhelmed by the tantalising smells emanating from further inside the home. His wife calls him to the dining table, groaning under the weight of a banquet that takes his breath away. He embraces her, chatters excitedly about her efforts, but she silences him with a kiss and demands he sit down to eat as her hard work is getting colder with every passing moment.

He takes the first bite, and his mouth explodes with delectable flavours. He beams his approval, and his wife sighs with pleasure. Together they savour the delicious meal and later, after quickly checking Weibo on his phone, the husband goes through everything he's packed for the trip, checks the alarm for the third time and gets into bed.

Five days later, he returns home. The meetings were successful, but he seems to have picked up some sort of a bug while travelling. He has a fever and a persistent cough, which is so bad that it's affecting his breathing. When he gets home, he sees his wife has it too.

Nobody knows or is ever likely to know who patient zero was for Covid-19. But it is likely that a scenario such as the one described here is as realistic as any other. What follows is a day-by-day account of the epidemic from the point of view of a medical professional, written contemporaneously at the time.

It is, in essence, a Covid diary of the available information on any given day, with added comments as Justin, the professor, reflects on the significance of the events unfolding around him and across the globe. Some of his reflections are quite wrong, painfully cringeworthy and embarrassingly so; at other times he predicts the future more accurately than Nostradamus. Underneath it all lies his search for the solution, a way to counter what would become the greatest health crisis of our time, and make a difference.

Professor Justin Stebbing received his training in medicine at Trinity College, University of Oxford, where he earned a first-class degree. After completing junior doctor posts in Oxford, he undertook training and a residency at the Johns Hopkins Hospital in Maryland, USA, before returning to London to continue his career at The Royal Marsden, St Bartholomew's Hospitals and now through Imperial College and its aligned Imperial College Healthcare NHS Trust. His PhD, funded by the Medical Research Council, was on the role of the immune system in controlling tumours and cancer-causing viruses, notably Kaposi's sarcoma-associated herpesvirus in the setting of HIV infection.

Professor Stebbing has published over 650 peer-reviewed papers in journals such as *The Lancet, New England Journal of Medicine, Blood, Journal of Clinical Oncology, Annals of Internal Medicine* and *Nature Medicine*, as well as presenting data at international conferences. He is a Fellow of the Royal College of Physicians, the Royal College of Pathologists and sits on advisory boards of a number of international cancer committees and biotechnology companies. He is Professor of Cancer Medicine and Oncology at Imperial College London. In 2016, he was elected to the American Society for Clinical Investigation and appointed editor-in-chief of Springer Nature's cancer journal *Oncogene*.

At the start of the pandemic he worked with BenevolentAI, a London-based company specialising in artificial intelligence, to find that an existing drug, a simple once-daily tablet, may be useful not just as an anti-cytokine, but also as an antiviral agent to treat people infected with SARS-CoV-2, the causative agent of Covid-19. His initial two pieces were published in *The Lancet* and *The Lancet Infectious Diseases*. Thereafter he led worldwide collaborations across continents, culminating in detailed molecular studies and global, randomised trials and an emergency use authorisation by the US Food and Drug Administration in November 2020 – ten months after the initial descriptions.

Professor Stebbing first started writing daily reflections on the Covid pandemic on 21 January 2020. Prior to that, the novel coronavirus from Wuhan, China, was background news, another minor illness that was affecting a specific region. While the virus may have been circulating among the Chinese population for months, only in January of 2020 was it starting to come to the world's attention. Chinese authorities had tried their best to suppress the realities of the outbreak, but, like the pathogen itself, the news couldn't be contained. Its secrets are still being unravelled on a daily basis.

Jem Duducu

January

21.01.20

I have decided to track this new, novel coronavirus from Wuhan, China. It could go two ways: it could be contained rapidly in the same way we stopped SARS, bird flu and swine flu, or it could become a mass outbreak, a major pandemic. The former is far more likely than the latter.

While we've become fairly adept at spotting these respiratory illnesses and neutralising them, there is always some collateral damage. I remember the grim story of gassing 20,000 chickens in Hong Kong back in 2014 to stop the spread of bird flu. Bad news for the chickens and chicken lovers, but it worked, and the virus was stopped. This time around, if it's a case of containment, then further lessons will be learned. I feel that this information will be important to capture for the future as it seems to me inevitable that we will have an outbreak of a new virus every few years. All you have to do is look at the previous thirty years. If, however, it is the latter scenario and there is a mass outbreak, then this could be the biggest news story of my lifetime.

There is now data showing cases outside of China. Of the 37 cases, nearly all (34) had been to Wuhan (36 were in China). There were 29 cases ex-China yesterday. In China itself today there are 2,741 confirmed cases, which is a fair jump from 1,985 yesterday, 5,794 suspected, 461 severe and 80 deaths, vs 56 yesterday. Some of this can be attributed to better reporting/diagnosis/ testing, but not all. Diagnostic criteria are already changing. Based on the numbers above, I don't see it plateauing yet, but it's getting much warmer in Wuhan by the day, and viruses are temperature-sensitive organisms – just my take. I have been looking at day/night weather forecasts and humidities/ temperatures for a while now. When Wuhan plateaus, I think the virus will decline internationally and the fear will dissipate, but we're not there yet. I also see that the WHO director is in Beijing now.

There is still no case outside of China without a close relationship to it; the one outlier is a close family contact in Vietnam, though 'investigations into their travel history are ongoing'. As with the rest of the world, attentions were turned elsewhere, and it took time for the Chinese regime to release more figures on the coronavirus situation inside its borders.

Earlier this month there were two other relevant points. First, on 4 January, I'd written to my close friend and confidante, the remarkably eloquent, truly decent, super-smart historian Niall Ferguson, to say I was worried about the unusual case of pneumonia from China. Second, with much more global relevance, the Shanghai Public Health Clinical Center & School of Public Health, in collaboration with the Central Hospital of Wuhan, Huazhong University of Science and Technology, the Wuhan Center for Disease Control and Prevention, the National Institute for Communicable Disease Control and Prevention, Chinese Center for Disease Control, and the University of Sydney, Australia, (I could go on) released a coronavirus genome from a case of a respiratory disease from the Wuhan outbreak. The sequence was also deposited on GenBank. I love the disclaimer that accompanied the sequence:

> Please feel free to download, share, use, and analyze this data. We ask that you communicate with us if you wish to publish results that use these data in a journal. If you have any other questions – then please also contact us directly.

> Professor Yong-Zhen Zhang, Shanghai
> Public Health Clinical Center & School
> of Public Health, Fudan University,
> Shanghai, China.

The *NEJM* has now published the first case of Covid-19 in the USA; a thirty-five-year-old man presented to an urgent care clinic in Snohomish County, Washington, with a four-day history of cough and subjective fever. On hospital day 6 (illness day 10), a fourth chest X-ray showed a nasty pneumonia, so treatment with intravenous remdesivir (a novel nucleotide analogue prodrug in development with previous activity against Ebola) was initiated on the evening of day 7. No adverse events were observed in association with the infusion. On hospital day 8 (illness day 12), the patient's clinical condition improved. Supplemental oxygen was discontinued. Who knows what would happen without remdesivir.

Dr Antony Fauci, President Trump's top medical advisor and director of the National Institutes of Allergy and Infectious Diseases (NIAID), has contributed to an editorial in *JAMA*, and I love the title: 'Coronavirus Infections – More Than Just the Common Cold'.

23.01.20

A cordon sanitaire has been placed in and around Wuhan, preventing free movement. Seems brutal.

24.01.20

The *NEJM* reports:

> In December 2019, a cluster of patients with pneumonia of unknown cause was linked to a seafood wholesale market in Wuhan, China. A previously unknown betacoronavirus was discovered through the use of unbiased sequencing in samples from patients with pneumonia. Human airway epithelial cells were used to isolate a novel coronavirus, named 2019-nCoV, which formed a clade within the subgenus sarbecovirus, Orthocoronavirinae subfamily. Different from both MERS-CoV and SARS-CoV, 2019-nCoV is the seventh member of the family of coronaviruses that infect humans. Enhanced surveillance and further investigation are ongoing.

At the same time, *The Lancet* reports on forty-one patients from Wuhan: 'The 2019-nCoV infection caused clusters of severe respiratory illness similar to severe acute respiratory syndrome coronavirus and was associated with ICU admission and high mortality. Major gaps in our knowledge of the origin, epidemiology, duration of human transmission, and clinical spectrum of disease need fulfilment by future studies.' They comment that the number of deaths is rising quickly. Good to see the big journals on this.

26.01.20

Niall Ferguson writes in his *Sunday Times* column: 'If it's climate change the WEF-ers are most worried about, you should probably brace yourself for a coronavirus pandemic. Talking of cognitive dissonance, what the hell were we all doing at a massive global conference last week? Fact: at least three of the WEF attendees were from – you guessed it – Wuhan.'

29.01.20

Professor Peter Richardson at BenevolentAI, a true outside-the-box thinker, and myself have spoken and decided that we should use our natural language processing technology, covering 180 million documents, 2 billion curated edges, to find an existing drug that has both anti-cytokine activity and antiviral activity. We know that damage is likely to be caused by the inflammatory response to the virus, involving small molecules called cytokines that our own immune system produces. But we also want a drug that can stop the virus from replicating. If we search for existing drugs, at least they're made already and we know their safety profile – for better or worse. Joanna Shields and Ivan Griffin, who run the company and always want to make a difference, are incredibly supportive as there are already signs that this virus might be a big deal. It will take a few days to get the programming right, and up and running.

30.01.20

There have been four confirmed cases in the UAE in travellers from Wuhan. While the percentage of new cases of the total is slowing from 24% to 22%, the tick up in net new cases is still growing.

The WHO and WEF have together set up 'the pandemic supply chain network' (PSCN) for data sharing and operational coordination. The WHO will re-decide today whether to call it a global emergency.

Data continues to be controversial; for example, there is no evidence that exit or entry screening helps travellers, and the animal source (seafood/bats?) is being questioned since we have the genetic sequence. It's not identical to any animal virus, but it has similarities to some.

Read a paper that R0 (the number of new infections one person causes) and the case fatality rate (number of deaths divided by number of cases) is 2.6–2.9 higher than seasonal flu's 1.3. Mortality rate is 0.1–4% given reporting biases.

Another paper suggests an early February peak. I'm not convinced.

Anecdotes of asymptomatic spread heighten concerns that there will be no way to contain the infection in China (and potentially beyond), given how far it's spread. It is masked by the background cold/flu season, which further complicates the ability to control it. That said, from my lens, the fact pattern doesn't match rampant asymptomatic spread at this point, which means it may very well be containable in most of the world.

Any vaccine will take nine to twelve months minimum. Some are saying longer.

31.01.20

At the end of the month there is no doubt that this epidemic is turning into a pandemic, the definition of which is 'an epidemic occurring worldwide, or over a very wide area, crossing international boundaries and usually affecting a large number of people'. The following points apply, methinks:

- The number of cases is on a steady rise, along with the number of deaths/number of severely ill, but the net number of new cases as a per cent of the total has fallen from 39%, to 24%, 22% and then 20% in the last five days.
- The Emergency Committee on the novel coronavirus (2019-nCoV) under the International Health Regulations (IHR 2005) says it constitutes a public health emergency of international concern (PHEIC – rolls off the tongue?).
- First confirmed cases of 2019-nCoV acute respiratory disease in Finland, India and the Philippines. All had travel history to Wuhan.
- The WHO recommends that the interim name of the disease causing the current outbreak should be '2019-nCoV acute respiratory disease' (where 'n' is for novel and 'CoV' is for coronavirus).
- It's been cold in Wuhan, especially at night (2 °C), but now is getting much warmer. I think, perhaps erroneously, this is relevant, but if I say the viral life cycle is five days, and it's properly warm night and day in Wuhan from Sunday, then the end of next week should see a plateau or decline. I've listened to several doctor/epidemiologist calls and no one is prepared to say anything emphatic regarding the trajectory.
- Align Technology said on its call yesterday not to expect any more revenues for quarter 1 (Q1) from China. They make Invisalign orthodontic aesthetic products. Thought it a pretty bold statement to make. What do they know that I don't?
- The best work I have seen in modelling suggests a peak in week two of February. Historically, these have typically overestimated the severity – the very nature of the epidemiologic mindset. I'd say a week today we'll see it level off.

February

01.02.20

There are two new cases in Italy, and the two new ones in the UK had been to Wuhan.

The life cycle of this virus clearly has a five-day latent period and a five-day recovery period. The reproductive number is 2, i.e. one person can typically infect two individuals. Although this is bad, it's worth putting into context with a disease like measles, which has an R0 number of 12–18, which means every person infected is likely to infect twelve to eighteen others.

BenevolentAI's tech, which I think is super cool, has shown us that several cancer drugs might be useful. We can't use those. Way too toxic. It also suggests that an existing approved drug to treat adult rheumatoid arthritis, a simple once-daily pill made by Eli Lilly, a global pharmaceutical company headquartered in Indianapolis, might be useful. It's well tolerated, though there's perhaps a small clot and infection signal in some of the larger randomised Phase 3 studies. It's a tablet, which is great, but most importantly, it has the dual mechanism we've been looking for. One is that it blocks the secretion of cytokines via its known mechanism of action, inhibiting the Janus kinase, the so-called JAK-STAT pathway. Second, remarkably, it looks like it can prevent viral replication by blocking two human proteins – called AAK1 and GAK – that SARS-CoV-2 uses to spread. These are kinases, like Janus kinases, in general a type of activating protein that adds phosphate groups to other proteins to turn them on, working in orchestral signalling cascades. These all look like important conductors of the orchestra here. It's an interesting concept to have an antiviral that doesn't directly attack the virus but our own machinery that the virus co-opts for its own evolution and molecular piracy. What I can't work out is why other JAK inhibitors, and there are several, don't come up as having activity in our algorithms. That's the beauty, though, of AI. It makes higher-order correlations that, with all the time and thinking in the world, mere mortals like me could never begin to predict. I am writing a paper on it.

03.02.20

I've just sent the paper to the editor of *The Lancet*. Within 3 minutes he writes back and wants to publish it now, today. Nice. Hopefully, it will be widely read. I call my head of department at Imperial to let him know the good news. Instead, he is concerned I am publishing a modelling study and thus treading on Imperial's Professor Neil Ferguson's toes. I explain this is drug modelling using AI, not epidemiologic modelling. Typical academic jealousies and rivalries, nothing new to me: politics and positioning above patients and helping people. Always been the way. The stakes are just so low in academia.

Main observations today:

- No new countries have reported cases in the last 24 hours, but the first death outside China has been reported (Philippines).
- The WHO has announced a task force to deal with spurious info on social media, the so-called 'infodemic'.
- There are, as yet, no real new numbers beyond what I sent yesterday, though we now have the severely ill. If the net severely ill as a per cent of severely ill is a relevant number then that's a big decline.
- I note Apple is closing all of its forty-two stores (out of 506 worldwide) in China until 9 February (obviously might be extended). China is 17% of total revenues; each week closed in China is a loss of $850 million or -1.3% of its revenues.

A paper in *Nature* reports: 'Full-length genome sequences were obtained from five patients at an early stage of the outbreak. The sequences are almost identical and share 79.6% sequence identity to SARS-CoV. Furthermore, we show that 2019-nCoV is 96% identical at the whole-genome level to a bat coronavirus. Pairwise protein sequence analysis of seven conserved non-structural proteins domains show that this virus belongs to the species of SARSr-CoV. In addition, 2019-nCoV virus isolated from the bronchoalveolar lavage fluid of a critically ill patient could be neutralised by sera from several patients. Notably, we confirmed that 2019-nCoV uses the same cell entry receptor – angiotensin converting enzyme II (ACE2) – as SARS-CoV.' I don't really understand the term 'almost identical' in a *Nature* abstract when it's only 79.6% identical. That's not almost identical, especially at the gene level. Another one on the same day shows it's 89.1% similar to a bat virus.

04.02.20

Starting to look much better to me: big decline in the severely ill, net percentages all falling. This is excellent news.

The WHO has copied the Hopkins tracker and developed a dashboard in real time.

WHO is also developing a '2019-nCoV kit' similar to prepared treatment kits used for outbreaks of other high-threat pathogens. In the coming days the costing, procurement and assembly of these kits will be a priority.

Some treatment thoughts today:

- If you take serum from one of the 667 recovered patients and give that to a sick person they get better.
- Our BenevolentAI-discovered baricitinib arthritis drug, manufactured by Lilly, will hopefully be trialled. Gilead apparently has a drug called remdesivir, previously tested against Ebola. The drug is currently not approved, but in animal studies it was found to be effective against other coronaviruses, such as MERS and SARS. Treatment with remdesivir was initiated on a patient in one of the first US patients reported in the *NEJM*. The next day the patient's condition improved significantly, though who knows the natural history.
- Countries tend to stockpile drugs if they work, and Roche's Tamiflu did $3.2 billion at its peak (2009 H1N1 outbreak), but flu is a yearly occurrence. China would be a good place to do rapid clinical trials, but any commercial opportunity will take another nine months at least (do the trial, show it works, approve it rapidly).
- Listened to a couple of the analyst/expert calls yesterday in which there was a wide fan of views, including gradual spread, fadeout in the summer, then resurgence in the 2020/2021 flu season (double-flu) as a severe next wave. Other possible outcomes include containment, which I think is more likely, and sooner rather than later, or a massive global pandemic with a mortality rate of 1%+ or anything in between.

05.02.20

No new countries in the last 24 hours have reported any cases. The WHO and others have stopped reporting suspected cases. I was probably too positive yesterday; I note that the number of new severely ill is up sharply off the Hopkins tracker website, which is more current than the WHO. I'll try to use both.

06.02.20

Very clear to me from various data sets that the situation is improving, with small downward inflexions in the important parameters.

Belgium had a case.

I have spoken this morning to both of my doctor contacts in China, as well as to a couple of other people there, who say the situation is clearly improving. The Tencent alarm going around yesterday was fake news.

If consistent tomorrow, as I expect, the worst of it is over.

07.02.20

No new countries have reported any cases in the last 24 hours. The new UK case, the third one, caught it in Singapore.

The WHO has completed a global set up of diagnostic reference labs for molecular detection, a hub-and-spoke model with smaller local labs.

All the data shows me it's getting better.

08.02.20

No new countries again in the last 24 hours.

Travel restrictions increasing, e.g. two-week quarantine in Hong Kong for anyone arriving from China. Dinner parties are banned there.

To me, you have to consider the lag time as it takes a while to become severely ill.

Read a report that said it can be transmitted in tears. Separately, very bad if pregnant (pretty obvious). Interesting the strength of psychological interventions also occurring in China.

10.02.20

After a quiet few days of data, there is now a glut. Information from WHO websites have doubled numbers affected. Previous 24-hour numbers (like net severely ill) are needing revision every day.

No new countries for four days.

We're now at 136 infected on the *Diamond Princess* cruise ship in Japan (3,700 onboard). Passengers are confined largely to cabins, and everyone is told to wear masks when leaving them.

New concerns that API (source material) for drugs from China might be impacted, leading to supply shortages. The US is dependent on China as an API provider for generics.

Headlines, such as those in *The Sunday Times*, of an epidemic here don't help – we had our fourth case yesterday. In the US, hospitals are preparing for a potential influx of admissions; anecdotally, infectious disease specialists and respirologists are busy with these preparations.

The WHO estimates that 82% of cases are mild, 15% severe and 3% critical, which creates a large pool of 'milds' to transmit. This could mean a less transmissible strain seeding outside of China or detection efforts lagging meaningfully behind the outbreak.

11.02.20

The Director-General of the WHO has said, 'We are very encouraged by the current trend. There have only been 3 cases in the past week, and no cases in the past 3 days ... Now to coronavirus. First of all, we now have a name for the disease: Covid-19. I'll spell it: C-O-V-I-D hyphen one nine – Covid-19.'

No new countries since 5 February. Following its release Saturday evening in China, users can scan a QR code via mobile apps like Alipay, WeChat or QQ to enquire if someone nearby has the virus. After registering with a phone number, users enter their name and ID number to find out whether they were in close contact with someone infected. A sign of how modern technology can be used to fight the old enemy of disease.

12.02.20

The virus has now been designated Covid-19, which makes it seem like last year's thing.

13.02.20

Among the unpredictability and the infodemic, there is nothing on the WHO website or its real-time dashboard regarding the new cases.

Still no new countries since 5 February. Ex-China cases, which are obviously very important as they are diagnosed properly on the whole (I don't believe three in India, though), are not rising steeply.

The sharp increase, the largest daily increase so far, may be due to a change in diagnostic criteria, i.e. they are using lung scans of symptomatic patients because in Wuhan they're short of reagents to diagnose the virus.

The *Diamond Princess* cruise ship now has 174 cases, the largest outbreak outside China (39 new cases).

A ninth case found in the UK, in London.

I am not sure this virus is getting better, actually. We've now published a follow-up piece on stitching together baricitinib's dual antiviral and anti-cytokine properties in *The Lancet Infectious Diseases*.

I am getting daily emails from desperate doctors all over the world filling my inbox. No one has any idea, other than with mechanical support, what drugs may help, but at the same time they're keen to undertake decent studies to give us the answer. Doctors tell me all they can hear is coughing in their emergency rooms. We've only published a computer prediction – who will believe that? We have no human data, zero. The AI, however, is far better than a hunch or nothing. One of the emails is from Mario Corbellino, an infectious diseases doctor at the University of Milan. He remembered me from my days, two decades previously, when I published extensively about HIV and one of the viruses that co-infected people living with HIV, Kaposi's sarcoma-associated herpesvirus (KSHV). Our collaboration just clicks, and we've been talking early in the morning and late into the evening, on the same wavelength, wanting to cut through bureaucracy and red tape. We need ethical approval to give this to patients to get human data amid, as he describes it, the 'Dantesque mayhem'. He's committed and thoughtful and, quite simply, 'gets it'. Our calls last into the night and we publish a stern riposte together in *The Lancet Infectious Diseases* to doctors who think baricitinib will suppress the immune system. It's a delicate balance when it comes to this. We do want to suppress the cytokine storm, but also allow the immune system to clear the virus. Together we're writing a trial protocol for emergency ethical approval by the hospital review board.

The Chief Financial Officer of Lilly, Josh Smiley, has been in touch after we were introduced by Umer Raffat, a mutual friend, and he's keen to get to the bottom of this and whether baricitinib can help people, with patients first and foremost in his mind. It will never be profitable for them here as it's been given for years for arthritis – here we're proposing it for a few days. Hope he's interested.

14.02.20

Again, no new countries affected since 5 February. This is good news. Is containment starting to work? That would be amazing.

The WHO has commented on the extra cases reported from Hubei Province and said, 'For consistency, we are only reporting the number of laboratory-confirmed cases. Coronavirus cases are not rising dramatically outside China, despite a spike in Hubei Province.' The only exception was a cruise liner docked in Japan, where 44 new cases were reported, bringing the total there to 218.

I am speaking to my doctor friends in China, especially the excellent Dr Ling Peng. They're so organised and are keeping cancer services on track while also treating Covid-19. There will be lessons for us from this, I am sure, including their methods of tracking.

15.02.20

The first case in Africa (Egypt) has been reported in someone returning from China. And only 3 deaths outside mainland China (Japan, Hong Kong, Philippines). Data on the severely ill is looking dodgy, so I will keep my eye out for better info. If it's true, then basically all deaths are linked to China, so no community transmission. China is the key. Let's get this thing isolated and then neutralise it.

16.02.20

Graphs are encouraging, but I can't help thinking of the French death/ the Chinese doctor who died several weeks from the start of symptoms, so maybe we'll see more deaths now due to its ability to persist in some before eventually causing death.

Seeing alarmist reports in the media that pollution is still very high in China, despite factories not opening, due to cremations. I think this is fake news.

Cases on the Japanese docked cruise liner are up to 355. This is a floating petri dish. We'll learn so much.

For me, cases ex-China, especially in Africa, are key.

The University of Milan gives us ethics approval to use baricitinib in patients with severe Covid-19, approval number 14581/2020. But, we can only use it in four people, they've said. Everyone is wary. 'Do the least harm' should surely come before 'do no harm'. We have to try. Even statins to treat high cholesterol have side effects.

17.02.20

No new countries in the last 24 hours. Rate of net new cases slowing. Quarantine in some places extended to three weeks for travellers returning from Wuhan, based on two cases with long incubation periods.

Personally, I find the virus biologically fascinating, and negatives from China initially (slow reporting, etc.) are now more than compensated for by their ability to lockdown regions, etc. 'Cordon sanitaire' – fascinating term.

In Milan, we've immediately started giving baricitinib to four patients with Covid-19 pneumonia about to be ventilated. I am on regular calls with Mario, who has moved out of his family home to avoid exposing them to Covid contracted from patients. I am helped enormously by one of my Italian post-doctoral scientists, the super helpful, smart Silva Ottaviani. Every conceivable test we can measure is studied, alongside their interleukin-6 levels, which is probably a good measure of disease severity here and a marker of our own cytokine storms. I think hospitals can routinely measure interleukin-6 because it's a useful marker in some diseases, like the rare Castleman's disease, which we see in HIV and is in fact caused by co-infection with KSHV, a herpesvirus. It looks pretty useful here.

Every day we're collecting more data, and we're plotting all their inflammatory parameters twice daily. One of the patients is hallucinating, imagining people in his room. He's obese, sick, just avoiding ventilation and desaturating. But after one tablet of baricitinib he feels better and the hallucinations stop. It's probably correlative not causative, but one can't help think there's an association here since baricitinib, unlike so many drugs, crosses the blood-brain barrier.

Re our baricitinib study: Josh Smiley introduces me to Gary Krishnan from the inflammation and immunology team. Conference and video calls are now occurring between myself and Mario, other collaborators, Gary Krishnan and his team, including Anabela Cardoso and Jonathan Sims at Lilly. This is actually happening at breakneck speed. We are really making plans to link AI to the laboratory, to the clinic and back, though I don't think Lilly believes any of this. The collaboration and urgency is a reminder about how this is a global issue, and an increasingly serious one.

18.02.20

No new countries in the last 24 hours. The WHO has moved to include laboratory and non-laboratory confirmed cases. The CDC warns Covid-19 is going to be with us for a while and starting to hear real concerns regarding the 2020 Tokyo Olympics.

Five US cities to test for coronavirus in patients with flu-like illnesses and negative flu tests. This is the first attempt to truly capture the extent of the outbreak in the US. Only public health labs can test for now, which to me is a problem.

Millions of people in the UK could be told to self-isolate for two weeks if the number of coronavirus cases passes 100, suggesting sustained community transmission, beyond which testing for the virus in the UK might cease. The press is full of lots of panic stories.

19.02.20

No new countries for five days, including no more African cases after one in Egypt. A second death in Hong Kong – one may have thought more.

The markers of our baricitinib fabulous four are getting better, including everything related to inflammation like interleukin-6. Sure, most people recover, but it's not a bad sign, let's face it. Gary at Lilly is brilliant, and loves cricket too. Amid lockdowns he's keeping some Lilly laboratories open to find out if the AI hypothesis around infection and recovery rates is correct. He has somehow also managed to source samples from an old, randomised study using baricitinib in rheumatoid arthritis – these are not patients with any virus and the samples are from years ago. Am really surprised that no one has ever shown that baricitinib can reduce levels of interleukin-6 in patients. As they used two doses, we can also see if the higher dose leads to a greater reduction, a so-called dose-response. We are going to measure this in patient samples, comparing across diseases. He will also help with kinase assays to understand if baricitinib can inhibit SARS-CoV-2 replication via inhibition of AAK1 and GAK, as the AI suggests.

20.02.20

A mixed bag of news today:

- New infection numbers have just dropped in Hubei, where it was announced that there were 349 new cases yesterday, the lowest daily number of infections recorded by China in weeks. This appears to be partly due to a change in what is counted as a 'confirmed case'. Sadly, the global death toll is now at least 2,126 people dead from the virus, with all but 10 of those deaths in mainland China. The total number of infected worldwide stands at around 75,600.
- On the *Diamond Princess* cruise ship, two passengers in their 80s from Japan have died from the virus as the remaining passengers continue disembarking after a fourteen-day quarantine. A total of 624 cases have been linked to the stricken ship. This means more than 50% of those ex-China are on the cruise ship, making this one vessel more of a global hotspot than most actual countries.
- The mayor of the South Korean city of Daegu urged its 2.5 million people to stay indoors. Some 23 out of the 30 cases in that city are linked to a church that a 61-year-old patient had attended.
- And Sanofi announced that it is teaming up with the Biomedical Advanced Research and Development Authority (BARDA), part of the US Department of Health and Human Services, to develop a vaccine against Covid-19 infections.

21.02.20

Apart from some case clusters in South Korea (total 156, including 53 new, related to a church in Daegu now in special measures) and Beijing (36 new patients in one hospital), the situation continues to improve. Doctors on the ground are optimistic.

More than half the cases outside China are related to the cruise ship. The US reports no change at 15 people infected for a week. The WHO confirms that a new country, Iran, has been added to the list of countries reporting cases. Am sceptical about numbers there.

22.02.20

No new countries in the last 24 hours, but since 1 February only three new countries (Egypt, Iran, Finland) have been added. Obviously, it's extremely hard for me to ascertain any real data I would be happy to share from Iran or Africa, but I don't think there are major concerns.

The best modelling study I have seen predicts absolute peak now or last week (from the London School of Tropical Medicine and Hygiene). This is great news and, in general, the data would certainly back this up. If this started in November, then this would mean Covid-19 will be done by June 2020. Obviously, the above sounds very positive. But even I get alarmed when the front page of today's WHO situation report contradicts this.

More baricitinib studies are being set up now; protocols are being shared. It's super exciting, and I just hope it helps. I don't think AI has ever been used in a pandemic before, or so rapidly, pandemic or no pandemic. New way of developing drugs – hardly an original thought from me here.

23.02.20

Clear flattening of the curve in China, but increasing case numbers ex-China, so looks to me like we'll see two peaks – a China one that has come and is going, and an ex-China one that will do the same, but not yet.

Covid-19 has spread to two more countries (Lebanon and Israel) and the numbers of new cases and deaths outside China climbed, with special concern focused on South Korea, with 556 infected and 2 dead.

So, Iran, amid its election Friday/Saturday, has been especially keen to garner favour with China and not to have restrictions on flights/quarantine/travel, so they're saying the death toll is 6 and 28 infected. I think this is doubtful and that we shall soon see a large number of previously unreported cases.

I am not in the camp that believes the US is not testing adequately and/or has flawed tests – an old story. If the US can't do it, I have no idea what to believe ex-China and prefer the simple thesis that the lack of new cases in the US is indeed due to the lack of new cases in the US – as per the UK too.

I am also hearing of a global face mask shortage. I don't know how to feel about that. On the one hand, it's bad, but on the other, it's good to see presumably billions of people taking the simple precaution of covering their mouths and noses to fight a respiratory illness.

24.02.20

The China CDC has published its description of cases there. Lots of data here. Quick run through:

- 72,314 cases (as of 11 February 2020)
  - Confirmed cases: 44,672 (62%)
  - Suspected cases: 16,186 (22%)
  - Diagnosed cases: 10,567 (15%)
  - Asymptomatic cases: 889 (1%)
- Age distribution (N=44,672)
  - ≥80 years: 3% (1,408 cases)
  - 30–79 years: 87% (38,680 cases)
  - 20–29 years: 8% (3,619 cases)
  - 10–19 years: 1% (549 cases)
  - <10 years: 1% (416 cases)
- Spectrum of disease (N=44,415)
  - Mild: 81% (36,160 cases)
  - Severe: 14% (6,168 cases)
  - Critical: 5% (2,087 cases)
- Case-fatality rate
  - 2.3% (1,023 of 44,672 confirmed cases)
  - 14.8% in patients aged ≥80 years (208 of 1,408)
  - 8.0% in patients aged 70–79 years (312 of 3,918)
  - 49.0% in critical cases (1,023 of 2,087)
- Healthcare personnel infected
  - 3.8% (1,716 of 44,672)
  - 63% in Wuhan (1,080 of 1,716)
  - 14.8% cases classified as severe or critical (247 of 1,668)
  - 5 deaths

So, as China has clearly peaked, all attention shifts to ex-China. Two new countries (Bahrain and Kuwait) reported cases in the last 24 hours related to travel from Iran – clearly close ties to Wuhan for all sorts of reasons.

The clear focus for me actually now is on 152 cases (3 deaths) in Italy. Will there be travel restrictions in Europe after the lockdown in Italy, which, to me, does not seem enough? I have no idea about person-to-person community transmissions vs traveller transmissions from China/Japan, etc., but I think China is a better place to control movement than Italy. For me, governments will have to act quickly re: Italian spread/travel. Not sure stopping the Venice Festival two days early is enough. North Korea quarantined 380 foreign nationals over fears. Pakistan and Turkey have closed their borders with Iran. Australia is advising but not ordering citizens not to go to South Korea.

25.02.20

South Korea is testing 200,000 members of a religious group believed to be at the centre of the country's outbreak: 893 people infected, 9 deaths.

China will 'comprehensively' ban the trade and consumption of wild animals. About time.

A Chinese university research team said it had developed an oral vaccine for the virus and appealed for partners in clinical trials. Shares in Moderna were up 20% after they shipped their MRNA-1273 vaccine to the NIH for testing – that's making a vaccine within forty-three days. This is unbelievably fast-paced, as in I'm not sure many will believe it. I first visited them in 2011. If anyone can, they can.

Italy has moved all Serie A football games and Europa League games behind closed doors to help stop the spread of the coronavirus.

Hong Kong has extended the closure of schools until 20 April. It also closed its borders to South Korean arrivals.

Gilead has initiated two clinical trials in patients infected with Covid-19 to evaluate the safety/efficacy of remdesivir as a potential treatment for coronavirus patients.

Baricitinib work continuing apace. Our fabulous four are out of hospital and, in patients with rheumatoid arthritis without Covid-19 from an old, randomised trial, it inhibits interleukin-6. The higher dose of baricitinib lowers it even more. This is exciting data, and hard to believe it's the first time it's been shown, but sometimes the most obvious and simple things aren't done.

26.02.20

Snippets from the web report the US acting in an alarmist manner despite no new cases from the cruise ship evacuees (and a soldier in South Korea, not in the US) for nine days. As American media and news outlets are designed to shock and heighten tensions for ratings, this seems to be backfiring as they now have a real problem to report.

One new country in the last 24 hours – Algeria. Italian numbers increased from 229 to 322, 11 dead. Presume mortality ex-China is 2%, that should mean about 500 infected, so about right.

27.02.20

Estonia, Denmark, Pakistan, Georgia, Norway, North Macedonia, Greece and Romania are among countries to report their first case of coronavirus in the last day. This follows Algeria, Austria, Croatia, Brazil and Switzerland yesterday. This virus is clearly spreading, and unless centralised blockers are put into place, I fear this may become the biggest pandemic in my lifetime.

Australia (23 cases) has extended its travel ban on China and enacted its emergency response plan because 'there is every indication the world will soon enter the pandemic phase of the virus', Prime Minister Scott Morrison said. I think he's right.

US Vice President Mike Pence has been appointed by President Trump to lead and coordinate the US response to the coronavirus. President Trump said the risk to Americans is 'very low', but that plans are in place for a spread of the virus, which he doesn't think is inevitable, in contradiction to US health authorities who expect to see more cases. The National Institutes of Health (NIH) said a vaccine is at least twelve to eighteen months away, so will not help this current outbreak but may assist a seasonal return. The answer right now is containment. The quickest a vaccine has ever been developed previously is four years.

28.02.20

No new confirmed cases in the US for ten days, while China confirms only 327 new cases and 44 deaths – the lowest rise since this started. The 'Italy curve' is just not as bad as the South Korean one.

After President Emmanuel Macron's warning on Thursday that France was on the brink of a coronavirus epidemic, officials there have announced 20 new cases emerging in the past 24 hours.

In Beijing, supermarkets must allow an average of 2 square metres per customer – a mandate that not only forces shops to track how many patrons enter, but also means shoppers have to wait outside once stores hit maximum capacity.

The virus has now spread to around 49 countries. In a survey, 38% of Americans won't drink Corona beer because... America.

March

01.03.20

The WHO has upgraded the global threat to 'very high', so a sustained local spread in other countries ex-China is clearly occurring. The next announcement will be a pandemic. This is it; this is the moment of truth. If we don't track and trace this effectively this month it's likely that the infection rates will get away from us, and we could end up in a global health crisis.

Three new US cases appear unrelated to travel. Another very worrying sign that this virus is not under control; this is important. The US has also strengthened its travel advice, raising Iran and Italy to a level 3, advising people to 'avoid nonessential travel'.

The CDC has said it will have new coronavirus testing kits delivered to all states by the end of the week after the first lot of tests was found to be faulty.

In studies, the death rate for Covid-19 varied by location and an individual's age, among other factors. For instance, in Hubei Province, the death rate reached 2.9%; in other provinces of China that rate was just 0.4%. In addition, older adults have been hit the hardest. The death rate soars to 14.8% in those 80 and older; among those ages 70 to 79, the Covid-19 death rate in China seems to be about 8%; it's 3.6% for those ages 60 to 69; 1.3% for 50 to 59; 0.4% for the age group 40 to 49; and just 0.2% for people ages 10 to 39.

Australia recorded its first Covid-19 death, a 78-year-old man who had been a passenger on the *Diamond Princess*. The US also recorded its first death, a man in his 50s from Seattle who had underlying medical issues. Two more doctors have died in China, and the country's death toll has risen by 35 to 2,870. Infections have risen 573 to 79,824 (of which 41,825, or 52%, are listed as recovered).

02.03.20

Six new countries (Dominican Republic, Azerbaijan, Ecuador, Ireland, Monaco and Qatar) reported cases of Covid-19 at the weekend, taking the total number of countries affected to 59. This all seems to be going in one direction, and not the right one. Australia has announced its first two cases of local transmission of Covid-19.

Indonesia reported its first two cases of Covid-19. That country has a population of 270 million, the same as Brazil and Italy combined. It could be a huge problem if it's not caught quickly, and thus far it seems even G7 countries are having difficulty coordinating a response to this pandemic.

03.03.20

South Korea has declared 'war' on the virus. Let's see if the virus surrenders. Twitter told its employees to work from home. Amazon has said 'don't travel' to staff.

Italy, now Europe's worst-hit country, recorded a spike in deaths to 52 from 18 as the number of confirmed cases reached 2,000.

Health officials in the US, where 105 cases have been confirmed, said six people in the Seattle area of Washington state have died of Covid-19. If one presumes the death rate at its lowest is 1%, as per the *Diamond Princess*, the number infected must be six times higher at 600, showing testing isn't sufficient. The concept of track, trace and isolate is valid and has worked in the past, but it now appears that the world's health authorities are behind the curve with this virus. The window of opportunity for genuine containment narrows every day, and I am worried that we're losing.

04.03.20

Eight new countries (Andorra, Jordan, Latvia, Morocco, Portugal, Saudi Arabia, Senegal, and Tunisia) reported cases of Covid-19 in the past 24 hours, taking the total to 72/195 countries.

Facebook gives health officials free advertising to combat the virus.

05.03.20

Four new countries (Argentina, Chile, Poland and Ukraine) have reported cases of Covid-19 in the past 24 hours.

California's governor has declared a state of emergency after the announcement of the first virus-related death there. The state now has

53 confirmed cases. Not like them to panic. The White House moved on Wednesday to expand nationwide testing for the disease. There are now 159 reported US patients with Covid-19 in 16 states.

Japan's Olympics minister announced the games would go ahead in July as planned, saying that cancelling 'would be unacceptable for the athletes'. The country has 1,036 cases and 12 people have died.

Panic buying has continued around the world. Masks and toilet paper, in particular, remain in demand. Disruptions to the global supply of personal protective equipment (PPE) are leaving healthcare workers (HCWs) ill-equipped to care for patients. Am noticing a real lack of supply of masks/gloves/aprons/anything at Charing Cross Hospital in and around my clinic.

06.03.20

Events continue apace, with six new countries in the last 24 hours.

President Trump has admitted that the coronavirus 'might have an impact' on the US economy, but said it would pass. Vice President Pence has admitted the country does not have enough testing kits. If the world's largest economy has insufficient testing, the whole world is sitting on a growing pandemic. We can't even begin to track how vast it actually is.

07.03.20

Starting with some positive news: the rates of increase in Italy and South Korea are lower today; I am plotting these daily. It doesn't look to me like any of the worrying European countries (France, Germany, Spain), with many hundreds of cases, are going to do what Italy did and reach thousands of cases rapidly. Further, I think either a drug of reasonable effectiveness or a vaccine trial will change sentiment, although this will, of course, take time.

There are two large clinical trials of remdesivir now: the first in mild to moderate cases, and the second in cases of severe infection. Both are ongoing and are randomised, which is the right thing to do.

On vaccine development, China is saying they will have clinical trials starting next month. I spoke to Stéphane Bancel, CEO at Moderna, who said the FDA, based on the global burden, would consider approving their vaccine after a healthy patient study in the USA, starting next month. Not sure about that one. He mentioned the good thing about the mRNA platform is that you can tune it to the virus, so if the virus mutates you can change it. The structure of this virus, though, isn't like influenza or HIV – seems like the mutation rate will be so much less.

The feedback I am getting from Italy, from doctors such as Mario, indicates the seriousness of the outbreak there, with large numbers of patients ventilated – up to 10% – and a mortality rate of 3%.

08.03.20

In the US, the virus has reached Washington DC and a political convention attended by President Trump and Vice President Pence.

Italian Prime Minister Conte signed a decree enacting forced quarantine for the region of Lombardy – home to more than 10 million people and the financial capital Milan – and multiple other provinces, totalling around 16 million residents. The country has formally locked down more than a quarter of its population in a bid to stop the spread of the virus, where more than 5,800 cases of Covid-19 have been confirmed, an alarming increase of more than 1,200 in a single 24-hour period. 233 people have died.

An Australian doctor with flu-like symptoms treated 70 patients.

Almost 100 countries are now responding to outbreaks. There are so many stories that I'll leave it at that.

09.03.20

Eight new countries/territories/areas (Bulgaria, Costa Rica, Faroe Islands, French Guiana, Maldives, Malta, Martinique and the Republic of Moldova) have reported cases of Covid-19 in the past 24 hours, passing 100 out of 195 countries.

New guidance from the CDC urges travellers, especially the elderly and those with compromised health, to avoid long-haul flights 'and especially' cruises. A total of 34 states in the US have confirmed cases, and there are at least 21 people out of 3,500 with coronavirus aboard the *Grand Princess* cruise ship, which is expected to dock sometime today in Oakland, CA.

The UK is currently in the first phase – containment – of the government's four-part plan to tackle the spread: containment, delay, research and mitigate. Today's Cobra meeting is expected to consider whether the UK should officially move into the 'delay' phase, which could mean the introduction of 'social distancing' of at least 1 metre, maybe 2.

We'll see results of the US testing fiasco this week, though I am expecting it to pass 1,000 on Wednesday.

10.03.20

With 463 dead and 9,172 infected, Italy's fatality rate is running at 5% nationwide and 6% in Lombardy, far higher than the 0.7%–4% estimates elsewhere.

The US is now at 754 cases, although I fear this is just the tip of the iceberg.

Mainland China reported no new locally transmitted coronavirus cases outside of Hubei Province, where the outbreak began, for the third straight day. Major Chinese cities remained on alert for imported infections.

The WHO said the threat of a pandemic is 'very real', but stressed the virus could still be controlled. The global death toll has passed 4,000 and infections are now at over 114,000.

Passengers are disembarking from the *Grand Princess* in Oakland, California.

11.03.20

States of emergency have been declared in Michigan and Massachusetts as the number of Covid-19 cases in the US passed 1,000.

Australia announced a ban on people arriving from Italy. Three Formula 1 team members in Melbourne for the Australian Grand Prix have been told to self-isolate as they await test results for Covid-19.

A match between Arsenal and Manchester City has been postponed after an unspecified number of Arsenal players were required to self-isolate. Somewhat alarmingly, this shows that outdoor sports, and even a sport involving a sole individual literally sitting with a mask on in a single-seater car, can be affected by this growing health crisis.

Google has told all its staff in North America to work from home. Uber will give any infected or quarantined staff 'financial assistance'. The government here in the UK is considering a policy of 'cocooning' groups of people who are most vulnerable, such as older people in care homes, who may be kept apart from the wider population.

Churches are stopping contact during services, including sharing the chalice and shaking hands for the sign of peace.

The WHO has said this is a pandemic, but added it would be the first pandemic that could be controlled.

A UK health minister has been diagnosed with the virus and, following my two relevant pieces in *Lancet* journals, I have been asked to go to No. 10 tonight with Joanna Shields.

In the event, the room is packed. I'm not sure this is right as it's quite clear that close contact indoors is a major factor in transmission, and it is a known fact that some people in the government have tested positive.

Could it be that a major meeting to try and stop the spread of the virus could become a spreading event?

There is a sense that the meeting could become chaotic as everyone, in an attempt to get their point across, is talking across one another. Jonathan Van-Tam, Patrick Vallance and Dominic Cummings make impassioned speeches to work together alongside the NHS – with all the NHS leaders there. Boris Johnson sits down and, surrounded by everyone in the room, looks across to Joanna and says hello, his eyes rapidly surveying the space, a slight sense of foreboding in the air. He uses a sombrero hat as an analogy, and if we can make it flatter, then the pressure on the NHS will be less.

The elephant in the room, a national lockdown, is avoided. It is a tough situation for any national leader to be in. Logically, a lockdown should crush transmission, but it will similarly annihilate the economic output of the country. What leader wants to sign off on the guaranteed biggest recession in living memory? We discuss contact tracing and data integration, and Boris Johnson promises to lend Downing Street's weight to cut through red tape.

He is looking for a scientific solution, hoping us British doctors and scientists can invent and think our way out of the problem. It's a noble idea, but science takes time. A lockdown will buy us that time.

12.03.20

President Trump has announced sweeping new travel restrictions on Europe in a bid to combat the spread. The ban applies to non-US citizens who have been in the EU's Schengen border-free area within fourteen days prior to their arrival in the US. That's 26 countries. However, the virus is already spreading within America's borders.

The National Basketball Association (NBA) has suspended its season – very decisive. The decision came after one player for the Utah Jazz tested positive for the virus. Shortly after the NBA announcement, the Oscar-winning actor Tom Hanks announced that he and his wife had contracted the virus in Australia.

Dr Anthony Fauci, director of the National Institute of Allergy and Infectious Diseases, told Congress that the outbreak is 'going to get worse', and that what followed would depend on the ability to contain those infected. He cautioned against quick vaccine development, mentioning safety, and singled out Moderna's vaccine as the lead candidate.

UK tests still take about a week to come back. Let's see what happens with US testing, but Pence, the US vice president, has said that 'any American can be tested, no restrictions, subject to doctor's orders,' and that insurers had promised to offset the charges.

Four UK parliamentarians are in isolation. 'UK cases could keep rising for months,' Matt Hancock, the Health Secretary, said. The aim is to flatten the ramp of the bell curve so demand on health services reduces. Boris said that in the room at Downing Street. He added that the outbreak was unlikely to last a year. The implication is we're behind Italy in terms of timelines. The UK will, I am sure, move to the containment phase today.

Working from home is now clearly being adopted as the norm by many. I write this from a desk that I regularly use, but realise I am going to become intimately acquainted with over the coming months. Which reminds me, I'd better neaten it all up.

13.03.20

A female diplomat from the Philippines to the UN, Justin Trudeau's wife, the Arsenal manager and a Chelsea player are all positive for coronavirus. I can't see sporting events continuing, and I include the Olympics in that statement. However, Japan disagrees with me as, once again, Japanese authorities insisted that the Tokyo Olympics will go ahead this summer, hours after Donald Trump added to speculation that the coronavirus pandemic could force them to be postponed or cancelled. Disney World Resort in Florida and Disneyland Paris announced they would close through the end of the month, starting at the close of business Sunday. Maybe in Japan the lack of hugging/kissing/shaking hands is the solution?

The Melbourne Grand Prix is now cancelled due to a Covid outbreak in one of the teams, a reminder that the virus does not care about human plans. It's also a sign, to me, that the Olympics really are doomed.

New York State banned all gatherings with 500 or more people. Globally, many churches have suspended services, including the Vatican.

Ghana and Gabon confirmed their first cases to become the ninth and tenth countries in Sub-Saharan Africa to register positive cases.

More tests are being hampered by a lack of buffer to extract viral nucleic acids, the RNA inside the particles.

Just to be clear regarding this R0 thing (and this is very basic but works): R0 (R zero) is a measure of how many other people one person infects. R0 = 1: which means 1 infected person transmits to 1 other person. If that happens every five days (time from infection to transmission), it takes nearly 5 million years to infect everyone in the US or Europe. R0 = 2: 1 person infects two people, who then infect 4, 8, etc., until 135 billion people have been infected in about six months. So, R0 = 1: transmission peters out and never really takes hold. R0 is a function of social distancing. Take a highly contagious (could still be asymptomatic) person from Italy, put them in a room with 350 other pharma colleagues from Biogen at the Cowen conference in Boston (which is what happened this week or last, depending on the viral latency) to shake hands, hug, stand close, huddle together, and that person's R0 can be 70. Take the same person and put him or her on a desert island and their R0 will be zero. In crowded cities with cooler temperatures, R0 can be well above 2. Currently, in warmer weather, R0 appears to be <1. The evidence for that could change. If we see sustained transmission in warm weather, it will show evidence that R0 >1 and needs to be strongly contained. We haven't seen that yet, but we are looking for it.

The power of exponential growth, though, is immense. There's a story about an Indian king who played a sage at chess. To motivate his opponent, the king asked the sage for any reward he wanted. The sage modestly asked just for a few grains of rice in the following manner: the king was to put a single grain of rice on the first chess square and double it on every consequent one. The king accepted the sage's request. Having lost the game, and being a man of his word, the king ordered a bag of rice to be brought to the chessboard. Then he started placing rice grains according to the arrangement: 1 grain on the first square, 2 on the second, 4 on the third, 8 on the fourth and so on. Following the exponential growth of the rice payment, the king quickly realised that he was unable to fulfil his promise because at the twentieth square the king would have had to put on 1,000,000 grains of rice. And there are more chess moves possible than molecules in the universe. Lots of analogies to viruses and infections here.

People who are taking precautions, staying 3 feet from others, sanitising things, etc., until we learn more, are part of the group keeping the R0 <1. Those going to crowded bars in known hotspots, sitting close, kissing hello and shaking hands are at risk of driving the spread in the R0 >2 group.

14.03.20

Spain has had a staggering 66% increase in cases – now over 5,000 – and looks like another Italy, but nobody is talking about it.

Acting Brazilian ambassador Nestor Forster, who sat at President Trump's table Saturday night during a dinner at Mar-a-Lago, has tested positive for the coronavirus. Forster is the third person who visited the president's Florida resort last weekend to test positive for the novel virus. Trudeau is in isolation as his wife is positive.

15.03.20

Trump tests negative. The Spanish PM's wife is positive. Spain moves toward a nationwide lockdown, and France closes most businesses.

More than 200 scientists have written to the British government urging it to introduce tougher measures to tackle the spread of Covid-19.

They say the government's current approach will put the NHS under additional stress and 'risk many more lives than necessary'.

Re our baricitinib study: I am talking to Gary at Lilly. He is just superb. Mario and Giacamo and Silvia are marshalling the data together, but Gary is driving the show. I couldn't do this without him; in fact, I couldn't do this without any of them, and to cap it all off, we are getting outstanding data. I thought we'd tick the AI hypothesis as being correct, but I hadn't realised that the laboratory work would ever confirm it to this degree. Quite amazing. And it's happening in three different countries right now, each one validating the other's data: England, Italy and the US. What we've seen on the computer programmes seems to be validated in both patients and in the laboratory.

Stopped on the way home for some shopping and had the most surreal experience in a supermarket (of all places). I have never before experienced anything like this and had no reason to expect anything out of the ordinary, even when I approached it. It hadn't really dawned on me that I would have to battle it out for groceries – or that I should probably have brought a mask. In the back of my mind, I knew that there was an inherent risk, but then again, this was simple food shopping. How intense could it get?

I thought I'd get some pasta; it keeps forever and can be used as the basis for many meals. Unfortunately, my plan was thwarted when I found the right aisle but saw… nothing. The shelves, normally fully stocked with pasta, pulses and rice in every shape, colour and size were bare, seemingly stripped by locusts. The only hint of what had been there before was a packet of penne that had split and spewed its contents over a middle shelf, the victim of a bloodless massacre. When had Britain's stores ever run out of food? Was this my local shop or had I been transported to some third-world country? Is this what economic collapse looked like? It was sobering. I have gathered data but not applied it to everyday life. I had, naively, expected to walk into the familiar and find that it had remained unaffected by the pandemic news. How wrong I was. I was reminded of the phrase that civilisation is only ever three meals away from anarchy. If that is true, then right now it looks like it's one down and two to go.

And just when I thought things couldn't get any more surreal, they did. The aisle with toilet paper had been savaged. Not a single roll was left. Though it can happen with any infection, diarrhoea is not a significant symptom of Covid-19, but it seemed the local population were taking no chances. The lines to check out were ridiculous, and there were growls of complaint coming from impatient shoppers. Everyone was crammed together in haphazard lines. I looked at the throng and thought only of it as a cross-vector for contamination in living form. Someone coughed. A few people threw them dirty looks, but most seemed oblivious. Couldn't get out of there fast enough.

16.03.20

Right, back to work after my bruising encounter where Covid met panic buying.

Work on viral proteins is continuing apace, but from my discussions, remdesivir doesn't work very well and is intravenous. Roche's Actemra stops the body's a billionormal reaction to the virus by inhibiting a single cytokine, interleukin-6. Our own trials with Mario and others in Italy have begun in earnest, and others are taking up the challenge of using the drug in Madrid, Paris, Oslo and Nova Scotia. Late-night calls talking to doctors all over the world begin. Most have read my pieces in *The Lancet* and *The Lancet Infectious Diseases* and are desperate for a simple, quick solution. In a disease where most people recover, it's not going to be so simple to show this properly.

Some countries are doing better than us, like Germany. There are so many plausible and semi-plausible associations as explanations. I just don't know why. Maybe because the pneumococcal vaccine, Pneumovax, is used more widely in Germany? Maybe I'll get this for my friends and family, alongside hydroxychloroquine as a treatment. The laboratory studies that show it stopping the virus from infecting cells are rudimentary at best.

17.03.20

Some decent new case rate declines, but the total number of cases and deaths outside China has overtaken the total number of cases in China.

In the US, the Ohio presidential primary was delayed on health grounds.

Global infections passed 180,000. There have been 7,154 deaths and 79,433 recoveries worldwide.

France tightened its lockdown and ordered 100,000 officers to police it.

The Greek Orthodox Church have now suspended daily services.

Tom Hanks and his wife, Rita Wilson, have been released from an Australian hospital, five days after they were diagnosed with Covid-19.

Trump posted a tweet referring to Covid-19 as 'the Chinese virus'. Trump also warned that social upheaval caused by the outbreak could last beyond August. The White House is recommending, but not enforcing, stay-at-home orders. Trump has told Americans to avoid any gatherings of more than ten people over the next fifteen days and is advising all states with evidence of community transmission to close down bars, restaurants, gyms and other facilities. Californians are now urged to 'shelter in place'.

Canada has closed its border to everyone.

A paper in the *NEJM* has shown that the virus remains stable in aerosols for over 3 hours. SARS-CoV-2 was more stable on plastic and stainless steel than on copper and cardboard, and the viable virus was detected up to 72 hours after application to these surfaces.

Here, Prime Minister Boris Johnson has urged everyone to avoid unnecessary social contacts, to work from home where possible and to stay away from pubs and restaurants. People in at-risk groups will be asked within days to stay home for 12 weeks.

A document published by the Covid-19 team at Imperial College, Neil Ferguson's group, which is advising the government on its coronavirus response, warns the current public health threat is the 'most serious' form of a respiratory virus since the Spanish flu in 1918. They advise the UK government to adopt a strategy of 'epidemic suppression' for a period of potentially 18 months or more, rather than 'mitigation'. Epidemiologists have predicted 17 of the last 3 pandemics and are always mega-bearish, so pinches of salt are always required. I dropped him a line, but he didn't reply to me.

18.03.20

The immune response to the virus has been mapped, and the Moderna vaccine is among the new treatment hopes. I spoke again to Stéphane Bancel at Moderna, a friend since I visited Moderna in 2011, who said it is possible the FDA will approve their vaccine based on the healthy patient study. He also said their mRNA base technology lent itself to use against a virus that mutated, i.e. variants. I have always loved the way they make their mRNA to be not detected by the immune system like a viral attack. It's modified to prevent this, in fact.

Australia's Prime Minister Morrison stepped up the country's response to the coronavirus crisis by announcing sweeping new measures to try to slow the spread. This includes a ban on indoor gatherings of more than 100 people, a global do-not-travel order and strict new rules for visiting care homes.

British-Australian academic Kylie Moore-Gilbert has not been reported among the 85,000 prisoners temporarily released from Iranian jails out of fear coronavirus could sweep through the country's overcrowded prisons.

Las Vegas casinos close. It's the right move, but with travel becoming restricted and the main reason to visit shut down, you have to feel for the tens of thousands of workers either working in or supporting the gambling industry in that city. How long can they last without a pay cheque?

19.03.20

A very informative paper in *Nature Medicine* says as of 29 February there were 79,394 confirmed cases and 2,838 deaths from Covid-19 in mainland China. Of these, 48,557 cases and 2,169 deaths occurred in the epicentre, Wuhan. A key public health priority during the emergence of a novel pathogen is estimating clinical severity, which requires properly adjusting for the case ascertainment rate and the delay between symptom onset and death. Using public and published information, we see that the overall symptomatic case fatality risk (the probability of dying after developing symptoms) of Covid-19 in Wuhan was 1.4%, which is substantially lower than both the corresponding crude or naive confirmed case fatality risk (2,169/48,557 = 4.5%) and the approximator 1 of deaths/deaths + recoveries (2,169/2,169 + 17,572 = 11%) as of 29 February. Compared to those aged 30–59 years, those aged below 30 and above 59 years were 0.6 (0.3–1.1) and 5.1 (4.2–6.1) times more likely to die after developing symptoms. The risk of symptomatic infection increased with age; for example, at ~4% per year among adults aged 30–60 years.

The New England Journal of Medicine has released data that HIV medicines don't work for Covid-19, and this highlights why proper, randomised trials are needed when assessing all drugs and vaccines for Covid-19. An editorial I have written with Silvia Ottaviani on the importance of randomised studies has been accepted by *Cell*'s new journal called *Med*.

20.03.20

Rhetoric around IOC postponing the Olympic Games. It's a tough call but the right one.

The California governor issues statewide stay-at-home orders.

UK newly designated 'key workers' are allowed to keep children in school (not sure who will teach them).

China exonerates whistle-blower Doctor Li Wenliang, who died from Covid-19 last month.

Trump said yesterday that the FDA had approved hydroxychloroquine (HCQ) to treat Covid-19. The implementation of an antiviral treatment and prophylaxis (prevention) has several requirements, and I can't see this has come close to reaching any of these. I cannot overemphasise the importance of properly conducted randomised trials, which HCQ, among most others, has not been through thus far, whatever the lab studies show. I know am being boring repeating this.

21.03.20

Mainland China reported no new locally transmitted cases, but infections involving travellers arriving from other countries continued to rise.

The tally of infections has surpassed 1,000 in Japan, Australia and Canada. Across New York, Illinois and California, 70 million people will be largely restricted to their homes, starting this weekend.

In Britain, as if I need to mention it, pubs, cafés, gyms and restaurants closed for business on Friday night after the government announced a wage support scheme. Our death rate is now closer to Italy's than Scandinavian countries, Germany or Switzerland.

Lots of reports of irresponsible behaviour but nothing violent. In Sydney, officials have closed Bondi Beach after thousands flocked there on Friday. Once it reopens, if more than 500 people are on the beach at any one time, it will be closed.

A nationwide curfew has begun in Jordan, limiting the mobility of its 10 million citizens indefinitely.

What did the French trial of hydroxychloroquine (HCQ) show that led Trump to say the FDA had approved it? It showed most people recover – we know that already. What we don't know is if it's better than not having the drug. Bizarre for Trump to say this.

22.03.20

Singapore has banned all transit passengers. In China, all international flights due to arrive in Beijing will be diverted to other airports as their first port of entry.

The Russian military is helping Italy from today with transport planes. That's a lot of non-EU support for Italy (Jack Ma gave them millions of masks). Wonder where the politics of this is going?

Indian citizens are being asked to observe a 14-hour/day curfew. Just 332 cases have been reported there, but such a low number has to be down to the absence of widespread testing.

Have just gotten a call from my mother that her younger brother Mark, headmaster of a school in Yorkshire, had been admitted with pneumonia to hospital in York. I don't know what to say. No one can visit. No one can hold anyone's hand. Her other brother John died in the fires in Kinglake National Park, Australia, in 2009, where he worked as a zoologist. He used to show me how different prehistoric ant species could survive in the same habitat (eating different food at different times in different places). Mark is generally healthy, but it just didn't 'sound good'. All seems increasingly personal.

23.03.20

The stock market continues to fall as senators debate a $2 trillion stimulus package to protect the country's economy. The Dow Jones had been just over 29,000 points, an all-time high a month ago, but now it has sunk to 18,592, as trillions of dollars are wiped off the value of the world's largest economy. President Trump has inextricably linked his presidency to the stock market, and he seemed, initially, to have worked his charms on the Dow Jones. Its steady and substantial rise seemed to confirm the president's business acumen… except that its fall indicates the opposite. The virus has made him vulnerable, I think.

Trump has avoided the consequences of sex scandals, funding scandals and even impeachment. Just a month ago it looked like he was a sure thing for re-election, but now a virus and the ensuing economic meltdown associated with the growing pandemic might be the place where he is held accountable. He can't declare it fake news (although he has tried), and he can't ignore it or pay it to go away. It seems Trump has met his nemesis.

Coronavirus-related deaths worldwide are approaching 15,000. Confirmed cases reached 339,259, with the number of recoveries currently amounting to just under a third of these, at 98,834. In the UK, the government is considering stricter measures; present figures are 281 deaths, 5,683 affected.

Rapid testing procedures seem to be improving everywhere. The benefits are significant but simple: if we could all get tested quickly and cheaply, we could all go back to work, with all that that implies for our economy and our wellbeing. Lots of simple things to iron out; we need results quickly.

Losing the sense of smell could be a key clinical indicator in otherwise symptom-free carriers of Covid-19. It's also a warning of Parkinson's, I am reliably informed.

Angela Merkel went into quarantine after the doctor who saw her tested positive for the virus.

Harvey Weinstein tested positive for coronavirus. Prisons surely will be ravaged by this; anyone living in close quarters is at greater risk.

Canada said it will not send athletes to the Tokyo Olympics. New Zealand said it would consider boycotting Tokyo 2020, and Australia told its athletes to prepare for the games to be held next year, in 2021 – all in the wake of Japan's Prime Minister Shinzo Abe saying postponement could be an option. Olympics President Yoshiro Mori says the biggest concern is the cost of cancelling the games. I would argue the greater cost is the tens of thousands of likely infections and the subsequent deaths.

Nearly 1 in 3 Americans were under orders on Sunday to stay home to slow the spread of the coronavirus pandemic as Ohio, Louisiana and Delaware become the latest states to enact broad restrictions.

Today, we in the UK go into full lockdown for twelve weeks. Schools, offices and all non-essential shops are closed. We are allowed out only to food shop (where you must be 2 metres apart) and for brief, local, outdoor exercise. Key workers will continue in their jobs, but that's it.

I write this from home, hunched over a desk I will now occupy daily for the next three months. It's the right move but is unprecedented in its curbing of freedoms of movement for the entire population. It's the biggest call by a government outside of wartime. In short, this is extraordinary!

And so we come to an especially cruel aspect of disease prevention. While death is the ultimate price to pay, the reality is that billions of people on planet Earth will avoid catching the virus or be largely unaffected by it. But these same people are facing the loneliness, isolation and frustration of lockdown and quarantine. The rational, medical part of my brain knows that these are simple yet practical weapons to fight the spread of respiratory illnesses. But I am a human too. With the restrictions in place, am I allowed to visit my children? I share custody, so we are a family unit even though the law says we are not. Billions of people will miss hugs from loved ones, get-togethers with friends and the vital social interactions that mark our everyday lives and make them worth living. Restrictions undoubtedly save lives, but at what cost? I wonder what the lasting damage for all of this will be.

Mark can't breathe and is ventilated in intensive care in York hospital. This is bad.

24.03.20

Lots of increases in rates of infection with today's data: France and Spain are at 22% and 24% respectively; the UK is up from 13% to 26%; the US is stable at 32%.

In Tokyo, crowds took part in the annual cherry blossom Hanami parties, so the government will probably lockdown there. I hear dire things about Russia despite the public figures. Putin said, 'Stay home for 15-days or go to jail for 5 years. Statement is over'. Short, succinct and to the point.

25.03.20

Global confirmed cases around 400,000, deaths 20,000.

A *New York Times* editorial advocates a national lockdown.

I saw the *FT* article on herd immunity that says 50% of us may be infected, but the tests are not showing this.

NHS England is establishing a big hospital at the ExCeL conference centre in east London. The Nightingale Hospital will be ready for patients from next week, initially providing up to 500 beds equipped with ventilators and oxygen. The capacity will then continue to increase, potentially up to several thousand beds, should they be required.

I've volunteered online to help, as have many of my colleagues. The form we fill out is crude but useful: when did you last intubate someone, was one of the first questions, among many of that type.

26.03.20

The UN has warned of a global food shortage, and after my time in Whole Foods, I can believe it. But it's not just panic buying that could be responsible. If farmers, industry workers or drivers fall ill in significant numbers, bottlenecks could result at any point along the lines of distribution from source to consumer. Something to think about.

The UK government has ordered 10,000 ventilators from Dyson, though it could take a couple of weeks to move from the prototype to actual production. The NHS currently has just over 8,000.

Mark takes a turn for the worse, but the ITU doctors stabilise him.

Nature has rejected our first baricitinib in humans paper after having it reviewed extensively. At least they did it quickly and have told us it's not a randomised study. Yes, right, it's 4 patients not 400, and they all got the drug alongside laboratory studies. No idea why they reviewed it if they were going to reject it for the obvious point of randomisation in the first place. We'll have it published somewhere shortly. Lilly has this super annoying rule that you only get two bites of the publishing cherry. Our preprint has been downloaded over 2,000 times, but we need this properly published. *Cell* wants the paper, but it's too much of a risk to send it to another huge journal. They may ask for a monkey study or something similar. We're already completely stretched.

27.03.20

Clearly, long-term care facilities (LTCF) will be at risk of Covid-19, and the *NEJM* has published an important paper on this subject. After identification on 28 February of a confirmed case of Covid-19 in a skilled nursing facility in King County, Washington, Public Health – Seattle and King County, aided by the CDC, launched a case investigation, contact tracing, quarantine of exposed persons, isolation of confirmed and suspected cases, and on-site enhancement of infection prevention and control. As of 18 March, a total of 167 confirmed cases of Covid-19, affecting 101 residents, 50 healthcare personnel and 16 visitors were found to be epidemiologically linked to the facility. Most cases among residents included respiratory illness consistent with Covid-19; however, in 7 residents no symptoms were documented. Hospitalisation rates for facility residents, visitors and staff were 54.5%, 50.0%, and 6.0%, respectively. The case fatality rate for residents was 33.7% (34 of 101). As of 18 March, a total of 30 long-term care facilities with at least one confirmed case of Covid-19 had been identified in King County. 'In the context of rapidly escalating Covid-19 outbreaks, proactive steps by long-term care facilities to identify and exclude potentially infected staff and visitors, actively monitor for potentially infected patients and implement appropriate infection prevention and control measures are needed to prevent the introduction of Covid-19.'

New York is no longer driving US growth. That is the most interesting finding today. The US now has more cases than any other country. Apparently, there was a 'good' phone call between Trump and President Xi of China.

US and UK infection rates are both increasing. My hospital, Imperial NHS Trust, is now caring for 183 patients who have tested positive for the virus, and we've more than doubled our critical care/ventilator capacity to 143 beds.

Downing Street has just announced that Boris Johnson has contracted Covid-19, but symptoms are mild. Suddenly the chorus of anger and indignation directed at the PM from satirical news shows and the Labour Party have evaporated as everyone wishes him a speedy recovery, many presumably through gritted teeth.

In York, they try reducing the support Mark is receiving, but they're unsuccessful. I think it's over for him.

28.03.20

600,000 global cases, nearly 30,000 deaths.

Abbott Laboratories launches point-of-care diagnostics to detect the virus within 5 minutes. This is game-changing, I think.

For the first time, WHO is asking the general public and private donors for financial support. The project is a test run for the WHO Foundation, to be launched later this year. According to WHO, almost 30% of countries have no Covid-19 national preparedness and response plans.

Mark's kidneys have stopped working so he's getting dialysis, but his lungs have worsened. All these organs are interlinked.

29.03.20

The CDC has urged no domestic travel in several states on the east coast, and Trump has withdrawn the NY quarantine proposal.

Sam, Mark's son, messages me to say, 'Yep getting worse. I think he's in the process of dying xx.'

30.03.20

Numbers are going up. At Imperial we're now caring for 252 patients; 43 are ventilated due to Covid-19. Staff are being redeployed to deal with the virus and others are off sick. We're stopping routine intravenous chemotherapy, trying to switch to tablet treatments in a real hurry.

31.03.20

Impressive paper in *The Lancet Infectious Diseases* showing just how relevant age is as a risk factor, with 60 being the cut off for a big change in mortality. Also, new data suggests restrictions are slowing coronavirus infections. It doesn't solve the problem, but it buys us some time.

I ask Sam, who is an amazing actor – the star of the 'History Boys' on stage and film – if there is any chance with his father (and I am supposed to be the doctor here). He replies, 'I don't think so I'm afraid xx.'

April

01.04.20

Every country in my tracker, apart from France (17%) and the US (15%), now has single-digit daily death percentage increases, not double digits. Can't work out if this is good news.

While potential therapeutic strategies for Covid-19 grab headlines, diagnostics rather than therapeutics are better positioned to materially change the economic and medical outlook.

Dr Anthony Fauci said, based on modelling of the current pace of the coronavirus spread in the US, 'Between 100,000 and 200,000' people may die from Covid-19. Fauci said the figure is a middle-of-the-road estimate and much lower than worst case scenario predictions. He said preparing for 1–2 million Americans to die from the coronavirus is 'almost certainly off the chart,' adding, 'Now it's not impossible but very, very unlikely.' Fauci cautioned people not to put too much emphasis on predictions, noting that 'it's such a moving target that you could so easily be wrong and mislead people'. Yesterday Fauci and Dr Debora Brix projected 100,000 to 240,000 deaths as 'our real number'. President Trump said that as many as 2.2 million people 'would have died if we did nothing, if we just carried on with our life'.

Context

According to the CDC the seasonal flu has killed between 12,000 and 61,000 people a year since 2010. The 1918/19 pandemic caused 39 million, 2.1% of the world population; the US has a cumulative death rate of 0.52% (total: 550,000), including one in every 100 American males between the ages of 25 and 34. 2.1% of today's world population would be 163 million people. 0.52% of today's US population would be 1.7 million. So, here's another way to look at it:

- Worldwide, 59 million people die every year. So, roughly 160,000 people die a day. Around 60% of them are 65 or older.
- Since the outbreak of the Covid-19 pandemic in January, around 40,000 people have died because of it worldwide.
- Even if none of these people would have died anyway – unlikely given the age profile of the dead – that represents only a 0.28% increase in total expected deaths for Q1 2020.
- In 2018, 2.8 million Americans died, so around 7,800 Americans died each day. 74% of those were 65 or older.
- To date, 3,756 Americans have died because of Covid-19.
- Even if none of these people would have died anyway, that represents only a 1% increase in total expected deaths in March 2020.
- If we could get a total mortality number for March 2020, we could see if it was an exceptional month. As with the Momo data for Europe, I suspect it wouldn't even show as a blip.
- In aggregate, Covid-19 is increasing the mortality of seniors worldwide, but not on a massive scale.
- The US now seems to be going down the European (ex-Sweden) road of more drastic suppression of Covid-19.

Mark has died. Utterly devastating. No one could be with him. Can't imagine the funeral will be any different. So proud of him, everyone loved him, and the Selby food bank is an enduring good legacy for a good man. It's been hard to write anything after hearing the news. I am so sorry, Mum.

02.04.20

More than three months into the pandemic we still lack reliable figures on the virus' most important epidemiological characteristics: the proportion of asymptomatic cases and thus its true spread through a given population and the true infection or case fatality rate (CFR). These are very different variables. The infection fatality rate (IFR) includes those diagnosed and undiagnosed. Think the IFR is a much better measure than CFR. We can estimate those undiagnosed using antibody/serology tests.

Fauci has commented that Moderna's trial will be the ultimate game-changer but is twelve to eighteen months away, meaning that it won't be approved on the basis of clinical outcomes. There are some reasons to be hopeful. Given that patients who are infected with coronaviruses do mount immune responses, it should be possible for a vaccine to create antibodies.

The weekly campaign to step outside and applaud the NHS on Thursday night at 8 p.m. has started. A week later and support for this demonstration of appreciation and gratitude seems to keep growing.

03.04.20

Do we now have Schrödinger's virus? If we can't get properly tested, we can't know if we have the virus or not, so we have to act as if we've never had it because if we haven't, we're not immune. But at the same time, we must act as if we have the virus so we don't transmit it to others as new research suggests that the rate of asymptomatic infection may be higher and the real infection fatality ratio lower than was initially feared.

EMBO Molecular Medicine has agreed to take our paper on baricitinib, using reviewer comments from *Nature*. Really good of them. The editor and his associate editor are simply lovely. I hope I am as nice as editor of *Oncogene*.

A paper in *Nature Medicine* shows that surgical face masks significantly reduced detection of influenza virus RNA in respiratory droplets and coronavirus RNA in aerosols, with a trend toward reduced detection of coronavirus RNA in respiratory droplets. This means they could prevent transmission of human coronaviruses and influenza viruses from symptomatic individuals.

04.04.20

The CDC just announced that Americans should wear masks to protect themselves from Covid-19. Trump said he wouldn't. The recommendation comes rather late in an epidemic that is not far from its peak. The widely cited IHME model predicts that New York is only a week away from its peak death rate.

Boris Johnson's pregnant partner Carrie Symonds now has Covid-19.

Harsh editorial in the *New England Journal of Medicine* editorial, which had this to say:

> This is the dark side of federalism: it encourages a patchwork response to epidemics. States and localities may decide to implement aggressive disease-mitigation measures, but need not do so. The defining feature of the US response to Covid-19, therefore, continues to be localised action against a threat that lost its local character weeks ago. The US approach contrasts strikingly with those of South Korea and Taiwan, which have prevented widespread community transmission by rapidly implementing a centralised national strategy. Lacking strong federal leadership to guide a uniform response, the United States quickly fulfilled the World Health Organisation's prediction that it would become the new epicentre of Covid-19.

Clinicians with inadequate access to standard PPE have been compelled to improvise protective barrier enclosures for use during endotracheal intubation. Researchers now describe one such barrier that is easily fabricated and may help protect clinicians during this procedure. The barrier studied was an 'aerosol box,' which consists of a transparent plastic cube designed to cover a patient's head and incorporates two circular ports through which the clinician's hands are passed to perform the airway procedure.

Lots of junior doctors here have been put on Covid wards. I've noticed that the number of biopsies we're doing to diagnose cancer has fallen through the floor, and the chemotherapy services are almost grinding to a halt. So now we'll have an epidemic to catch up with late diagnoses and excess deaths, and excess deaths from lack of treatment for other conditions. Clearly routine presentations to A&E are down too, but that might just reflect people not going out.

05.04.20

A key here has been, as a colleague has mentioned, to establish prevalence, which is why a decent serology test is so important. Indeed, the CFR is turning out to be pretty useless. The IFR is a much more useful number of deaths divided by known and unknown cases.

The Bronx Zoo in New York reported that a 4-year-old female Malayan tiger had tested positive for Covid-19.

06.04.20

A few points this morning:

- One has to be concerned about the PM despite it being stated that admission to hospital was for 'precautionary tests'. In the evening it was announced that Boris Johnson is now in the ICU with Covid-19. He could become the first prime minister to die in office since Henry John Temple, 3rd Viscount Palmerston, in 1865. I really hope not.
- The US is entering what will likely be its worst week. New York may have already peaked, though yesterday's lower death counts could also be a blip. Either way, I think the US is not far from a shift away from the current focus on the virus' human cost and moving toward planning for an end to lockdowns and a return to some sort of normalcy.
- I listened to a replay of the International Sensitivity Index (ISI) call on serology with the CEO of Genalyte, which is yet another company making tests that I hadn't heard of. The aim was to debunk the hype as per the Citigroup note. The argument is that most tests

are not specific enough. That is, they have a high false-negative rate. Well, it also depends on how common a disease is. So much depends on the characteristics of the test and on the population being tests (i.e. low vs high prevalence of disease). For example, using a highly sensitive test in a low disease prevalence population (when the disease is rare) will give you lots of false positives.

07.04.20

The best ICU data set series is 1,591 patients admitted critically ill in Lombardy. Once a patient enters the ICU, the mortality rate is 26%. I was on the phone with Boris Johnson's brother at 1 a.m. He's on ITU. We're discussing all these new and old treatments, from convalescent plasma to stem cell therapies. I keep saying no, no, no. I think I am really boring. We lack randomised data – we just don't know if any of it works. The prime minister is clearly getting the best medical care in the world.

08.04.20

Interesting French survey with unusual methodology (derived from GP consultations), estimating 9% of the French population may have contracted Covid-19.

A report in the *New England Journal of Medicine* from South Korea where very clear contact tracing showed 3 out of 28 individuals in a small series transmitted it while asymptomatic.

On the treatment side, former FDA leaders have decried the authorisation of HCQ based on a lack of data. About time.

09.04.20

I have read a couple of fascinating articles: one an eloquent and convincingly written argument on why herd immunity won't work, the other on the effectiveness of non-pharmaceutical interventions (NPIs) in China. Masks and distancing work, and yet they are becoming politicised in America.

More calls to set up baricitinib trials across the world amid lockdowns. Trying to sort out an elderly focused study in Albacete near Madrid with my new collaborator Dr Pedro Abizander Soler, a geriatrician there. This is the thing about Covid: it encompasses everything from infectious diseases to statistics, molecular biology to rheumatology, cellular models to artificial intelligence and, of course, ethics to compassion. Every medical and scientific speciality is involved.

10.04.20

Four central points for me thus far:

1) In general, the virus only kills people that have left the workforce – it really is a killer of the elderly.
2) It is, for a number of reasons, not like influenza pandemics, making it different historically, and its R0 is higher than previously calculated as per CDC.
3) If we do everything possible to protect the elderly, then people should be able to return to work, especially if the IFR, the infection fatality rate, taking into account the asymptomatic cases, is as low as we think it is, and I am coming to the conclusion that even 0.3% is being conservative.
4) The key features of point 3 deserve a re-mention. Positive Predictive Value (PPV) is the probability that if a patient's test says they have Covid immunity, they really do. If 20% of a population is truly immune, then that same assay's PPV will be 69%, meaning 31% will have a false positive. Can you imagine if it turned out that 30–70% of patients who were told they have Covid immunity actually didn't? This is going to be really relevant when the number of people infected in a population falls. We'll be telling people who aren't immune that they are.

A paper in *JAMA Neurology* shows an altered sense of smell with Covid. Seems like an early sign of viral infection.

11.04.20

As of now, the global Covid-19 vaccine R&D landscape includes well over 100 vaccine candidates, of which 78 are confirmed as active and 37 are unconfirmed (development status cannot be determined from publicly available or proprietary information sources). Of the 78 confirmed active projects, 73 are currently at exploratory or preclinical stages. The most advanced candidates have recently moved into clinical development, including mRNA-1273 from Moderna, another mRNA candidate from Pfizer/BioNTech, and AstraZeneca's, Johnson&Johnson and CanSino's adenoviral constructs – replete with the virus' spike protein on the surface. There are also several inactivated virus candidates, and Novovax have a protein subunit vaccine with an adjuvant component to stimulate the immune system generally, too. Theirs is from the bark of the Chilean saponin tree. Numerous other vaccine developers have indicated they'll start in some form or another. Heat Biologics, run by the charming Jeff Wolf, has a candidate too and has been asked to sit on his scientific advisory board again to help assess the efficacy of the vaccines that got to trial.

12.04.20

Boris Johnson is discharged from hospital with, it seems, a collective sigh of relief. Now his critics can go back to criticising him, and everyone else can look forward to the return of the PM after a week of painful briefings from Dominic Raab.

Today is also notable for low, single-digit increases in cases across the board.

13.04.20

Iceland's testing suggests 50% of coronavirus cases have no symptoms.

Recovered coronavirus patients in South Korea test positive again in a blow to immunity hopes. I don't think reinfection occurs, but reactivation or lack of clearance seems to, and to me, going forward, it's a game of whack-a-mole for new clusters.

14.04.20

In the US, the piecemeal, state-driven decision-making process makes containment very challenging. The ability to travel freely between states means hot zones can seed cold zones and then be reseeded from other hot areas of the country. Now, as the president insists that he is the one who decides when the economy will reopen, a group of states are banding to form their own restart policy. New York, Pennsylvania, Massachusetts, Rhode Island, Delaware and now Connecticut have committed to a joint task force to decide how to reopen their economies. These include four of the top five states in terms of Covid-19 patient count, but many others are growing quickly. These are all broadly 'blue states', although Pennsylvania did vote Republican in the last election and Massachusetts has a Republican governor, though one who is seen as bipartisan. New York Governor Cuomo, who has been broadly applauded for his handling of Covid-19, notes that the restart decision must be approached as a regional issue and not driven by 'opinion and politics'.

Thus, one has growing interstate collaborations and conflicts as well as federal/state ones. Simultaneously, Bernie Sanders might be out of the election race, but he is still pushing his agenda. The US does have issues with healthcare and pharmaceuticals, especially when it comes to drug pricing, but the middle of a global pandemic is not the right time to bash the pharma industry.

Re our baricitinib study: the regular calls with myself, BenevolentAI and Lilly are showing us that in the real-life setting the AI prediction was correct. Gary and Anabela didn't believe this at first, but they've done the work to show themselves, us and the world that it really is for real – excuse the tautology. This isn't just great for Covid patients, but AI could be used in future pandemics too. The drug seems to have this dual mechanism, but we do need to personalise treatment. I am not talking about genetics, I just mean treating the right patients at the right time.

15.04.20

We have our usual consultants' meeting at Imperial, but this time it's different. Cancer services are in free fall, but I am aghast at our head of oncology at the NHS Trust stating we have a shortage of syringe drivers. This was in explicit reference to keeping cancer patients comfortable and ensuring a peaceful, rapid death in this crisis, just because they have cancer, i.e. if Covid-19 infects them, then ensure a rapid death. Really? Has it come to this? 'Don't even try' seemed to be the not-so-subliminal message. I looked around the room and think I was the only person aghast. Surely, just surely, it's not this bad. Are people not looking at the data, or are they interpreting it differently?

A *Nature Medicine* paper shows that 44% of secondary cases were infected during the index cases' presymptomatic stage, in settings with substantial household clustering, active case finding and quarantine outside the home. They say disease control measures should be adjusted to account for probable substantial presymptomatic transmission. To be clear, the difference between presymptomatic and asymptomatic is that presymptomatic patients later go on to develop symptoms, i.e. fever, cough.

The situation in China appears surprisingly well contained, though with stringent monitoring and surveillance that may be difficult to replicate in the USA and the libertarian West in general. If China prevents a second wave, this doesn't mean other countries will too, but if they do experience additional waves it will be a harbinger of challenges ahead. One important difference for the US is that the spread of Covid-19 has exceeded that of the benchmark countries, while testing has lagged. China, South Korea, Taiwan and Hong Kong appear to have passed their fairly small apices of new cases, while Singapore and Japan are seeing a recent increase with meaningful local spread; however, interestingly, the proportion of asymptomatic cases appears high, indicating better/more and perhaps earlier testing.

16.04.20

Fascinating article on disease transmission on the London Underground argues that influenza transmission is very highly correlated with public transport usage and negatively with cars. Makes sense, but the magnitude is impressive. This would explain why New York is worse than San Francisco but less so Germany vs Italy.

Complex article on the projection of transmission dynamics published in *Science*. An excerpt: 'The pandemic and post-pandemic transmission dynamics of SARS-CoV-2 will depend on factors including the degree of seasonal variation in transmission, the duration of immunity, and the degree of cross-immunity between SARS-CoV-2 and other coronaviruses, as well as the intensity and timing of control measures.' Argues for social distancing until 2022 and surveillance until 2024.

17.04.20

The only way to see if a drug truly works is in the context of a randomised trial. We have seen no randomised data. The latest news on the STAT website of doctors singing and dancing about remdesivir (a bit), isn't randomised data. They've increased the size of their largest RCT from 400 to >2,000 patients. There are two primary end points and it's a powerful study, meaning the ability to detect a difference if one exists because it's so big. They really only need one primary end point to work.

The latest news, that many sick people get better, isn't any new news. It's an intravenous pro-drug, a so-called nucleoside analogue, metabolised in the liver to an active drug, but the livers of these sick patients do not work that well. After the remdesivir single-arm *New England Journal of Medicine* publication, Gilead's CEO/chairman, the ex-head of Roche diagnostics, put out an open letter in response to criticism. Other companies involved, like Lilly, think a lot of Gilead's behaviour is 'underhand'. I should know as this is what they've said to me.

Why did the China severe trial on remdesivir not stop for overwhelming efficacy at the interim analysis in mid-March? That's very important as the China trial has a proper placebo arm. I looked at the statistics for this interim analysis: remdesivir needed to show >60% effect size vs placebo to stop at interim, and it clearly didn't. So how does one make sense of all this? It's not a panacea and we need to wait for the RCTs to see if it works or not and how large that effect size is.

I would bet on Moderna's vaccine working, and see they've just received a $0.5 billion BARDA grant from the US government and are announcing their Phase 2 begins in quarter 2.

18.04.20

Stanford and others ran a sampling test of the general population in Santa Clara County, recruited through targeted Facebook ads, which I now attempt to summarise:

- This is the county with the greatest number of confirmed cases in northern California.
- They tested 3,439 individuals using tests with a sensitivity of 90% and specificity of 99.5%.
- The number of positive cases was 50 or crude prevalence of 1.5%.
- Reweighing by zip code, race and sex, the estimated prevalence of Covid-19 on 4 April is thus 2.81%.
- This number is adjusted by three parameter scenarios: sample prevalence, sensitivity, specificity. The final range of seroprevalence is thus 2.49–4.16%.
- This is the equivalent of 48,000–81,000 people that have had the virus.
- This is 50–85 times the number of confirmed cases.

I get the feeling we're all going to need a crash course in statistics. In medical diagnosis, test sensitivity is the ability of a test to correctly identify those with the disease (true positive rate), whereas test specificity is the ability of the test to correctly identify those without the disease (true negative rate). If 100 patients known to have a disease were tested, and 43 test positive, then the test has 43% sensitivity. If 100 with no disease are tested and 96 return a completely negative result, then the test has 96% specificity.

20.04.20

Many are anticipating a second wave of Covid as restrictions are serially lifted to restart a desperate economy. The Restart America framework reads like a sequence of increasing R0 steps needed to restart the economy. Each stage increases the probability/size of second waves. But many people will remain wary, face masks will be used, and hopefully transmission will be partially mitigated.

We are buying time to better equip hospitals with important PPE and reduce the frenzy in some settings.

We can use PCR (identification of the actual virus' genetic material) and serology (antibodies against the virus) to identify and trace infected people. Serology can offset the significant limitations of PCR, but antibodies take days to develop so they can complement one another and give different answers to similar questions. But, the better we contact map/trace, the more we can limit second waves. But it's not just 'let's test a lot'. Contact mapping is labour intensive – perhaps too much so given the vast extent of the outbreak.

As the next waves emerge, an array of pharma drugs will hopefully move upstream to keep patients out of hospitals and ICUs.

We may see (more) socioeconomic segregation: some people may be forced to accept Covid risks so they can work. The government may look to find a balance between giving people 'easy' money to stay home vs forcing them into exposure. Some people have the means to stay 'in hiding'.

And then, vaccines will hopefully start to arrive early next year despite a *Fierce Pharma* article saying it will take five years (worth being aware of).

- As of 9 a.m. today (Monday 20 April), at Imperial NHS Trust we were caring for 314 patients who have tested positive for coronavirus.
- Of these patients, 118 were in critical care on a ventilator – from a total of 143 patients in critical care on a ventilator.
- As of 9 a.m. yesterday (Sunday 19 April), 537 patients with coronavirus had recovered and been discharged from hospital (please note, we gave an incorrect figure in last Monday's update).
- The total number of deaths reported for our trust centrally via NHS England is 278 as of today (Monday 20 April).

Calls to US poison control centres regarding exposures to cleaning products and disinfectants reveal they increased by more than 20% during the first quarter of 2020, compared with 2019, according to a CDC analysis.

21.04.20

Widespread improvements across the board, confirmed by doctors here and in the US. Maybe it's going.

22.04.20

There are some important trials reporting in the next ~4 weeks, and one of them has an interim analysis today concerning a trial using generic HCQ in preventing Covid-19. Looks rubbish.

There's a Korean story about a hospital worker who had Covid for two days and could have exposed 211 people. They were all started on HCQ, and no one developed Covid. That reads positively, except for one nuance: the worker with Covid was wearing a mask during those two days, and this is where masks work best, i.e. they prevent someone with the virus from passing it on.

Governor Cuomo, on New York State study of HCQ prophylaxis, said, 'Anecdotally, you will get certain suggestions it's been effective, but we don't have any official data yet'.

In the US the positive trends of recent days reversed yesterday, though this could also reflect a catch-up of weekend reporting lags as we have seen before (numbers reported by states today were collected Monday). There were 25.5k new cases reported nationwide by state health departments, up from 24.5k the day before and with a small uptick in the positive test rate, to a total of approximately 800k confirmed US cases.

Four more tigers and three lions at the Bronx Zoo have tested positive for the virus that causes Covid-19. They can clearly transmit it. Obviously pets will be able to also, but I don't know which ones.

23.04.20

Dear, oh dear. Trump floated the idea of using disinfectants to treat Covid-19 patients. He did not say Americans should ingest chemicals to prevent or treat the virus. Here's the full context:

> A question that probably some of you are thinking of if you're totally into that world, which I find to be very interesting. So, supposedly we hit the body with a tremendous, whether it's ultraviolet or just very powerful light, and I think you said that hasn't been checked, but you're going to test it. And then I said supposing you brought the light inside the body, which you can do either through the skin or in some other way. And I think you said you're going to test that, too. Sounds interesting, right?
> And then I see the disinfectant, where it knocks it out in one minute. And is there a way we can do something like that, by injection inside or almost a cleaning, because you see it gets in the lungs and it does a tremendous number on the lungs, so it'd be interesting to check that, so that you're going to have to use medical doctors with, but it sounds interesting to me. So, we'll see, but the whole concept of the light, the way it kills it in one minute. That's pretty powerful.

He also said, 'I hope people enjoy the sun, and if it has an impact, that's great. I'm just hearing this, not really for the first time. I mean, there's been a rumour, a very nice rumour, that you go outside in the sun or you have heat, and it does have an effect on other viruses ... I would like you to speak to the medical doctors to see if there's any way that you can apply light and heat to cure. You know? If you could? And maybe you can; maybe you can't. Again, I say maybe you can; maybe you can't. I'm not a doctor.'

Incredible for such a public figure to say this sort of stream of consciousness stuff, as no doubt some people will ingest bleach to treat it. I am assuming that people outside the medical profession know that bleach and humans do not mix well.

I've now sent my latest baricitinib work to Howard Bauchner, the editor at *JAMA*, though it's not a randomised trial, as if I need reminding of this, and our discussions move on to the above Trump comments after I send him a picture of Dettol in a whisky glass replete with ice. He writes back with respect to the above comments: 'God save me – Tony Fauci and I are good friends – we do a live stream every two weeks – have done four now. I don't know how he keeps his sanity – and how he keeps his integrity intact is a tribute to 40 years in public service, his intelligence, and his calmness. I wonder what he is thinking sometimes.'

There's so much nonsense out there, said and written. Just based on feelings. The good thing about research is that it gives different results to what we 'think and feel'.

The interim analysis of the HCQ prevention trial I referred to yesterday indicates they can continue the study, which to me means no outstanding efficacy signal mandating early stopping, but no terrible toxicity. The next analysis is 6 May.

There are further costs to this pandemic: the American Dental Association Health Policy Institute released a study that quantifies the economic damage to dental practices from Covid-19. As expected, the situation looks dire, with nearly 85% of dental practices reporting patient volumes at less than 5% of what is typical.

24.04.20

Couple of points from yesterday:

- An estimated 13.9% of New Yorkers have likely had Covid-19, according to preliminary results of coronavirus antibody testing released by Governor Cuomo. Next, Bill Bryant (Head of Science and Technology Directorate at Homeland Security) presented results of a study at the White House, concluding that Sars-CoV-2 doesn't last in sunlight (gone in minutes). He then delivered the recommendation to shift activities outdoors… having said the virus won't survive in the sun. Would have been nice if he had mentioned that outdoor air disseminates viral particles quickly and limits spread. Too bad it took two months to realise that being outside is a good thing for limiting viral transmission. Telling people to lock themselves indoors with other people creating aerosolised 'Covid clouds' that can fill a room if it has poor ventilation has probably accelerated transmission – especially in overcrowded inner cities. Probably explains why the numbers in the US continue to skyrocket.

25.04.20

We can see cases go up in the US, but hospitalisations go down as more are tested.

27.04.20

Tonight, the headlines will be about the US moving through a million cases (Spain will go through 250k, Italy through 200k cases). 'Social distancing will be with us through summer,' declared Deborah Birx, the White House Coronavirus Coordinator, earlier today. 'Opening Up America Again', may be the plan trumpeted by Trump's political advisors, but his health experts are warning otherwise. Whatever the merits of Birx's advice, she is right that reopened economies will need to maintain substantial social distancing, in some cases enforced by law, in others, by social practice.

Interestingly, last Thursday's stimulus bill contained $1 billion to boost the CDC's testing capacity, contact-tracing capabilities, morbidity and mortality surveillance programmes and other containment measures. The allocation is a positive step towards Phase 2 containment of the US Covid-19 response plan in which a national surveillance system is a crucial prerequisite to other containment measures.

The current national surveillance system aims to draw from a combination of data sources – from existing influenza and viral respiratory disease surveillance, syndromic surveillance, case reporting, commercial lab reporting and ongoing research platforms at state and local levels.

Clearly, many people's hopes rest on a vaccine, but how much will that cost? When determining the price for a drug, payors typically look at the cost of a QALY (Quality Adjusted Life Year), meaning, how much did we spend to give someone a good year of life? Many healthcare organisations, such as the UK's NICE, have decided that every QALY is worth between $40–50k, but many in the pharma world believe that's too low, causing the usual tensions; most speciality drugs cost much more than that. A QALY in the US is $50–150k. Certainly more than with NICE in the UK.

At Imperial NHS Trust we are caring for 212 patients who were positive for coronavirus, representing the seventh successive daily reduction in the number of inpatients with Covid-19. Of these patients, 85 were being cared for in critical care on ventilators. We had a total of 103 patients being cared for in critical care on ventilators. This is still a 50% increase on our usual critical care/ventilator capacity of 68 beds, but a reduction in demand, compared with the recent peak of need, when we had 156 beds available. We had reported a total of 337 deaths of patients with coronavirus via NHS England. As of yesterday (Sunday, 26 April), 583 patients with coronavirus had recovered and been discharged. It really does look like this virus comes in waves. And goes in one, too.

29.04.20

When it comes to science leading us out of this, the best hope for the elderly/vulnerable is vaccines. Johnson & Johnson has very much thrown its vaccine hat in the ring. *The New York Times* has commented that the UK's very own Vaccitech is ahead. And yesterday Moderna issued what I think is a very bold press release, although I strongly suspect BARDA would have been aware of this to have given them $0.5 billion for manufacturing this month. It is initiating a Phase 2 study of its Covid-19 vaccine based on a sequence of the spike protein and laid out a specific trial design. They must be seeing an impressive immune response in Phase 1, which is ongoing. Specifically:

- Moderna is moving into Phase 2 with 600 subjects (with the same vaccine construct, i.e. mRNA plus a lipid nanoparticle).
- They are testing a dose as low as 50 micrograms, but aiming to go higher too.
- They will have two cohorts, including a higher-risk population: older adult cohort (age 55+) with no upper age limit.

30.04.20

Yesterday *The Lancet* published the China placebo-controlled, randomised remdesivir study in 237 severe patients, showing not only that there were no benefits, but that there was no reduction in viral load with remdesivir, which for an antiviral is truly bizarre. You have to look at the supplementary tables to find this bit, annoyingly. Just like the lopinavir/ritonavir study from China which was randomised, it doesn't work here at all. Just to be clear, a negative RCT is really important, just like a positive one. I can't see any subgroups of patients where it might work better either.

In the US, there were about 27k new Covid cases reported by state health departments today, up from 24k and now averaging 29k over the past week. The cumulative total is 1.03 million confirmed cases in the US, but tests also jumped back up to 225k from 190k.

New deaths increased significantly for a second day to just above 2.6k, which is a new single-day high. There are now 55k Covid-confirmed deaths in the US (plus 5k probable Covid deaths reported by New York City).

One of the most confusing things for me is the data from children. Globally, governments are taking different approaches to reopening schools as part of the initial phase of lockdown relaxation, e.g. Denmark opening only for younger kids at first; Germany phased reopening with masks in corridors; Austria is aiming to reopen with split classes in mid-May; US schools are mostly closed until August/September, etc. Some reports are coming out that suggest children are not an important vector of transmission. It is interesting that in a study from Padua in northern Italy, no kids were infected despite 13 of them living in households with close contact and infected individuals. Slightly confused by this.

Earlier this year, retired army captain Tom Moore decided to celebrate his 100th birthday by walking 100 lengths of his garden to raise £1,000 for the NHS. What began as a local family fundraiser was picked up by major news outlets, because right now we could all do with a good news story. Captain Tom is 100 today. He has raised over £33 million for the NHS. Truly, he is one of the greatest generation. Happy Birthday, Captain Tom.

May

01.05.20

A paper in *Science* has shown combined data from Tencent, a huge social media/technology company, with a dynamic/Bayesian analysis to look at the spread from China. They show 86% of cases were undocumented before travel restrictions were put in place. Before travel restrictions and isolation in China, the transmission rate of undocumented infections was more than half of known cases, but because of their bigger numbers, undocumented infections were the source for around 80% of documented cases. After travel restrictions, 65% of cases were documented.

A group analysed 58 known superspreader events for Covid-19, where lots of transmission has clearly occurred. Of these, at least 70% involved one of four types of activities: parties or liquor-fuelled mass festivals (19), religious services (9), business networking events (6) and funerals (5). None of these events were linked to airports or air travel. More research is needed. I am writing my own review on superspreader events, seeing if I can classify them by activity/location and so on, so maybe we can prevent them from happening. We just need to learn more.

Denmark and Austria, which started to exit strict lockdowns in mid-April, provide some hope that schools are not major vectors for SARS CoV-2 transmission.

In the US, around 30k new cases yesterday, up from 27k and rising for a third straight day. And over the course of April we have seen this weekly pattern repeat, with lower numbers coming out of the weekend due to reporting lags, and rising over the course of the week, averaging 29k over the course of the month. The seven-day moving average is trending down, though only very slightly.

02.05.20

Another elegant piece in *The Spectator*: 'More than 70% say they'll be nervous about leaving their house even once the restrictions are lifted. In Northern Ireland, the executive has decided not to reopen schools until September at the earliest because it has calculated that 90% of parents simply wouldn't send their children back before that. In England, around 20% of pupils are eligible to go to school as the family of key workers, yet fewer than 2% are in class.'

The New York Times on vaccine timelines with some half-decent graphics: 'If you want to make that 18 month timeframe, one way to do that is put as many horses in the race as you can.' Is anyone considering that the vaccines actually have to work?

In the US, the number of new cases increased again, though also with an increase in tests to a new high as the positive rate declined, while net hospitalisations, ICU admissions and new deaths also declined.

It's striking that the Asian countries indicate containment should be possible, whereas the US and so many other places in Europe are struggling so dramatically. Theoretical explanations include prior virus exposures, general health, behaviour, genetics or more.

- China continues to report low numbers of new cases, with 3–22 new daily cases reported over the last week (not including asymptomatic cases).
- South Korea reported only 9 new cases on 1 May (8 imported); the country is beginning to reopen.
- Singapore and Japan are still seeing new cases with predominantly local transmission, though may be seeing signs of decline from the peak.
- Taiwan has had no new cases for the past six days and Hong Kong has reported 0–2 new cases per day.

Remdesivir has been given an EUA by the FDA; it is notable Gilead has spent $1 billion on it this year. Drug development is super expensive.

Meanwhile, the toxic mixture of American exceptionalism and the Second Amendment led to a confrontation at a Family Dollar store in Michigan, where an employee told a customer their daughter was required to wear a mask to enter the store. The employee was shot dead.

03.05.20

In the US, after increasing four days straight, the number of new cases reported decreased to 30k from 33k, following the same day-of-the-week fluctuations as the last couple of weeks – thus expect further decreases today. The seven-day moving average continues to decline very slightly. Total Covid cases reported by state health departments stands at 1.12 million. New deaths dropped for the third day, though slightly, from about 1.8k Friday to 1.7k yesterday, for a total of nearly 61k deaths confirmed by state health departments (plus 5k probable Covid tests reported by New York). Gross and net hospitalisations and intubated patients continue to decline gradually.

04.05.20

The key now will be keeping the effective reproduction R0 number close to 1, though not necessarily below it, and shielding high-risk people as effectively as possible. When it comes to vaccines, which to me is science's best way out, it's clear that vaccine manufacturing is one of the most complex, challenging and highly regulated areas of the entire biopharma industry. The manufacturing process is as unique and important as the vaccine itself, and large-scale vaccine manufacturing plants, even for known processes, can take years to build. For example, GSK expects its new Shingrix facility to take around 5 years to complete. While development timelines are being significantly accelerated to find a Covid-19 vaccine, with hopes that one can emerge within the next 18 months, manufacturing facilities with sufficient scale to supply likely global demand could take longer to come online, in my view, largely owing to 1) uncertainty on the type of vaccine that will succeed, influencing the facility specifications, and 2) the sheer scale of production needed to meet demand. There are so many candidates in development now from different classes; notably, the mRNA platform, the replication-defective live-vector platform, the recombinant-subunit-adjuvanted protein platform or the attenuated replicating live-vector platform.

It seems mRNA-based vaccines could be the simplest and quickest to produce at scale as these are generated synthetically, albeit complexities remain with the need for a delivery vehicle. Adjuvants could reduce the volume of antigen needed as these can be added to vaccines to provoke a stronger and longer-lasting immune response through various interactions with the immune system. The use of an effective vaccine adjuvant could potentially allow smaller quantities of antigen to elicit an immune response, which could help ease manufacturing strains.

The next phases of the pandemic might well be marked by increasing divisions, factions and conflict, driven by:

1) Ongoing Covid waves
2) Competing interests (geopolitical, corporate, employees, consumers)
3) Elections

4) Freedom of speech, civil liberties/social media
5) Incomplete information
6) Individual assessment of facts and acceptance of risk

A growing number of media reports are focused on conflicts, all resulting from the nuances of Covid-19 such as asymptomatic transmitters, relatively low fatality and its predilection for the elderly.

05.05.20

Points today:

- Susceptibility and vulnerability can be used in the same way, according to one paper pointed out to me. A great study. 'Here we demonstrate that individual variation in susceptibility or exposure (connectivity) accelerates the acquisition of immunity in populations.'
- I think remdesivir pricing is very interesting. We know that Gilead is donating the drug to around 300,000 people. Also, there are hints that Gilead is structuring agreements with generics companies for remdesivir in developing countries (perhaps akin to what Gilead did in HIV and hepatitis C). So, what's a good comparison for remdesivir pricing? Since remdesivir is launching into a public health emergency, a $3k price implies $99k to save 1 death. $99k to save an event is well within the ICER thresholds for cost-effectiveness. ICER, the Institute for Cost-Effectiveness Research, has suggested $4,500 per course.
- The confusing situation with children continues, concerning not just their role in transmission and how susceptible they are, but also a possible inflammatory syndrome they suffer with.
- I've read some interesting articles on so-called immunity passports. These could become the future of travel in the Covid age. They raise all sorts of ethical issues.

06.05.20

A new publication from Los Alamos National Laboratory, pretty much run by the legendary Bette Korber, with whom I've had many interesting discussions over the years on HIV mutations, collaborating with Sheffield here is making the rounds and leading to a bunch of questions/concerns. It notes that a mutation seems to have led to a more contagious version of the virus than was seen earlier. It's important to differentiate between 'isn't that interesting' facts and 'that's going to be a problem' facts, and

I would put this in the former category. It looks like a dominant strain of SARS-CoV-2 emerged, which makes sense; some strains will be more infectious than others and will take over transmission dynamics. Just as SARS-CoV-2 is more infectious than SARS-CoV-1, so we have more of the second variant.

Smokers are less likely than non-smokers to fall ill with Covid-19 according to one paper I just read. Isn't that because smokers are much more socially isolated than non-smokers these days? The catch to that argument being that even when they are infected, they're still less likely to fall ill.

I was involved in lots of chatter last night regarding the role of children, and it's becoming clearer to me that they can transmit but have lower potential to do so. There is an important new study on the role of children and their infectiousness. The authors have obtained viral loads from over 3,000 samples and grouped them according to age. Then they compared them pairwise and found no statistically significant difference in the viral load, although this is not the only parameter when it comes to transmissions as children are not 'harmless'. Of course, in other respiratory diseases, their viral load is way higher than in adults, making them great spreaders.

Finally, in the US there were roughly 22k new cases reported yesterday, which is flat and also down from last week. However, ending five days of declines, new deaths spiked back up to 2.4k from 1k. Increases on Tuesday have been typical after weekend reporting lags, and the seven-day moving average is essentially unchanged at 1.8k.

07.05.20

The UK moves past 200k cases, yet mainland Europe, particularly France and Germany, are noticeably lower in cases. The *NEJM* publishes the final paper of the negative trial of HIV medicines (lopinavir and ritonavir) to treat hospitalised patients with Covid-19, a proper randomised study, meaning that patients are assigned (randomly) to one of two groups so there's no bias. Great to see a proper trial, performed in warlike conditions in Wuhan, with a real answer, albeit a negative one. Sometimes it's not about knowing what to do, it's about knowing when to do things and, most importantly, when not to. First, do the least harm.

08.05.20

Was reminded yesterday that Greta Thunberg said at Davos, 'Bring the world to a halt to protect the climate.' It's taken a pandemic, but pollution levels and CO_2 emissions are down. What's bad news for humanity might be good news for the planet.

Excellent discussion on heading back to school today with a case study of what Taiwan did. It wins the gold medal for me for any country because of its containment strategies, roll out of test, track and trace and the speed with which it's done this.

New Zealand has now eliminated Covid-19. They recorded in total fewer than 1,500 confirmed cases of Covid-19 and just 20 deaths. On 23 March, a month after the country had recorded its first case, New Zealand committed to an elimination strategy. A few days later, Prime Minister Jacinda Ardern announced a strict national lockdown when it only had 102 cases and 0 deaths. Her swift decision-making has won lots of international praise, including from WHO. The decision to pursue an elimination approach was a vastly different approach to the usual pandemic planning, which has historically been based on a mitigation model and focuses on delaying the arrival of the virus, followed by a range of measures to flatten the curve of cases and deaths.

Chile is poised to become the first country to provide certificates to people who have recovered from Covid-19 to give patients confidence in the months following their illness. But some call the move premature because of questions about whether the virus confers immunity and, if so, for how long, and about when a patient can be considered to have recovered. Brazil, on the other hand, has had a 'so what' attitude to the virus. Low-middle income, densely populated countries like Pakistan and Indonesia will be an important focus going forwards.

A big HCQ randomised trial vs placebo in 1,446 hospitalised people showed no benefits. HCQ is starting to look like junk. Might be harmful junk too.

On the vaccine side, the NIH has completed enrolment of a Phase 1 study of Moderna's mRNA-1273 in 45 healthy volunteers to assess safety and immunogenicity. Subjects are receiving 2 doses. In an interview in *National Geographic*, Dr Fauci said, 'A final vaccine could be available for general use as early as January' and that 'the animal trials so far show that modest doses of the mRNA vaccine for coronavirus have generated a strong immune response'. The spike protein of the virus has 1,273 amino acids, thus the name MRNA-1273. There we have it.

There were 27k new cases reported in the US yesterday, up from 25k, still following the pattern of recent weeks (low numbers coming out of the weekend and rising over the course of the week). The seven-day moving average is flat and right in line with the 27k increase. Testing capacity continues its recent steady rise, reaching a new single-day high (excluding a couple of backlog-inflated days) of 302k new test results, up from 270k and lifting the seven-day average to 266k.

The National Institute of Allergy and Infectious Diseases (NIAID) is sponsoring the ACTT-II trial starting now. Right now, it's baricitinib versus placebo. This is hugely exciting, spurred by BenevolentAI's and our other work. It's amazing to see a proper, well-powered, randomised study starting three months after publication of computerised prediction AI work. This is utterly staggering, regardless of whether it works or not. Having said that, I think it will work. While the interferon response may be important for very early viral infections and blocking, JAK-STAT signalling might block that response. This is true for Covid-pneumonia for sicker patients. We are trying to save lives here.

09.05.20

In an article published in the *Journal of the American Medical Association*, a group evaluated the association of public health interventions with the epidemiological features of the Covid-19 outbreak in Wuhan by five periods according to key events and interventions, including the cordon sanitaire, traffic restrictions, social distancing, home confinement, centralised quarantine and universal symptom survey. They then determined the effective reproduction number R0 as an indicator to measure the transmission of SARS-CoV-2 before and after the interventions. The authors show the extraordinary change in the rate of transmission of SARS-CoV-2 associated with reducing social interaction. In other words, lockdown, quarantine and stay-at-home orders may be blunt tools, but they work. China seems to have done well as they acted decisively and rapidly. No surprises there.

10.05.20

In the US, another 25k new cases were reported yesterday, down from 27k Friday, as the seven-day moving average continues to trend downward very slowly. New tests dipped to 292k from 310k, but the rolling average trend is still steadily upward. The positive rate has now stayed at the low point of 9% for a sixth straight day. New deaths dropped to 1.5k from 1.7k, but the seven-day moving average is still relatively flat. Hospitalisations in the 38 states reporting net numbers declined for a fourth day in a row. New York State released additional antibody test results on front-line workers in New York City, showing positive rates below the 20% level for the general New York City population, for transit workers (14.2%), HCWs (12.2%), New York Police Department (10.5%) and the Fire Department of New York (17.1%).

At this rate, with a lack of centralised control of the situation and Trump wanting to reopen the country with no sign of the crisis reducing to manageable numbers, I can only conclude that deaths by the end of the year will be Second World War levels of mortality, only taking months to reach those statistics rather than years. It is still very much not over.

11.05.20

In Germany, the Robert Koch Institute (RKI), which is providing very decent data, said at the weekend the R0 value had risen to 1.13 from 0.7 from the end of the lockdown (April 2020), with some statistical variations. I wonder if this influenced the PM's speech where he was clearly more worried.

In Asia, where restrictions are being lifted and the situation as a whole remains well contained, some new clusters have emerged this week. We will have to see if the speed of response is sufficient for preventing larger outbreaks. China reported 14 new symptomatic cases on Saturday following a recent cluster in Shulan. Across the rest of China, theatres and other indoor venues will be gradually reopening and travel/ tourism increased over the Labour Day long weekend, though remained meaningfully lower vs previous years. But Shanghai Disneyland is opening today with tickets sold out.

Similar to South Korea, China is seeing some cases of reactivation. It's unclear if these are false test results/dead viral remnants or if viral latency is possible. South Korea has been well contained, though a new cluster has emerged, caused by an infected patient who visited several clubs/bars before testing positive. Seoul is now shutting bars/clubs, and President Moon Jae-in has warned that it's 'not over until it's over'.

Japan's new cases continue to decrease along with the percentage of positivity, while Singapore is still struggling with migrant worker clusters. Taiwan and Hong Kong remain extremely well controlled. Schools are reopening across Asian regions, and some areas are considering gradually easing some border restrictions.

In the US, 21.5k new cases were reported yesterday, down from 25k, as the seven-day moving average continues its slow but steady downward trend – now at 24k. On Monday the percentage of the population under original, full, statewide, stay-at-home orders will be down to 37% as states continue the phased reopening of certain businesses (with many restrictions still in place). It has been around two weeks since Georgia and some other early states started the reopening phase, and so far there hasn't been any notable uptick in trends of new cases or hospitalisations, but it is still early.

12.05.20

A bulletin from the American Association of Poison Control Centers refocuses on Trump's comments on disinfectants on 23 April 2020. In January, February and March of 2020, accidental poisonings with household disinfectants were up 5%, 17% and 93% respectively over the same months in 2019. In April, which includes an eight-day period from the 23rd of the month to the 30th, following Trump's comments, the increase was 121%, compared to April of 2019. In the first ten days of May things settled down some, with poisonings up 69% over the same ten-day period in 2019. For bleach, the numbers are less dramatic, but still telling. In January, February and March 2020, poisonings were up 7%, 1% and 59% respectively over each of the same months last year. In April they leapt 77%. As with disinfectants, May has similarly improved a bit, with the first ten-day period showing an increase of 51% over the same ten days last year. Critically, association is not causation, and with a frightened public doing whatever it can to protect itself from the virus, the same increases in poisonings might have happened regardless of Trump's remarks. But the presidential megaphone is a powerful one, and even dangerous ideas projected through it can influence an awful lot of people.

Researchers are noticing some curious and unexpectedly positive side effects of the abrupt shifts in human behaviour in response to the pandemic. Skies are bluer, fewer cars are crashing, crime is falling, and some other infectious diseases are fading from hospital emergency departments. There's greater community spirit, widespread appreciation for NHS and those now deemed key workers, and a greater sense of responsibility for the elderly and vulnerable. Many working parents are spending quality time with their children and people are enjoying box sets, exercising more, eating healthier diets and drinking less alcohol (but the converse is also true). Many people who could never have envisioned working from home find they now can, and in the future will, to a greater or lesser extent, continue to do so.

There's also been a sharp decline in paediatric admissions for respiratory illnesses. These include diseases such as influenza, parainfluenza, respiratory syncytial virus and human metapneumovirus. Probably a reflection of kids not being in day care or school. Hospitals are testing fewer patients, which could be because more children might be staying home with respiratory symptoms. But more serious cases and intensive care unit admissions are down as well, suggesting a true decline in life-threatening illnesses. Children will see the value of handwashing and how to handle infections.

Clearly, a pandemic is a terrible way to improve environmental health, but it may, however, provide an unexpected vantage to help understand how environmental health can be altered. NASA satellites have documented significant reductions in air pollution, 20–30% in many cases in major cities around the world. Based on those declines, a Stanford blog mentioned that two months' worth of improved air quality in China alone might save the lives of 4,000 children under the age of 5 and 73,000 adults over the age of 70; a more conservative calculation estimated around 50,000 saved lives.

Similarly, road accidents, including those involving an injury or fatality, fell by half in the US after the shelter-in-place order on 19 March.

Whereas average traffic speeds increased by only a few miles per hour, traffic volumes fell by 55%.

The role of the media and social media in healthcare advice has been remarkable. At this time, when we are marking our gratitude to health service workers by clapping on Thursday evenings, it is important to remember that, until recently, the NHS has been repeatedly castigated for being more concerned with sickness than health. Yet, right now, we are desperate for an efficient and well-equipped sickness service backed up by compassionate social care. Perhaps the coronavirus crisis can finally broker a shared understanding that a DNAR, a 'do not attempt resuscitation' order, is not a death sentence or the devaluing of life but an attempt to ensure dignity in dying.

For me, personally, the most incredible thing has been the speed, scale and depth of collaboration among academics, industry, HCWs and epidemiologists to reach conclusions. Economically, the size of the fiscal stimulus available has been in numbers I didn't think possible. At a biological level, we are fostering more global collaborations to help us link the patients with Covid-19 to the laboratory and vice versa. We want to personalise all of this – who, when, where and how to treat. This will decrease the IFR.

13.05.20

Soon the global confirmed death rate from Covid-19 will go through 300k. I am still confused by children, their symptoms (or lack of them) and their ability to transmit, which seems lower than adults. A group has now presented startling new evidence on the potential rise in maternal and child mortality in low- and middle-income countries (LMICs) if essential health services are disrupted as a result of Covid-19. It's so important to understand all of this, and the potential of children to transmit – for schools, their education, their parent's work. Building on lessons learned from previous outbreaks of Ebola virus disease and SARS, the authors estimate a devastating increase in the numbers of maternal and child deaths resulting from reductions in routine health service coverage.

Children are at risk not only of infection, but also of losing or being separated from family members and caregivers. Mothers and children are affected by the disruption of essential preventative and curative support and supplies resulting from suspensions in services and transportation systems, as well as by financial constraints. Even before the crisis, UNICEF was working on an initiative to extend digital infrastructure to ensure all children can learn, no matter who and where they are, and this work needs to be brought quickly to scale.

Following the NHS England alert at the start of the month, there are infrequent but growing reports of an unusual vasculitis (inflammation of blood vessels) similar to Kawasaki disease in children associated with Covid-19, as well as reports of a related multisystem inflammatory syndrome. Kawasaki disease is extremely rare, tends to affect children of Asian descent (boys > girls) and is characterised by the inflammation of mid-size arteries; coronary artery inflammation is most concerning (risk of aneurysms, i.e. burst vessels). Why is this emerging now?

1) Previously unappreciated, awareness of Covid link is increasing reporting.
2) Extremely rare, only seen after a large enough denominator of infections.
3) Delayed reaction to infections weeks ago.
4) A new strain?

It's also unclear why in children, not adults? Maybe there's a variant presentation of the same thing happening in adults? Maybe due to a relatively immature immune system? The implications are causing concern for parents and schools. Until recently, kids were thought to be minimally affected. It raises questions about vaccines/children: should children be vaccinated? Could inflammation be a risk from vaccines as well as the virus? For which ages? There is no reason to think the risk with vaccines would be higher than with infection, but it still needs to be considered.

The *NEJM* reports transmission between cats. The domestic type, not lions, though I note the popularity of *Tiger King* on Netflix.

14.05.20

Trying to think six months ahead of Covid-19 isn't easy in terms of second waves. It's plausible we could have a vaccine available by year end or early 2021, which will create a new round of discussions, such as will employers or schools force employees/students to show documentation of vaccination or immunity? That seems aggressive, especially for a brand-new vaccine that has flown through development in record-breaking time. Who will be the appropriate candidates for a vaccine in limited supply? Are there groups for whom the risk of Covid-19 is less than the risk of a vaccine? To some extent, that answer depends on what's happening with the pandemic then.

There will be important unknowns that can only be addressed with longer follow-up. What if we have a situation where the economic restart and ongoing extensive spread of Covid-19 have led to a state of partial herd immunity by year end, especially if some estimates that natural infection rates don't need to be that high to reach herd immunity? It might not be comprehensive, but it could meaningfully dampen transmission before we're given the choice of a vaccine. We may have had some 30 million people in the US infected with SARS-CoV-2 over the past three months; most of those would have been over the past two months. We might start to see regions that are burning out naturally by the time we get to the winter, with pockets of herd immunity being established. Then what do we do? It might make for some challenging choices, but fortunately, those will be good choices to make, albeit reflecting extensive spread of a very bad virus (in older people).

People over the age of 65 have the most to gain from being successfully vaccinated. Younger people can develop severe complications but have the 'least to lose' since their outcomes are generally very good. Ideally, a vaccine can address all ages, if possible. What is the dose? The higher the dose required for each vaccine unit, the more supply inputs needed. It doesn't matter on a small scale, but if we're talking billions of doses, it might. How many doses? The first dose is called the 'prime'; subsequent doses (if needed) are called the 'boosts' (there can be 1–2 boosts), typically administered at 1 and then 6 months after the prime. Covid-19 vaccines may need boosts for optimal effect, although viral vector approaches believe a single prime may be adequate. Ideally, a Covid-19 vaccine would consist of a prime only, but a one-size-fits-all approach may be challenging.

I genuinely don't understand why older people are affected so badly. To help answer this, yesterday the UK announced a new 35,000 whole-genome sequencing project, which will sequence 20k severely ill and 15k mild/moderate symptom patients. The goal is to understand whether an individual's genetic makeup influences outcomes. Obviously we need to sequence the virus too.

15.05.20

It's good that we now seem to have animal models to help us, and many are being published. Non-human primate (NHP, i.e. monkey) challenge data is important because it provides direct evidence for disease protection – not just immunogenicity. It's preclinical, but a new *Nature* article shows macaques have a similar viral shedding pattern to humans, so are a reasonable model for moderate Covid-19.

I thought it was really disappointing data from Abbott's quick PCR test. They sought to evaluate the recently released Abbott ID NOW Covid-19 assay, which is capable of producing positive results in as little as 5 minutes. But it missed a third of the samples.

Following a 2.5-hour choir practice attended by 61 people, including a symptomatic patient, 32 confirmed and 20 probable cases occurred, making the attack rate over 50%. Three patients were hospitalised and 2 died. No doubt singing at someone isn't great.

16.05.20

A Moderna and Lonza board member, Moncef Slaoui, ex-GSK head of R&D, has become the Coronavirus Vaccine Czar, and the team is called Operation Warp Speed (OWS), with a clear aim to deliver a few hundred million doses by year end. Was a bit surprising when the Sanofi CEO said the US would have priority over a vaccine, but then he backtracked.

I keep seeing various over-the-counter solutions to Covid-19; it really frustrates me that I see all this hard work going into clinical trials and some very smart people coming up with ingenious solutions to a deadly pandemic, and yet people still turn to alternative medicine. Let me be clear: the difference between 'medicine' and 'alternative medicine' is alternative medicine is either medicine that has yet to be proven to work or medicine that has been proven not to work – well, not any more than the placebo effect. When people talk about the efficacy of certain herbs, they are correct. Aspirin is synthesised from willow bark; it is a known painkiller and blood thinner. The same with opium from poppies. This is why both products are now part of our efforts to aid a patient's health. But just because something was used 'in ancient times' or it's from the 'East' doesn't grant it automatic healing powers. For the Europeans who look to Chinese traditional medicine, it is worth pointing out that in China right now health workers aren't using dried herbs, incense and maps of the body's chi to counter Covid-19; they are in hospitals and ICUs using the same procedures as you'd see in a hospital in Australia or Austria. If energy chakras really were a thing, do you not think the Chinese hospitals would be using them, and I would be reading dozens of papers on their effectiveness against Covid? It's not a conspiracy the drug companies want to hush up; it's that nobody reputable is using this. That's why there are no papers in the likes of *The Lancet* or *Nature*. There are none even in the journal *Oncogene* where I am co-editor-in-chief. And I'd be keen to publish well-conducted negative or positive studies.

We pride ourselves on how evolved we are, how far we've come, and yet the superstitions of the medieval era lurk just beneath the surface. There are churches, particularly West African ones, with holy water or various potions that have been blessed by [insert name of preferred deity here] that will stop Covid-19. No, it won't. It's snake oil, the same snake oil those tricksters on the frontier of America used in the 1800s.

We laugh at renaissance doctors using leeches for all kinds of ailments, and yet today, there are people who believe that magical auras can be used by energy healers to manipulate the very energy of the universe (an energy, I hasten to add, that is undetectable by any scientific instrument) to check your chakras, use the power of reiki and flush out the negative energy of Covid-19. Yes, use it as complementary therapy, not as an alternative, i.e. in addition to, not instead of.

There are some impressive claims made for the efficacy of alternative medicines, so can I look at the clinical data? What do you mean, 'modern science doesn't understand how it works'? Am I just meant to take your word for it? That's not how medicines are approved. Billions are currently being spent to come up with vaccines and drugs to counter Covid, and it is inevitable that some of that money will be spent on dead-end projects that yield no results. That is the nature of research. However, at the start of the project there will be some background evidence, some logic to justify the investment of millions in a particular drug, and yet none of that cash is going to homoeopathic or energy-based healing remedies because everybody knows it will not result in an effective vaccine, not even one made of... magic. If you have a heart attack, will you call for an ambulance or reach for your homoeopathy pills?

It seems that when we humans are scared we will try anything to fix the problem. After all, what's the harm? Well, the harm is if you feel like you are invulnerable you might be less inclined to wear a mask and to observe social distancing, and then you become part of the problem, not the solution. Fear might be as toxic and as contagious as Covid.

17.05.20

South Koreans thought to be reinfected turned out to be false positives. In this respect, it will be interesting to see how the story develops around the thirteen US sailors who recovered from Covid but have now tested positive for the virus. I presume they became PCR negative and are now PCR positive. Details are scant.

Here, UK cases/tests are at 4.3%, the lowest it's ever been. I think the test positivity rate is a really important metric.

In the US, 24.5k new cases were reported yesterday, dropping <1k vs Friday, also pushing down the seven-day moving average.

18.05.20

Why should we expect vaccines to work against Covid? Some initial thoughts:

- There aren't credible reports of Covid reinfection. This means that the immune response to the virus is robust. And most people don't have severe symptoms, so healthy/prepared immune systems are already effective.
- Vaccines mimic infections, so we can look for immune responses with vaccines that approximate those in people who recovered from an infection.

- Anti-Covid antibody titres (levels) are increased 10–100 times for people infected versus people who aren't. A similar magnitude of response is seen with mRNA vaccines for similar viruses like Zika or CMV; many platforms can achieve this type of immunity. Plus, Moncef Slaoui pretty much just told us he saw preliminary Moderna data, and it looks solid.
- Antibodies don't tell the whole story, but understanding gaps in the leading vaccine approaches helps fill in the gaps. Vaccines that have worked really well usually stimulate a strong antibody response in the past.
- Past vaccine failures reflect immature platforms and knowledge. We have better constructs and adjuvants now.
- Vaccines don't have to take years to develop. We can learn much of what we need to know in a single season if we pour enough resources into them.
- Most rare/concerning vaccine adverse effects would have also happened from the actual infection, but at a much lower rate than with a vaccine.

So, the vaccines should be safe and effective – probably not perfect at either. Could a leading approach run into some unexpected difficulty, including side effects? Maybe, but we know a lot about them. Now we just have to wait and see what the pandemic will be like towards the end of the year to figure out if we'll even need the vaccines. Could it 'magically disappear' before then? Donald Trump seems to think so, but I would say medical precedent shows that to be unlikely. Could we establish herd immunity? Possibly. But if we haven't, the vaccines should be there to bail us out.

19.05.20

Am starting to wonder if track and trace is a hopeless waste of time. The job of Test Track Trace Isolate (TTTI) is to identify the people with active infection, isolate them, find all their relevant contacts, isolate and test them, then trace and isolate the contacts of the positive contacts, etc. This is a manageable thing to do if the number of infected people is fairly small, as several countries have proved. So, what's relevant is the number of people who currently have an active infection and are infectious to others.

Patrick Vallance, the government's Chief Scientific Advisor, said last week that the antigen arm of the Oxford study suggested a central estimate of around 140,000 people with an active infection in the UK. It's also very worrying that over 3,000 new cases are still being diagnosed every day in the UK after eight weeks of lockdown. That seems to be a larger number than any other country in Europe (excluding Russia), which is partly why the government is continuing its current policy and suggests our lockdown has been the least successful in breaking transmission chains. It is said that most transmission is related to health and social care facilities, which if true, is evidence of the weakness of our infection control procedures in the places where they should be most effective.

It's unclear in post-lockdown conditions what would be the average number of contacts of an infected person in the UK. Say it is 5, then that would mean 700,000 potential contacts. If R0 is 1 and one of the five contacts is positive then that's another 700,000 people to contact, and so on. That's clearly not feasible and certainly not with the 18,000 people being recruited to the TTTI teams. The task is also greatly complicated by the fact that people can be infectious without being symptomatic, so virtually impossible to detect unless you do mass screening of whole populations as the Chinese are planning for 11 million in Wuhan. Contact tracing is also made more difficult because infection may be spread to people the case doesn't know, e.g. on public transport. That is where the app is supposed to help, but how many infected people will use it, and how many contacts will act on advice to self-isolate and get tested remains to be seen.

When it comes to tracking technologies, the Google/Apple API programme has gained significant momentum in the past few weeks, and over this same period, several European countries have embraced the decentralised Google/Apple system. Germany, Italy, Ireland, Austria and Switzerland are all now using Google/Apple or a compatible system and Belgium and the Netherlands are moving in that direction. Even Margrethe Vestager, the EU's Competition Czar, who has led many cases against big tech, supports a united technology. The UK is also developing a backup app that works with the Google/Apple system, but worries over data privacy continue to hamper adoption.

On the international front, numbers are mixed. At the high end, >4 million Australians have downloaded their government's tracing app out of ~16 million, and nearly 40% of Iceland's population has downloaded its tracing app. Singapore's TraceTogether app, long a beacon of hope for contact-tracing app success, has been unable to expand past 1.4 million users, just short of a quarter of its population and much below its desired 60% uptake. If they can't do it, I'm not sure how we can.

20.05.20

A really fascinating big paper from *Nature*. A person who had SARS seventeen years ago had an antibody that also appears to inhibit SARS-CoV-2. This bodes well for the longevity of antibody responses.

The *British Medical Journal* has an article on how Covid-19 has forced a reckoning in the UK over how the government has much to learn from low-income settings. I don't disagree, but I also don't see the nation's social housing being upgraded any time soon, particularly with the government spending more money than any other peacetime government. At the moment it pays for furloughs, PPE and everything else.

Also, lots of speculation that mortality in BAME (black, Asian and minority ethnic) individuals may be due to low vitamin D, indicating a role for vitamin D in the response to Covid-19 infection. It has been postulated that vitamin D might help to reduce the inflammatory response to infection with SARS-CoV-2. Not convinced by anything related to vitamin D and never have been. It's a sign of bad health not a cause of it, in my view.

21.05.20

Really important paper in the *NEJM*. Been chatting to William Li from Harvard, one of the authors, and this provides a very central piece of the jigsaw. They examined 7 lungs obtained during autopsy from patients who died from Covid-19 and compared them with 7 lungs obtained during autopsy from patients who died from acute respiratory distress syndrome (ARDS) secondary to influenza A (H1N1) infection and 10 age-matched, uninfected control lungs. 'The lungs from patients with Covid-19 also showed distinctive vascular features, consisting of severe endothelial injury associated with the presence of intracellular virus and disrupted cell membranes. Histologic analysis of pulmonary vessels in patients with Covid-19 showed widespread thrombosis with microangiopathy. Alveolar capillary microthrombi were 9 times as prevalent in patients with Covid-19 as in patients with influenza ($P<0.001$). In lungs from patients with Covid-19, the amount of new vessel growth, predominantly through a mechanism called intussusceptive angiogenesis, was 2.7 times as high as that in the lungs from patients with influenza.' What does this mean? SARS-CoV-2 has a predilection for blood vessels, causes localised clots and is very different to the flu.

Also, another paper showed a pooled analysis looking at the infection fatality rate (i.e. number of cases/those diagnosed and those undiagnosed): 'Seroprevalence estimates ranged from 0.113% to 25.9% and adjusted seroprevalence estimates ranged from 0.309% to 33%.' That's pretty wide, depending on location. It continued, 'Infection fatality rates ranged from 0.03% to 0.50% and corrected values ranged from 0.02% to 0.40%.'

Also, sticking with the science today, a paper in the *NEJM* describes the clustering effects of long-term care facilities. In King County in

Seattle they described a total of 167 confirmed cases of Covid-19 affecting 101 residents, 50 healthcare personnel and 16 visitors found to be epidemiologically linked to the facility. Most cases among residents included respiratory illness consistent with Covid-19; however, in 7 residents no symptoms were documented. Hospitalisation rates for facility residents, visitors and staff were 54.5%, 50.0%, and 6.0% respectively. The case fatality rate for residents was 33.7% (34 of 101). As of 18 March, a total of 30 long-term care facilities with at least one confirmed case of Covid-19 had been identified in King County. Staff working in multiple facilities while ill and transfers of patients from one facility to another potentially introduced Covid-19 into some of these facilities.

A paper in *The Lancet* describes additional suicides from unemployment. In one scenario, the worldwide unemployment rate would increase from 4.9% to 5.6%, which would be associated with an increase in suicides of around 9,570 per year. In the low scenario, the unemployment would increase to 5.1%, associated with an increase of about 2,135 suicides. There are around 800k suicides per year worldwide. Unhappy reading.

With Trump's criticism of WHO and China, the key question is could the pandemic of the century have been averted? The process by which WHO decides whether to declare a Public Health Emergency of International Concern (PHEIC) under the International Health Regulations has drawn criticism. Reports have condemned the four-month delay by WHO after the international spread of Ebola in West Africa before declaring a PHEIC. The Democratic Republic of the Congo (DRC), now experiencing the second-largest Ebola outbreak in recorded history, notified WHO of the outbreak on 1 August 2018, but WHO required four Emergency Committee meetings, including on 17 October 2018 (216 confirmed cases, 139 deaths, and 64% case fatality ratio) and 12 April and 14 June 2019 (4 confirmed cases in Uganda). Justifying their response, the Emergency Committee said that 'the cluster of cases in Uganda is not unexpected'. A PHEIC was finally declared at the fourth Emergency Committee meeting on 17 July 2019 (2,501 cases and 1,668 deaths), almost a year after initial notification.

The purpose of the declaration is to focus international attention on acute public health risks that 'require coordinated mobilisation of extraordinary resources by the international community' for prevention and response. Clearly it can panic people too. The all-or-nothing nature of the assessment generates confusion. The clear purpose of a PHEIC declaration is to catalyse timely evidence-based action, to spur increased international funding and support, and to limit the public health and societal impacts of emerging and re-emerging disease risks.

22.05.20

It's worth a recap on the four major respiratory pandemics up to the current time:

1) 'Spanish flu' occurred during 1918–19. Precise information about its spread and the number of fatalities is not available, in part because it started during the First World War, and governments actively suppressed media reporting. Spain was not in the war and was a neutral country. As such, while it did not originate there, the press was free to report what was happening, thus the name. It is thought to have resulted in 20–40 million deaths worldwide, with 675,000 in the US, where GDP growth averaged 2.1% in the five years before and 3.7% in the five years after. Indeed, rather than leaving permanent scars on consumer psychology, the Spanish flu was followed by the 'roaring twenties'.

2) 1957 Asian flu is generally thought to have originated in north Asia, quickly spreading throughout China, the US and Europe, ultimately resulting in between 1 and 4 million deaths, with 116,000 in the US. In the US, GDP growth averaged 3.5% in both the five years before and after, with consumption growing by 3.3% on average in the following five years compared to 4.1% before.

3) 1968–69 Hong Kong influenza also started in north Asia before quickly spreading through China, Europe and the US. Ultimately it killed an estimated 1–4 million people, including 100,000 in the US. Both GDP and consumption growth did slow a little in the five years after (despite a vaccine), but in large part that was due to other factors such as an oil shock.

4) The 2009–10 swine flu is thought to have originated in Mexico but was first detected in the US. However, even with this relatively recent pandemic, no one is sure how many people were impacted, but it is estimated that around 1.4 billion people were infected, with between 150,000 and 575,000 fatalities. In the US, GDP growth averaged 2.4% in the five years before and 2.2% in the five years after, with consumption growing by 2.3% in the following five years compared to 2.5% before. This pandemic happened on the heels of the 2008 financial crisis.

So, as the US and the rest of the world move to reopen their economies, a key question is whether these reopenings will engender a resurgence of the epidemic, thereby holding back the pace of economic recovery. The risk cannot be ruled out, and the large uncertainties about how SARS-CoV-2 works means we should be wary of definitive comments. But thus far, about a month after the initial reopenings, there is not much evidence of a resurgence.

However, a paper in *Science* suggests multiple waves of infections, extending even into 2025. Oh joy.

23.05.20

Now the US is planning, as part of OWS, a 100,000-person vaccine trial in aggregate, in some of the most promising candidates, to deliver a safe and effective vaccine this year. To get the quickest answer, vaccines will be tested in HCWs and communities where the virus is still spreading to show whether they reduced new cases of Covid-19. Washington DC, which has not reached the peak of its outbreak, is one likely test site. Trials may be conducted abroad, including in Africa, where the virus has just started to spread.

We need a vaccine, not least because another paper in *The Lancet* shows that HCQ may do more harm than good in nearly 15k hospitalised patients. This is the largest observational study published to date.

The other main news is about a new cluster in China in the northeast. Patients found in the provinces of Jilin and Heilongjiang appear to carry the virus for a longer period of time, take longer to test negative, and fewer end up hospitalised. They are probably reimported from Russia. Cases are low, but a 108-million-person lockdown seems imminent there.

24.05.20

In the US, there are around 22k new cases, down from 24k Friday and in line with the unchanged seven-day moving average. There are 43 states reporting and ICU declines remain steady as well. The trend in gross new hospitalisations remains flattish in the 31 states reporting this metric.

25.05.20

There are times to talk about medicine and then there are times to talk about the world around us. Today, how could I do anything other than record the sickening events in America? I watched in dismay at the footage of the man lying face down on the ground, his body pressed against the cold tarmac of the street. His head was only inches away from the rear wheel of the police vehicle, which made it look as if they had thought about running him over before pinning him to the ground. George Floyd was a big man, but his plaintive calls of 'I can't breathe' and later, 'Mama' and 'Please' were heartbreakingly fragile. The grown-up man had become a scared child again. People congregated, called for an end to the brutality and witnessed yet another crime even as Covid lurked in the background. There will be protests.

26.05.20

Here, a public inquiry into the UK's response to Covid-19 now seems inevitable, with political and public demands for one that can command widespread support. While a comprehensive inquiry at some point will be essential, the traditional model as used with Bloody Sunday or the Iraq War takes years, and we don't have that kind of time before a possible second wave.

In the US, all four police officers involved in the killing of George Floyd have been fired from the Minneapolis Police Department, but I have to wonder why they haven't been arrested. The anger generated is immense, all the more so because this was not the first such incident, not by a long shot. Dozens of cities were on fire as peaceful protesters mixed with those intent on damage and destruction. Some clearly felt they had a point to make, while others took advantage of the anarchy to smash store windows and grab a new 4K TV. Riot police were on the streets dressed in black or drab military colours. They looked like the police force of a brutal dictatorship or figures from some dystopian future, not that of the most powerful democracy in the world. Similarly, the vehicles the police deployed looked like military-grade equipment more suited to suppressing the locals in some authoritarian regime than law enforcement in suburban America. Meanwhile, Trump only has words of condemnation for the protestors; all of this and a deadly virus that is fast approaching a death toll of 100,000 Americans.

27.05.20

Yesterday was notable for Merck throwing its previously quiet hat in the vaccine ring. Considering their expertise in immunotherapy, vaccines and virology, I've been amazed by their quiescence. How does a big pharma, trying to be nimble but the size of an oil tanker, get into Covid-19? Well, I guess this is how. Their three new programmes are announced the same day to almost no fanfare:

1) A nucleotide analogue (a so-called 'nuke') for Covid-19, like remdesivir, but it's oral, cytosine-based, and it has broad, potent preclinical efficacy.
2) A vaccine collaboration with a non-profit using a validated rVSV vector for delivery (same tech as MRK's Ervebo, their FDA-approved vaccine for Ebola).

3) Purchase of another vaccine company, Themis, with a measles-based virus (related to GSK's Priorix, which is GSK's MMR vaccine).

28.05.20

First, most Americans expect a vaccine against Covid-19 to be available by some point in 2021, but only half say they will get vaccinated, and many are unsure, according to an AP-NORC survey. I'm not quite ready to share my thoughts on anti-vaccine sentiment, but I know I'll get there. Let's just leave it as staggeringly dumb, irresponsible and selfish for now if the data is as good as I think it'll be.

A total of 60% of Americans are sceptical that tracking someone's location through their cell phone would help curb the outbreak. At the same time, the public holds mixed views on when – and if – this type of monitoring is acceptable; 40% believe this would help a lot (16%) or a little (22%) in limiting the spread of Covid-19. Still, Democrats (46%) and independents (42%) are more likely than Republicans (31%) to say that if the government tracked people's locations through their cell phones during the outbreak, it would help at least a little to limit the spread of the virus.

Amid this tension between personal privacy and public safety, here 45% say it is acceptable for the government to use cell phones to track the location of people who may have had contact with someone who tested positive for Covid-19, while 55% describe this type of tracking as unacceptable.

The CDC has published some reopening guidance. It feels to me a little like they are doing it through gritted teeth or after being shouted out by the White House.

29.05.20

Bit of a mishmash today; a couple of papers to start with. First, one in *The Lancet* showing that men don't have a higher mortality vs women, in Massachusetts at least; the message is you need to consider both absolute and relative mortalities. Second, in the *NEJM*, in a large cohort in Louisiana, 76.9% of the patients who were hospitalised with Covid-19 and 70.6% of those who died were black, whereas black people comprise only 31% of the population. Black race was not associated with higher in-hospital mortality than white race, after adjustment for differences in sociodemographic and clinical characteristics on admission. In other words, you are more likely to die if you are poor and old than young and affluent, rather than racial characteristics being a factor.

A *New York Times* article is missing many relevant points, including a declining R0 and that the world is still far from herd immunity. I don't think this journalist is well qualified to comment based on feelings.

30.05.20

Not a hoax, monkeys in India have stolen some Covid-19 positive blood samples. Sometimes you need a laugh, particularly in a Covid world.

Anyway, back to something more serious: Covid-19 is testing the FDA's leadership. One of many challenges facing the FDA is whether to keep in place or rescind the EUA for chloroquine and hydroxychloroquine (HCQ) and how to explain its decision. An honest explanation is essential because the public needs to know that FDA is prioritising its interests, that it is making decisions based on science, and that it has resisted the political pressure that appears from the outside to be influencing its decisions. The implication now though is that contingency planning will be perceived or punished as defeatism. That runs counter to science-based public health policy. The chloroquine and HCQ EUA raises concerns that this fear has seeped over into FDA's decision-making. As data accumulates, demonstrating that malaria drugs don't cure or even help Covid-19, the FDA will have an opportunity to show that it will be guided by science and the public interest. And if we do get some decent treatments or a vaccine, we can be sure they're guided by the right science.

Recently, France banned use of HCQ for Covid-19, to which Dr Raoult, who made it famous, responded, 'It's just another opinion. I don't really care.' And the WHO suspended enrolment in the HCQ arm of the Solidarity study, to which he lamented, 'The WHO isn't about science.' He also lashed out against the recent *Lancet* publication in his weekly video press conference. In the article he boasts he's invented ten treatments, of which half are prescribed all over the world, and yet he's never conducted a double-blinded study. Yikes!

So, what's next for treatments? We'll hear shortly about the remdesivir study in moderate patients, and Merck has started a trial of its new oral nuke. There are fourteen baricitinib studies on clinicaltrials.gov, and I think it's interesting because of the work I've been lucky to be part of showing it has antiviral and anti-cytokine activity. This now includes ACTT-II, which is plus-minus remdesivir, i.e. recruiting more than 1,000 hospitalised patients who will be randomised to receive either remdesivir or remdesivir with baricitinib, with time to recover the primary end point. This is a proper randomised study, and if it doesn't work that's as clear a message as if it does work. It's also important to hit the primary end point; otherwise, you might as well throw a dart on the floor and paint the target around it afterwards.

All of the science out just now is useful and emphasises the importance of the features of the virus' transmission above all else. For this, handwashing and maintaining social distancing are the main measures recommended by the WHO to avoid contracting Covid-19. Unfortunately, these measures do not prevent infection by the inhalation of small droplets exhaled by an infected person that can travel a distance of many metres in the air, carrying their viral content.

Despite this, no countries or authorities consider the airborne spread of Covid-19 in their regulations to prevent infection transmission indoors. Indeed, transmission lessons point toward an approach that we might think of as a combination therapy akin to a drug cocktail. Its elements are all familiar: hygiene, screening, distancing and masks. Each has flaws, and if you miss one out the treatments won't work nearly as well. But, when taken together and taken seriously, they shut down the virus. And I've vacillated until recently on the last one, masks, but think there's real data that they're important now. They're all pieces of the same jigsaw.

Let's start at the beginning with hygiene: People have learned that cleaning the hands is essential to stopping the transfer of infectious droplets from surfaces to the nose, mouth and eyes. But frequency makes a bigger difference than many realise. A study conducted at a military boot camp found that a top-down programme of handwashing five times a day cut medical visits for respiratory infections by 45%, and research on SARS found that washing hands more than ten times a day reduced people's infection rate by even more.

Disinfecting surfaces might help too, and frequency may also matter, although I haven't found good research on this, so I just don't know. The key, it seems, is washing or sanitising your hands every time you go into and out of a group environment and every couple of hours while you're in it, plus disinfecting high-touch surfaces at least daily. We know that different surfaces harbour the virus for different durations. Copper is doing well here, even leading to explanations of why copper-deficient patients are susceptible to so many infections. But, remarkably, I read somewhere that environmental transmission may account for as little as 6% of Covid-19 infections. Only last week I discussed that respiratory infections occur through the transmission of virus-containing droplets and aerosols exhaled from infected individuals during breathing, speaking, coughing and sneezing. Traditional respiratory disease control measures are designed to reduce transmission by droplets produced in the sneezes and coughs of infected individuals. However, a large proportion of the spread of Covid-19 appears to be occurring through airborne transmission of aerosols produced by asymptomatic individuals during breathing and speaking. Aerosols can accumulate, remain infectious in indoor air for hours and be easily inhaled deep into the lungs. For society to resume, measures designed to reduce aerosol transmission must be implemented, including universal masking and regular, widespread testing to identify and isolate infected asymptomatic individuals.

Identifying infected individuals to curb SARS-CoV-2 transmission is more challenging compared to SARS and other respiratory viruses because infected individuals can be highly contagious for several days, peaking on or before symptoms occur. These 'silent shedders' could be critical drivers of the enhanced spread of SARS-CoV-2. In Wuhan, China, it has been estimated that undiagnosed cases of Covid-19 infection, who were presumably asymptomatic, were responsible for up to 79% of viral infections. Therefore, regular, widespread testing is essential to identify and isolate infected asymptomatic individuals.

However, the 2-metre/6-foot rule isn't some kind of law that droplets obey. Public health guidelines, in fact, originally set the at-risk distance at 3 feet, based on experience in previous outbreaks, such as the 1981 meningitis outbreak in a Texas elementary school classroom, which began in a cluster of five girls seated together on one side of the room.

Clearly, under the right conditions of temperature, humidity, and air circulation, forceful coughing or sneezing can propel a cloudburst of respiratory droplets more than 20 feet. In outdoor environments, numerous factors will determine the concentrations and distance travelled and whether respiratory viruses remain infectious in aerosols. Breezes and winds often occur and can transport infectious droplets and aerosols long distances. Asymptomatic individuals who are speaking while exercising can release infectious aerosols that can be picked up by air streams. Viral concentrations will be more rapidly diluted outdoors, but few studies have been carried out on outdoor transmission of SARS-CoV-2.

Given how little is known about the production and airborne behaviour of infectious respiratory droplets, it is difficult to define a safe distance for social distancing. Assuming SARS-CoV-2 virions are contained in submicron aerosols, as is the case for influenza virus, a good comparison is exhaled cigarette smoke, which also contains submicron particles and will likely follow comparable flows and dilution patterns. The distance from a smoker at which one smells cigarette smoke indicates the distance in those surroundings at which one could inhale infectious aerosols. In an enclosed room with asymptomatic individuals, infectious aerosol concentrations can increase over time.

June

01.06.20

There is much focus on pictures regarding closely packed protestors without masks following the George Floyd death. The problem is a respiratory virus doesn't know the difference between a gathering for a good cause or a bad one, or a house party. Protesting in the Covid world creates risks seen and unseen, knowable and unknowable. Reminds me of the Rumsfield known unknowns. And the Nixon rule: if two wrongs don't make a right, try three. And with this, today sees the staggered reopening of schools in England. Of course, it will take weeks to see if this leads to a significant uptick in infections, but research from schools in other countries would indicate it's a reasonable risk.

Gilead have reported a randomised study showing a five-day course of remdesivir is associated with quicker recovery than standard of care. We are in the middle of starting the ACTT-II randomised trial, and because the A stands for Adaptive, the placebo arm is now replaced with remdesivir, so the trial becomes baricitinib plus remdesivir versus remdesivir. Gary has called Gilead to congratulate them, though pretty clear Gilead don't want baricitinib to be trialled. Surely we can do better than remdesivir, and I'd like to think Gilead know this? The Chinese data didn't show any viral load decrease for a study of an antiviral, i.e. remdesivir. We have to get the best drug combination to patients. On the wards, the Covid-19 pneumonia chest X-rays and CT scans look so similar, with so much damage. It's hard to see that once this damage is established, if any treatment will make any meaningful difference and clear the damage.

02.06.20

Have just seen an interesting story in a medical journal reporting on an Italian family. The patient, an 87-year-old woman, was admitted on 10 March to the Infectious Disease Unit, University Hospital of Foggia, Italy, with mild to moderate Covid-19. The patient was part of a family cluster. The index patient received supplemental oxygenation, anti-HIV medicines, hydroxychloroquine and baricitinib. Therapy was successful and she recovered. In contrast, her husband (90 years old) and son (59 years old), who received the same therapy with the exception of baricitinib, showed rapid disease progression and after a few days they died of respiratory failure. Sad, and at the same time hopeful for baricitinib. Hard to draw conclusions from case reports, and the one rule for all that should apply is that we need properly conducted trials. This wasn't one of them. It's not proper science, and the plural of anecdote is not data.

France is set to roll out its contact-tracing app, the so-called StopCovid app. But some at Spain's health ministry are raising their eyebrows at a similar app they plan to pilot soon in the Canary Islands. Many are concerned the app could overwhelm the country's health centres with false alarms of people coming into close contact with anyone, regardless of whether they're sick.

I was surprised to see that in Israel there has been what looks like a superspreader event related to schools.

As mentioned, I am coming to the conclusion that no treatment makes a major difference once the pneumonia is moderate or severe. I hope I am wrong. Another trial evaluated the safety and efficacy of five-day and ten-day dosing durations of remdesivir administered intravenously in hospitalised patients with moderate manifestations of Covid-19. Thought the data completely underwhelming and not sure what it's taught us. Am not sure why such a large treatment duration trial has been performed – the patients could have been randomised to different therapies or combinations. And in Russia, the antiviral drug favipiravir made by Fujifilm will be available to patients suffering from Covid-19 from 11 June, aiming to treat 60k people per month. The trials aren't out yet, but it's hard to criticise this, considering the FDA's approach to HCQ.

Elsewhere, Lilly has begun trials with its therapeutic anti-SARS-CoV-2 antibody, slightly ahead of Regeneron's antibody cocktail programme.

The first participants in the Phase 2 study of Moderna's SARS-CoV-2 vaccine, mRNA-1273, have been dosed in each age cohort, 18–55 years and 55 years and above, following promising top-line interim data where we've seen neutralising antibody responses.

In Europe, all major countries, including the UK, are in the terminal phase. New cases continue in a sustainable decline even with the reopening of the economies. I do note, however, that the UK has started to plateau versus other peer countries. Given that Sweden does not have a lockdown, I would expect cases there to continue to grow.

Asia's new cases remain low. Singapore and South Korea appear to have been able to control their new clusters of cases.

The Middle East continues to see significant spread, as well as Latin America. The spread in Brazil has accelerated again and now has a similar level of daily new cases to that of the US. The best model in the world to me is Los Alamos, which projects around 2 million cases. This may be optimistic given the ongoing significant community spread. The Middle East appears to be having a second wave during Ramadan. The scope of the outbreak in these countries appears underappreciated.

03.06.20

Two French doctors sparked an intense backlash over comments made during a live television discussion about Covid-19 trials in Europe and Australia by saying that the studies should be done in Africa first 'where there are no masks, no treatments, no resuscitation,' reasoning that certain studies on AIDS had been carried out on prostitutes 'because we know that they are highly exposed and that they do not protect themselves'. Territorial colonialism may have ended long ago, but this contemporary global health crisis can serve as a reminder that the colonisation of medicine, economics and politics remains alive.

There's an important mechanism through which the pandemic is allowing external agencies to gain more control over healthcare financing in low-income countries. There is currently unprecedented political momentum for low-income countries to achieve essential reforms by investing 1–2% of their gross domestic product from 2021 to 2023 towards building universal, publicly financed health systems that cover their entire populations. However, external debt repayments that are currently being negotiated are threatening this opportunity to realise universal health coverage and will weaken the health systems in many countries. If you ask anyone what their rights are, very few will come up with a right to life.

To free up financial resources to address Covid-19, these countries can apply for the postponement of their principal debt and interest payments from 1 May to 31 December 2020. However, their debt will not be cancelled and will become due between 2022 and 2024. In fact, deferred payments will be adjusted to ensure creditors face no losses at the time of repayment; therefore, countries will have to repay more at the end of the suspension.

There is another study that supports universal face mask use because masks were equally effective in both healthcare and community settings when adjusted for the type of mask use. Growing evidence for presymptomatic and asymptomatic transmission of SARS-CoV-2 further supports universal face mask use and distancing. In regions with a high incidence of Covid-19, universal face mask use, combined with physical distancing, could reduce the rate of infection (flatten the curve) even with modestly effective masks.

04.06.20

I watched the Moderna science day. Their science is doing nicely across mRNA, protein engineering and delivery, and they showed intriguing results from collaborations with the International AIDS Vaccine Initiative (IAVI), NIAID and the Bill & Melinda Gates Foundation on an HIV vaccine.

Moderna has been heavily criticised over the years, and I have heard much of this. In a recent symposium, where I was 'co-talking', Greg Poland (head of vaccines at the Mayo Clinic) said they put economic considerations above scientific ones, but I really don't think this is the case. They're just trying to move very quickly and have done so since they were founded in 2011. In some ways the company came before the science, and it's never been their intention to publish as Oxford do.

Elsewhere, there is clearly some suspect science going on. For example, I find the science suggesting that SARS-CoV-2 was made in a lab very dodgy, based on personal views, and I haven't seen a decent paper on it. These views are based on the fact that no natural virus matching to Covid-19 has been found in nature despite an intensive search to find its origins. On the other hand, bats have a close version of it, and pangolins and other unusual animals an even closer version. Maybe it was released from a lab by mistake, but to make a virus like this I doubt, if only because it's too good at being transmitted and not killing people – too clever, in fact, despite the damage it causes.

The potential of HCQ for treating Covid-19 has become a political flashpoint, and the questions on HCQ in *The Lancet* paper have provided new fodder for the drug's supporters. French microbiologist Didier Raoult, whose own widely criticised studies suggested a benefit from the drug, derided the new study in a video, calling the authors 'incompetent'. On social media, some speculated that the paper was part of a conspiracy against HCQ. This is the pressure cooker atmosphere science is having to work in at the moment.

The Lancet and *NEJM* have had to retract cardiovascular Covid-19 studies by Surgisphere. An issue with preprints is they're not peer reviewed. An issue with peer review is it takes too long. An issue with a pandemic is wanting to get the truth out quickly. And journals are under pressure to publish leading science, which sometimes isn't that leading after all.

05.06.20

Some decent studies out in the last 24 hours. Starting to see some papers on host genetic factors and severity of Covid-19. Having type A blood was linked to a 50% increase in the likelihood that a patient would need to get oxygen or to go on a ventilator, according to the new study that is very comprehensive, looking at the genomes of a decent cohort of patients and controls in Italy and Spain. Interestingly, ACE2 variants made no difference.

An article in *The Lancet Public Health* assessed the impact of NPIs on viral transmission in the UK. It was a big study tracking 66 million people aggregated to 186 county-level administrative units. It found only lockdown periods were sufficient to bring R0 near or below 1. They suggest that because of the features of the virus, intensive interventions with lockdown periods are needed to control it and prevent cases overwhelming hospitals.

Another interesting study: To contain the spread of the disease, a cordon sanitaire was imposed on Wuhan city on 23 January 2020, and travel restrictions were subsequently imposed on other cities across Hubei Province the next day – as we know. After 61 days of lockdown in Hubei, the province reopened again on 25 March 2020, and after 76 days of lockdown in Wuhan, the city reopened again on 8 April 2020. The screening of individuals in these areas provides essential information on how immunity, and potentially herd immunity, is shaped in the community that has so far had the longest chain of community transmission but also some of the strongest physical distancing measures.

Today, clinicaltrials.gov listed a remarkable 215 Covid-19 trials with HCQ, 61 of which were focused on prophylaxis. Should they stop now? They really should, shouldn't they?

With regard to the Floyd protests, one measure of wealth inequality is the Gini coefficient, which in the US is well above the 0.4 threshold that the UN suggests poses a risk for civil unrest. The Gini coefficient is a calculation of wealth inequality measured from 0 (complete equality, where everyone has the same wealth) to 1 (complete inequality where the wealth of a population is held entirely by a single individual). The latest US estimate is 0.486. It's been observed that 1 in 5 Americans aren't saving, and 60% can't afford an emergency $1k expense, reflecting this inequality. Unfortunately, we might see wealth inequality exacerbated by Covid-19 as unemployment is spiking in unprecedented ways, leading to more consequences. Inner cities might take a disproportionate Covid hit, which could further amplify this. Within this framework, it's no wonder that at some point civil unrest will ensue. The Gini coefficient calculation can be used to express inequality of various forms, including wealth, income or even healthcare provision. Indeed, an analysis has estimated that if unemployment in the US reaches 20%, 25–43 million people will lose their health insurance.

06.06.20

Lots of quick facts today to get a flavour for the state of the world at the midpoint in the year: a US survey of social distancing preferences in around 6,000 adults finds 37% of people are reluctant to accept any increased risk of transmission, 26% were willing to accept increased risk to restart the economy, 13% wanted to get right back to normal immediately despite risks, and the rest wanted to wait a little longer to reopen.

An AI prediction, not mine I hasten to add, says it will all end this December anyway. So that's good news, although it could of course be wrong, like so many other AI predictions.

New data in *Science* suggests Rt is the actual transmission rate at any given time, and some say this is what we really should be talking about instead of R0 (which is more a description of how fast the virus wants to spread).

The New York Times published an article on how the CDC messed it all up in the moment of need, as if that's news. Also, the brains behind Sweden's plan to not aggressively quarantine when Covid-19 hit now apologises as the country has one of the highest Covid mortality rates in the world.

Now on to vaccines: Dr Fauci says we don't know how long immunity lasts. But he says a vaccine is doable by year end. OWS selects its five vaccine candidates, which seems to assume large US pharma must be the best at everything, and of course Vaccitech/AZN, which has said they'll make 2 billion doses if it works (which is a heck of a lot but guess we have to divide most of these things by two, i.e. for 2 doses). We'll have to see if vaccine timelines need to be adjusted to reflect delays from the selection process.

At the same time, China is ramping up vaccine production. 'Xi Jinping vows to share a Chinese-backed vaccine with the world.' Are vaccines the new soft power in the world? I would think, for the next couple of years, they would be a major lever of power and international diplomacy. Provided they work.

And Switzerland has called for a loosening of patent protection around Covid-19. No doubt we'll hear more of all of this sort of thing.

As well as all the baricitinib work I am doing my best to drive forward, let's show that you can't get Covid-19 from sports balls. With Michel Pelisser at Phoenix Hospital Group, I am covering various sports balls in inactivated SARS-CoV-2, wiping them, dropping them, throwing them and seeing if afterwards you can swab them and amplify the virus by PCR. A straightforward experiment that will hopefully reassure people involved in outdoor sports that it's safe. We've chosen a cricket ball, golf ball, tennis ball and football; tennis balls were just too furry. There's actually some science behind this. And it's good for morale and health if we can get people involved in sports again.

07.06.20

In the UK regional differences continue to be marked (perhaps the lockdown in the 'more susceptible London' led to a greater change than realised). In the US, a sharp jump in new cases was skewed higher by Michigan, which retrospectively added another 5k probable cases based on symptoms and an epidemiological link, similar to what we have seen other states do. China also reclassified cases. In addition to the sharp acceleration in testing, these retrospective revisions have been a factor in the slower declines in reported new cases vs hospitalisations and also deaths.

New tests spiked to a new single-day high of 519k, far above what we have seen before, and the moving average is up to 446k.

The WHO and others have said, contrary to some (I think erroneous) reports, the virus isn't losing potency.

And four new cases of Ebola in the DRC for the WHO to deal with. Ebola – remember that?

08.06.20

Let's start with something we can easily fix: a report was released stating 'elevated cholesterol appears to increase risk of Covid-19'. Not sure I am surprised?

As we talk about masks, it's very clear Covid-19 can be transmitted through eyes/tears, which we already knew but the media doesn't talk about. Perhaps we should encourage everyone to dress as Darth Vader or, more nicely, Neil Armstrong. It would cut down transmission and every day could be a Halloween party (except nobody is allowed to gather in groups outside their home). I guess to prove the point above, doctors ranked activities most likely to spread Covid, and drinking in a bar is number one.

Asia continues to exemplify models for safely reopening; case numbers remain low as their economies open up. Small clusters have emerged, though these have been met with rapid and efficient local responses that have curtailed spread. The US is starting to reopen from a substantially higher caseload and without comparable infrastructure or precautions, which makes me a little nervous that a possible second wave here could be problematic and further set the US back behind other countries. The CDC is right about one thing: the US isn't prepared for any further pandemics.

In China, the outbreak remains under control, with limited local transmission; it reported only 6 new cases on 6 June (5 imported). The Jilin cluster in north-east China that led to a dramatic lockdown has subsided, and the region lowered its response level to low – no new recent cases. Wuhan's mass testing effort is now complete. They found only around 300 asymptomatic cases and no infections in close contacts – remarkably low given the size of the initial outbreak.

A study from Hong Kong continues to support the role of superspreaders in the outbreak, finding that 20% of cases resulted in 80% of transmissions. Japan's outbreak has come under control despite limited testing; Singapore is starting to show encouraging signs as well, with new case numbers dropping.

South Korea is still seeing small clusters driven largely by indoor gatherings; the latest sources include churches, door-to-door salesmen, logistics centres and table tennis clubs. Schools continue to close/reopen. The most informative superspreading event (97 diagnosed) at a call centre in South Korea showed 58% were infected in the same room, 44% of those on the same floor, but only 0.3% of those on other floors.

The impact of the pandemic and of lockdowns on those with severe mental illness from *The Lancet*:

> Although the Covid-19 situation is frequently described as having changed everything, in some cases it has simply accentuated pre-existing trends – including neglect by the media, the public, and too many professionals – of those with severe mental illness. There have been innumerable opinion columns and reports on the mental health effects of lockdown, and on the situation on medical wards and in primary care. But there has been far too little space dedicated to the status of those with severe mental illness who would usually receive community support, or on the problems faced on inpatient mental health units.

09.06.20

In a sad sideshow to the human pandemic, authorities in the Netherlands began to gas tens of thousands of mink on 6 June, most of them pups born only weeks ago. SARS-CoV-2 has attacked farms that raise the animals for fur, but the Dutch government worries infected mink could become a viral reservoir that could cause new outbreaks in humans. So do I.

Another study I read had a good discussion of the potential persistence of Covid-19 in the body, something that still isn't well understood, and there are important implications since it determines how long people might be infectious. Is it possible some people could be chronic carriers with persistent low-grade lung inflammation?

Places in the US with the highest risk of Covid-19, none of which I'd have guessed: Glades FL, Nobles MN and Montgomery NC top the list. Covid-19 levels in swing states before the election are clearly key if elderly voters are going to turn out or not. Could a virus once again influence political history? I think of a minor moment: when Nixon was recovering from illness in the first televised debate in 1960 he looked sweaty and nervous compared to JFK, and he lost the election. Or the much bigger moment when the American delegation at Versailles in 1919 all came down with Spanish flu (including President Wilson), so they couldn't stop (and didn't want) the punitive repayments Germany had to make to France, a key point that is seen as a time bomb for the causes of the Second World War.

Brazil has stopped reporting Covid-19 figures as the data didn't look good; if you don't report the data, then it never happened, right? A bit like Samuel Shem's *The House of God* – if you don't measure a fever, a patient can't have one. And Iran is bracing for a second wave but only ever had a partial lockdown in the first place.

We should remember that vaccines may not work and/or be safe. No human safety data is available to the public, though some companies have issued press releases claiming safety without releasing the data. This is a concern as we are contemplating eventually giving vaccines to 2–3 billion people, or more. One vaccine with an adverse reaction can result in many millions either injured or killed. We don't know if they will protect anyone from infection. Yes, they raise antibodies in experimental animals, but it is still unclear whether the animals are protected.

An article from Harvard in *Nature Biotechnology* raises the valid point that worsening of Covid-19 infections could occur if we don't get the vaccine right. For certain diseases, patients who have been previously infected by one strain of a virus and who are later infected by another strain can suffer outcomes that are worse than those infected only once. Antibody-dependent enhancement (ADE), which blighted one of the Dengue vaccines, is a real concern, i.e. the vaccine is worse than the disease.

10.06.20

WHO retracted statements on only symptomatic cases transmitting the virus. Sometimes I wonder if they are making it up as they go along.

A new *Nature* modelling paper looked at data on local, regional and national non-pharmaceutical interventions and estimates that early infections of Covid-19 exhibit exponential growth rates of roughly 38% per day. They find that anti-contagion policies have significantly slowed this and estimate that in six countries (US, China, France, UK, Iran and Italy) interventions prevented or delayed 62 million confirmed cases, corresponding to averting roughly 530 million total infections. Big numbers.

In the US, there are around 17.5k new Covid cases, up slightly, while the rolling seven-day average is flat again. I note that the acceleration in testing in recent weeks, plus the retrospective additions of probable cases into some state counts have been factors in the slower declines in reported new cases nationally vs hospitalisations. New tests decreased for the fourth day in a row after reaching a new high point on Saturday, and the seven-day moving average remains flattish. The positive rate ticked up to 5% from 4% on Monday. It has been in the 4%–5% range for the past nine days. New reported deaths increased slightly, but the seven-day moving average is still flat.

Our sports balls experiments show that wiping the ball removes all traces of virus. Going for a quick paper here in a public health journal. If we can get more people out playing sports safely that must be good for morale.

11.06.20

A letter initiated by Denmark and signed by France, Germany, Spain, Belgium and Poland points out issues with medical supply shortages and uncoordinated responses to the coronavirus by EU member countries. One key proposal is to create a stockpile of critical medicines, protective gear, medical devices and vaccines that could supply the entire EU for three months in an emergency. The six countries also propose coordinating the development of a coronavirus vaccine, 'possibly' with EU funds, 'as this would accommodate the urgent need of enabling the EU to speed up the time from the outbreak of a future pandemic to the successful deployment of a vaccine'.

In the US, the trend and scope of new virus cases continues to be worse than other Western countries. The reproduction number there remains slightly over 1. The peak is significantly flatter and wider than other countries, and the total predicted infections now stands at 2.5 million (versus about 2.3 million last week). Many states have started to reach new highs in cases as well as hospitalisations. While testing volumes have increased, I do not view this rise in cases as purely driven by tests as many European and Asian countries have been able to lower cases while increasing testing volume, and hospitalisations are now starting to increase in the most impacted states as well.

Asia's new cases remain low. Singapore and South Korea appear to have been able to control their new clusters of cases. The Middle East continues to see significant spread, as well as Latin America. India, Brazil and various Middle Eastern countries remain the most concerning areas globally as the spread of disease remains significant. Brazil slowed somewhat, but given the new data restrictions by the government (despite states still independently reporting data), I am unsure what to make of the trend. Importantly, some Middle East countries appear to be entering the terminal stage of their outbreaks.

The *Wall Street Journal* reported that the US government plans to fund and conduct the decisive studies of three experimental coronavirus vaccines starting this summer: Moderna, AZN/Oxford and Johnson & Johnson (J&J).

J&J also announced an acceleration of its vaccine studies. I am unclear how it would start a Phase 3 study so soon, but it's a big pharma so it has a ton of resources. Per the *WSJ*, each vaccine study is expected to include roughly 30,000 people, with some receiving the experimental shots and others placebo shots, and each study will be conducted at more than 50 sites, possibly some internationally. Researchers hope the trials will yield answers within six to eight months of their starts, but their view is consistently that shots could become available for emergency use on a shorter timeline, possibly as soon as the autumn.

12.06.20

Have found it interesting that locations of major Floyd protests (or riots, depending on where one lives and/or political considerations) are not foci of new infections. The police video went viral (to be clear, most police violence involves guns so this was unusual in that it didn't), and no doubt there will be a decline in police activity in many areas, with that in itself having major implications: who needs cities? With our newly discovered ability to work from home, big locational changes will occur, I think. This plus the virus together make for an interesting dynamic.

Lots of people ask me about the second wave. Well, it's here in nearly 20 states, and that means the states that are okay now might not be okay by Labor Day (7 September) if everyone is travelling. In the US, over 22k new cases were reported yesterday, up again from 20k Wednesday, though the rolling seven-day average remains flat at about 21k. New York State and Italy provide two examples where testing volumes can increase, but cases continue to decline.

Arizona is really very hot just now, destroying the warm weather argument I made for dissipation of the virus. Every day there's an incremental pathology paper. A decent paper out from *The Lancet* showing why Covid-19 isn't just bad flu. In a post-mortem series from Italy, the predominant pattern of lung lesions in patients with Covid is diffuse alveolar damage as described in patients infected with severe acute respiratory syndrome and Middle East respiratory syndrome coronaviruses.

Regeneron has begun studying the anti-SARS-Cov-2 antibody cocktail in patients who have active Covid-19 infections (in both hospital and non-hospital settings). These are the first two of four trials. The trials are adaptive Phase 1/2/3 studies that allow for flexibility and rapid clinical advancement.

So that's the news on treatment, but also, every day there is incremental vaccine news. Moderna has formally announced that it expects to begin the Phase 3 trial of its vaccine at the 100-microgram dose level in July, with 30,000 participants. The Phase 2 in younger adults (n=300) has also been enrolled, as has a cohort of older adults. As the trial is event-driven, relying on accrual of symptomatic cases, the completion timeline has not yet been disclosed, although there are clear reports suggesting a potential EUA of the Moderna vaccine by this autumn. In time for the US election or not. This virus is turning into Trump's nemesis. Will a vaccine save him?

13.06.20

In Europe, the observed decline in cases and deaths could be due to lockdowns, social distancing and other interventions. This would imply that the epidemic is still at a relatively early stage and that a large proportion of the population therefore remains susceptible. First, in such a scenario, there is a high risk of renewed transmission if interventions or behavioural modifications are completely relaxed. Second, the observed decline in cases and deaths could be due to the achievement of herd immunity. This would imply that a large proportion of the population is now protected from infection either through acquisition of immunity following previous infection or through other natural means (such as cross-protection from other coronaviruses). In such a scenario, a further decline in cases and deaths is to be expected even in the absence of interventions or behavioural modifications. Putting it simply, countries that went into lockdown early experienced fewer deaths in subsequent weeks.

14.06.20

Beijing is now in partial lockdown with mass contact tracing; the rest of China is unaffected. On Thursday (11th), Beijing announced its first new infection in two months. I have heard there are two symptomatic cases, actual symptoms unclear. Imported salmon implicated off an 'infected chopping board' and two Chinese doctors have told me it means it can live on surfaces for longer – so to me it's interesting they look at the worst case. It could, of course, all be hay fever and false positives. But in a 100% susceptible population, it's not implausible that there is some form of outbreak, despite the measures seen.

The *BMJ* has an interesting critique of the current test-trace-isolate system in the UK. One of the biggest challenges with test and trace is that delays inevitably hamper every stage. A symptomatic person organising and then receiving a test; the test reaching a laboratory and the laboratory analysing the sample; the test results getting to the contact, tracers and councils and follow-up action being taken. Boris Johnson has promised that test results – except those from samples returned by post – will be turned around in 24 hours by the end of June, but anecdotal evidence, certainly from people I speak to, suggests that two or three days is currently more typical.

15.06.20

Rather emotive daily update today. First, an extraordinary editorial in the *NEJM* re: 'I can't breathe', reveals George Floyd was Covid-19 positive at post-mortem. Two headlines merged into one. Two great blights on society become a single focal point. And, of course, his plaintive cry is a defining statement.

On a more positive note, England's schools are now fully reopened and so are shops – with various restrictions. I had never before appreciated that just walking into an ordinary store, that doing something so 'normal', could now feel almost exciting. I have gotten too used to Whole Foods and Amazon as my main retail points. The country is slowly, cautiously, coming out of hibernation, and the fabulous weather has made the lockdown more bearable.

16.06.20

It will be interesting to observe the current new Beijing outbreak to see if they can contain it – and how rapidly. The Xinfadi wholesale market is absolutely enormous, and the focus of 79 cases in four days but very few symptomatic cases. This looks like the shape of things to come. If they can't control it, it doesn't bode well for Italy, Spain and the US. For example, going forward to preserve the economy, will states in the US take the excess mortality if necessary? Around twenty areas in Beijing are now quarantined. Local Chinese news is saying it's from an imported European salmon – like some kind of Monty Python sketch. They say it's a Covid strain that, genetically, comes from Europe. But if you want humour, this *Onion* headline is more amusing: 'City enters phase 4 of pretending coronavirus is over.'

The European alternative of opening progressively, following Austria's lead, has seemed the best method to me, thus far. The Netherlands opened on 1 June with restaurants/bars, and although numbers are small, there's been an upsurge in ICU admissions since Friday, when they'd been declining (8 yesterday, the highest since March).

Interestingly, there is a study that has shown loss of smell is a predictor of milder disease. I hadn't realised there's a global consortium for chemosensory research.

Lilly finally started its very own, or our own, big Phase 3 trial of baricitinib vs placebo called COV-BARRIER, and the important points about this are twofold: first, they feel it's ethically fine to do a placebo trial so remdesivir is not standard of care, and second, this was a pharma company that didn't believe in AI and is now embracing it. So, if treatments don't work, we're waiting to be infected, not infected or vaccinated. Sinovac, Beijing-based, has announced that its inactivated live virus induces neutralising antibodies in 90% of 743 people in Phase 2. I have to say their monkey data, if one believes it, published last month in *Science*, was decent, to say the least. Let's see publications of their human data.

AstraZeneca's BARDA contract has led to a deal for European delivery. This is the first contract signed by Europe's Inclusive Vaccines Alliance (IVA), a group formed by France, Germany, Italy and the Netherlands to secure vaccine doses for all member states as soon as possible. Britain, having 'Brexited' from the EU, has gone its own way on this. Only time will tell which way of doing things is better.

With respect to the various vaccine companies, the major differences for me are around how the vaccines work. All of the projects about to head into large OWS studies in the US use different modalities: AZN and J&J use an adenovirus that cannot replicate itself to introduce the SARS-CoV-2 spike protein, in the hope that the body generates a response. Moderna and BioNTech are delivering mRNA in a lipid coating that should prompt the body to manufacture key parts of the virus and subsequently provoke an immune response that would protect against encountering SARS-CoV-2 in the wild.

We know vaccine development has historically been a long and costly endeavour, and it's worth mentioning these as the same still applies, and these reasons haven't gone away:

- Durable efficacy is usually required so trials are long.
- Trials are usually in healthy patients and a good outcome is that they do not become sick, which takes time to ascertain.
- Since the ultimate recipients are usually healthy individuals, the safety bar is very high: trials with large patient numbers are usually conducted to ascertain if there are rare (but potentially serious) side effects or antibody-dependent enhancement (ADE).
- Lengthy trials with many patients are expensive, and so is building the complex production infrastructure necessary to manufacture consistent and reliable supply.
- The production process itself can be long (months to get a dose from start to finish).
- Here, timelines have been drastically shortened to something that would be the fastest-ever process for creating a new vaccine (other than repurposing flu vaccines for an outbreak, where the production process already exists).

- The need to show durable efficacy has essentially been removed (for now).
- Plenty of activities are being undertaken 'at risk'. This includes the government's purchasing plans.
- Phase 3 trials are being planned while Phase 1 trials are still in progress.
- Large-scale manufacturing is being organised (with some assistance from the government in the US) already.
- Distribution networks are being developed (the Department of Defence may be involved in the US).

In other words, what is usually a long, cautious, sequenced process is now being parallelised to some degree, and risks that would usually be considered unacceptable from a return on investment perspective, are now tolerable based on some public funding and explicit expectations from some companies that profits on a coronavirus vaccine are not a priority. Of course, there are other potential consequences: long-term safety data will, by definition, not be available for some time. The Phase 3 trials planned so far are at least large, which should offer some comfort. What does success look like? In the immediate future, it looks as though 'good enough will be good enough', given a total lack of existing options.

17.06.20

There have been 136 cases in Beijing in the last six days, with schools closed now, but it seems under control – typical quick actions. The New Zealand government has so far identified 320 close contacts of the two infected women who were not tested before they were released from quarantine on compassionate grounds. In the US, around 23k new Covid cases were reported by state health departments Tuesday, up from 19k Monday. The seven-day moving average moved back up to 22k.

New York State provided an update today on its random sampling for serology tests, with only a small uptick in the positive rate. Still, it's an important metric.

Oxford has come up with the only drug to reduce mortality. It's oral or intravenous and a cheap generic, with results shown in a randomised study though we've yet to see details, and I don't really understand the mechanism. In March 2020, the RECOVERY (Randomised Evaluation of Covid-19 thERapY) trial was established as a randomised clinical trial to test a range of potential treatments for Covid-19, including low-dose dexamethasone (a steroid treatment). Over 11,500 patients have been enrolled from over 175 NHS hospitals in the UK with an easy consent form, and joined up protocols between hospitals. Based on these results, 1 death would be prevented by treatment of around 8 ventilated patients or around 25 patients requiring oxygen alone. It looks a proper result, though it has come in for criticism for being announced in a press release. We do need to see the paper. This time I am sure we will.

I have no idea about the virus reality in Africa. The DRC reported its first case on 14 March, and by 9 May a total of 274 confirmed cases and 10 deaths had been reported; today there are around 5k cases/112 deaths out of a population of 8 million. Very few countries in Africa have sufficient and appropriate diagnostic capacities, and obvious challenges exist to handle an outbreak of this extent. A question that the DRC and other member states in the region must ask themselves is, are they seeing only a gradual increase in the detection of cases? Are they missing infections? A probable answer is that people with symptoms do not present to healthcare facilities because of their concerns about fragile health systems, social stigma and quarantine in suboptimal facilities. Other questions still to be resolved are related to the dynamics of viral transmission across geographical regions, between humans, across different ecosystems, within different genetic backgrounds and whether any protective herd immunity exists.

Paper in *Journal of Physics Fluids* (it's real!) shows flushing the toilet generates a 3-foot virus aerosol if infected. Gross but important news. The solution is simple: put down the lid.

Gary, Mario and I now want to find a blood marker in Covid patients to work out who will become sick, and to distinguish different disease patterns. Gary has access to O-Link's mass spectrometry technology, so they can measure 186 blood markers and cytokines from a tiny sample. Lilly also have their own home-grown interleukin-19 assay, a marker of dendritic immune function – the cells that prime the immune response. I need to help collect these samples from all over the world and get them to Lilly. As well as comparing healthy people with mild, moderate and severe Covid-19, the crucial thing is to have longitudinal samples over time, so we can work out patterns of response, comparing those who do well against those who don't, and let's not forget, whether baricitinib improves the situation. If we can predict who will do badly, we can give those patients specific therapies earlier to help prevent them from crashing.

18.06.20

Food today. Norwegian salmon is not to blame for new traces of the coronavirus at a Beijing food market, Chinese and Norwegian authorities said together. No surprise. It's worth taking a step back here, however. Seafood consumption provides nutrients linked to reductions in malnutrition and disease for nearly half the global population. Almost half of the world's seafood comes from small-scale fisheries (SSFs), which also employ 90% of the world's fishers and provide crucial food and livelihoods in coastal communities globally. This important industry virtually collapsed in January 2020. The closure of a single dominant market highlighted the growing vulnerability of SSFs to global market shocks as many such fisheries increasingly rely on a limited number of foreign buyers rather than less lucrative domestic markets. Furthermore, local management strategies available to SSFs can be effective at maintaining local fishing stocks but are incapable of ensuring the stability of a globalised market.

Food impacts include habitat loss (which is implicated in the spread of zoonotic diseases like Covid-19), water resource depletion, perturbation of biochemical cycling (including greenhouse gas emissions), pollution and waste, to name just a few. The performance of the food system therefore matters a great deal. The systems we employ influence who has enough to eat and who does not, how much environmental degradation we cause, and where it accrues; they also influence the extent to which people consume healthy and sustainable meals across the wealth spectrum. The global food system produces enough for everyone, yet hunger is still a huge problem. The 'Global Report on Food Crises', just published, estimates that 135 million people were food insecure in 2019, the highest number in the four years of the report, revealing a concerning trend towards increasing hunger. Who knows what it will be for this year?

Conflict was identified as the main driver of food insecurity, with weather extremes and economic shocks becoming increasingly significant. If that wasn't bad enough, projections by the World Food Programme, which incorporate the effects of Covid-19 and its economic ramifications, suggest that 265 million people in LMICs will be suffering acute food insecurity by the end of 2020 unless mitigatory action is taken.

In other words, Covid-19 could roughly double the number of people living with acute hunger in just one year, a devastating scenario. There are many ways that the Covid-19 pandemic and its control measures are expected to impact food systems. In the first instance, food supply is expected to be relatively unaffected, although lack of labour mobility and access to markets will likely reduce some food supplies and will certainly increase food waste, particularly of perishable items.

The 'to do' list for sorting this is long: we need more sustainable foods that are less harmful to the environment, and to produce healthier and more nutritious foods and fewer unhealthy ones. We need to find ways to distribute food more equally, and it is now clearer than ever that we need to build much more resilience into our food systems, particularly for vulnerable groups. Weaknesses in our food systems are likely to be just one test among many yet to come.

On the subject of food: in Germany, Agriculture Minister Klöckner has said that it could make sense to test pets for coronavirus if they live in the same household as humans known to be infected. Klöckner said that while there is currently no evidence that humans can pick up an infection from animals, positive coronavirus tests in pets could help scientists find out more. Glad this is relevant to food.

19.06.20

China's old school vaccine approach, using an inactivated virus, continues to yield interesting albeit unpublished data: of the 5 vaccines in the clinics in China, 4 are inactivated whole virus. Of the other 126 vaccines in development outside of China, only 5 are inactivated whole virus. For example, the China National Biotec Group just reported 100% neutralising antibodies in their Phase 2 trial. Am not sure what that means. I thought it was dependent on the level of antibodies. Mind you, many are referring to antibody levels similar to those seen in convalescent plasma. Which can be very high, or very low. This just refers to the plasma fraction of the blood, which is sometimes used as a treatment for patients as it's got all the antibodies in it, akin to a blood transfusion in some ways but without the red cells, white cells, platelets and other factors – apart from the antibodies.

Meanwhile, OWS is supporting seven vaccines and the WHO is hoping for hundreds of millions of doses this year, billions next. That's incredibly ambitious, but necessary if we are going to return the world to a functioning state again. But then again, the CEO of AstraZeneca has said their vaccine will protect for one year only. It seems like it's hard to project too far ahead.

The European Commission is asking global leaders to cooperate to buy Covid-19 vaccines to avoid harmful competition (I thought competition was partly how/why they've moved so fast). Let's see how that goes. And simultaneously, the EU is trying to secure supplies of Covid-19 vaccines from J&J and others. So much for that cooperation, and what about Sanofi-GSK?

Data suggests that antibodies post-Covid remain stable for at least two months; 2–9% don't seroconvert. The more severe, the more likely to have elevated antibodies. In other words, the sicker you get from Covid, the longer you remain resistant to it afterwards, it seems. A woman in Dallas tested positive for Covid a second time, but symptoms and signs the second time (headache, elevated blood pressure) were different from the first time (dry cough). Was it a persistent antigen without a live virus? Reactivation in blood vessels? Reinfection? Fortunately, still very rare.

Next, the Equal Employment Opportunity Commission yesterday stated that 'requiring antibody testing before allowing employees to re-enter' was not allowed under the Americans with Disabilities Act. Vaccination discrimination is now a thing.

A leaked CDC document contradicts Pence's claim that the virus is stabilised. Not sure why some say 'leaked' as it was on the CDC website, but what do I know? And Dr Fauci is worried spikes will turn into proper outbreaks if people don't wear masks. Even the Governor of Florida has said there won't be another lockdown, but people must wear masks. Most importantly, we will have trusted information as *Sesame Street* will do an episode for kids on Covid and mask wearing. We are now at the point in America where children's TV shows are giving out better health information than some state governors.

20.06.20

Since the early days of the pandemic, medical protectionism has emerged as nations scrambled for their own stocks of PPE and ventilators. Covid-19 vaccines could be the next example. Already there is a danger of a vaccine bidding war, with governments competing for a limited number of doses well before a vaccine even reaches the market. Enormous amounts of public money and resources poured into vaccine research and development have resulted in more than 150 Covid-19 vaccine candidates, 10 of which are now in trials in humans. The most advanced candidate is AZD1222, sometimes called ChAdOx1, first developed by researchers at Oxford/Vaccitech, with public and philanthropic funds from CEPI, then licensed to AstraZeneca. Last month, the UK government boosted its national vaccine programme with £65 million towards the Oxford vaccine. In return, 30 million doses will be reserved for people in the UK by September, part of an agreement to deliver 100 million doses in total. The US government also spent big: $1.2 billion to secure 300 million doses of the same vaccine for use in the US as part of OWS to accelerate the development, manufacturing and distribution of Covid-19 medical countermeasures. But neither a nationalist nor a free-market-driven approach will lead to equal access to vaccines.

Earlier this month, France, Germany, Italy and the Netherlands formed the Inclusive Vaccines Alliance to persuade pharma to make Covid-19 vaccines accessible and affordable to EU states. A portion of vaccines will be made available to low-income countries, including in Africa; less clear is how big this portion will be, which countries will benefit from it, and who will make these decisions. Many middle-income countries might be left out.

Political leaders, including Macron, Merkel and Xi Jinping, have called for Covid-19 vaccines to be a global public good – a people's vaccine, available to all. At the Global Vaccine Summit on 4 June, world leaders, including those from the UK, Germany and Canada, together with the Bill & Melinda Gates Foundation, pledged $750 million to AstraZeneca for 300 million doses of AZD1222 on a no-profit basis as part of the Gavi Covax Advance Market Commitment. The Serum Institute of India will also produce up to 1 billion doses for low- and middle-income countries. Covax's initial aim is to raise $2 billion to accelerate the manufacture of a Covid-19 vaccine on a huge scale and to distribute it according to need, rather than ability to pay.

This commitment is commendable. It delivers a powerful message to governments and vaccine developers that, if legally binding, solid measures will be put in place and money pledged, meaning that vaccines can be made available and affordable universally. However, many big questions remain: Have the funders agreed to equitable access? How will the vaccines be priced? Will governments commit to sharing vaccines according to fair allocation rules being developed by WHO? Can technology be transferred royalty-free to multiple manufacturers? The question of who will get priority access to vaccines is core to the global public interest. We need to get the governance of these decisions right; otherwise, there will be tremendous resentment and unnecessary deaths, not to mention decreased capacity to get this pandemic under control. I think, but do not know, that GAVI/COVAX is a step in the right direction.

21.06.20

Seems likely that going forward we will see numerous outbreaks in multiple locations. Israel registered 294 new coronavirus patients in the past 24 hours, the Health Ministry announced late on Saturday after single-digit daily cases in May. Israel has had an aggressive early hospitalisation policy from the beginning, so that can't really explain it (would explain UK/Italy observations potentially). But we might just be better at treating Covid. It may also be that if there is an inoculum dose effect (minimal evidence thus far, but a reasonable enough hypothesis) that people are getting infected with lower doses. I should note that there does appear to be some lag in deaths, so don't read too much into the above. But it's worth watching this space.

Meanwhile, by comparing open states versus closed states in the US, daily new cases continue exhibiting an upward trend in open states, although note the cyclical weekly fluctuations. A clear decreasing trend remains among the closed states. A similar trend in open vs closed states is also observed in the latest fourteen-day trend.

22.06.20

Busy start to the week, one in which I could spend the entire entry talking about worldwide outbreaks, from Iran to a poultry factory in Yorkshire, England, and from several clusters in San Diego to slaughterhouses in Germany, where unidirectional air-conditioned drafts clearly nicely spread the virions between closely assembled workers. In the US, Covid cases continue to spike in 12 states, infecting younger people who are less risk-averse and not adhering to face masks/social distancing but interestingly again not in George Floyd protest locations. As expected, young people also have less severe disease. Question is, will they spread to vulnerable people and/or affect reopenings, or will wearing face masks save the day as mandated in much of Arizona and now Vegas?

And you can cross Nebraska off your holiday list as the federal government has said mandating masks will mean no funding; even Iran's President Rouhani is considering mandating masks. Sinovac from Beijing thinks its Phase 2/3 trials using inactivated virus will be done and ready by this autumn. Beijing also claims to be able to test 1 million people per day. Not to get too technical, but that's a lot. Indeed, Beijing's confirmation of a Covid-19 case on 11 June ended a run of 55 days without reported local transmissions. Since then the outbreak has burgeoned, but it is now gone as the city responded with fierce determination. As of today, it has tested >400,000 people, confirming 140 cases, the vast majority asymptomatic. The city has locked down some residential compounds, closed all schools and cancelled hundreds of flights.

Lilly has started its own Phase 3 trials with baricitinib. The main one is a global study versus placebo, called COV-BARRIER. The existing ACTT-II trial, sponsored by the NIAID, is using baricitinib plus remdesivir versus remdesivir alone. Both will have over 1,000 patients. I'm in regular contact with the main investigators here, and they are quite simply the world's best doctors, people like Ray Schinazi and Vincent Marconi (a fellow Hopkins alumnus) from Emory. I do wonder how the use of steroids in both arms of these studies will confound and confuse any data we produce, and I know Gary is concerned about this too. But it also means that if baricitinib hits the primary end points in these studies or reduces mortality, the reality will be better than the data. I think baricitinib is a lot more than just steroids, especially with specific antiviral effects.

23.06.20

I was really flattered to receive this:

Dear Professor Stebbing,

Re: DHSC/UKRI Global Effect on COVID-19 Health Research call – Invitation to join College of Experts

In recognition of your expertise in the field, I am writing to invite you to join a College of Experts that we are establishing to support a new

DHSC/UKRI Global Effect on COVID-19 Health Research funding opportunity ... This is an exceptional and time-critical activity and the College of Experts will be crucial to ensuring that robust decisions are made. I understand that this is short notice, but I would very much value your participation in this important assessment process...

Yours sincerely,
Dr Debbie Willis
Senior Programme Manager – Global Health

A report is circulating that the D614G strain, a mutation that started to circulate in Europe and affects the spike protein at position 614, changing one amino acid for another, 'escapes' the neutralising antibodies that Covid-19 patients in Wuhan developed. This strain is now very dominant.

An 'escape' would be one of the more significant concerns for the vaccine field. Many of the first wave of vaccines were constructed prior to the D614G strain emerging and, as such, would not be designed to incorporate it. It does code for part of the spike protein, but the most important thing to note about the D614G mutant study is that among the 41 patient blood samples tested, 93% could still neutralise both the original and the mutated strain. Only 1 patient failed to neutralise the mutated strain. Mutation is natural and inevitable; it's why there's no cure for the common cold and there are annual flu jabs. But mutation shows the complexity and importance of the race the vaccines are in. They may come out by year's end and be perfectly capable of dealing with the original strain, only to be faced with an adapted winter strain that makes all that hard work mean nothing.

24.06.20

In the US, the trend and scope of new virus cases continues to be worse than in other Western countries. The R0 in the US has increased to 1.14 (vs 1.1 on 21 June), an indication that spread is accelerating and new case growth is also accelerating. As per my comments on chessboards and exponential growth back in March, a small change in R0 can make a big change in case numbers.

In Europe, all major countries are in the terminal phase. New cases are either stable at a low level or continuing in a sustainable decline despite the reopening (Italy, France and Switzerland). Spain reported a large daily increase last week due to a backlog and resumed stabilisation. Germany had a significant outbreak in a meatpacking plant and has established a new lockdown around the plant. The UK continues to improve but at a slower rate than its peers.

Another paper on low- and middle-income countries (LMICs). At the current time, it isn't possible to predict with any certainty the exact number of cases for any given country, the precise mortality and disease burden that will result or the benefits and drawbacks of the different approaches to control of the virus that are currently being implemented. A full understanding of these will only be available retrospectively. They show that even moderate levels of changes in behaviour can avert many infections and hence save millions of lives.

I'm excited about baricitinib in LMICs as it's a once-daily tablet and can be used at home – you don't need a hospital, another potential epicentre of infection for this. Although taking it for years for rheumatoid arthritis is not cheap, taking it for 7–14-days is. It has 2 doses, so can be used at a lower 2mg dose in the elderly or those with impaired renal function (unlike remdesivir, which can't be used in this group) and doesn't interact with other drugs. It has a short half-life of many hours, meaning that the body gets rid of it quickly, much less than antibodies like Actemra, which stay in the body for a couple of weeks. This means that if there's a problem, one can stop the drug. We've been worried about blood clots with it because the virus can cause this, and the original trials in rheumatoid arthritis had a small clot signal. I'm mining the FDA database of drug side effects to see if there is a real clot signal, kindly helped by Dr Ling Peng's diligent team from China and Silvia at Imperial; we don't see anything of any meaning to report, so we will publish this. Have had a few late-night discussions with the busy, dynamic Lorenzo Cecchi in Italy too, working with his team in Prato. Of all the risk factors for Covid-19 and problems with it, we seem to be circling around the fact that asthma may be protective because of the type of immune response that occurs there. All very much worth investigating.

Over 33k new Covid cases reported by state health departments in the US, up from 27k the day before, and the highest number I have seen in my dataset since 1 May. The seven-day moving average also continues to climb for an eighth straight day, reaching 29k and breaking above the narrow range around 21–22k that had held from mid-May through mid-June.

Tuesdays are typically a high point of the week for hospitalisations due to weekend admission patterns and reporting lags, but yesterday's increase in net hospitalisations was still notably large at more than 1k. Gross new hospitalisations for states reporting also increased on a seven-day rolling basis.

25.06.20

Utterly shameless plug now: David Sinclair from Harvard, who runs their ageing programme and wrote the amazing book *Lifespan*, wrote an editorial to accompany the full print of my paper in *EMBO Molecular Medicine* on my team's work on baricitinib/AI. Thank you! I quote:

A typical drug development program takes at least 5 years to move from bench to bedside. This timeframe can be shortened to months by repurposing existing drugs. The question is, how to rapidly identify which existing drugs to test in patients? A possible breakthrough was made in February by Stebbing and colleagues, a London-based team, who used an artificial intelligence platform called BenevolentAI to identify baricitinib as a possible Covid-19 therapy. While there are few specific details available on how BenevolentAI works, conceptually similar platforms are increasingly being used to generate novel hypotheses that are speeding drug repurposing efforts … Beyond these immediate next steps, the study also has broader, longer-term implications. Other deadly viruses, such as those that cause Ebola, hepatitis C, dengue fever, and other coronavirus diseases, rely on similar mechanisms for entry into host cells and also cause systemic inflammation. Baricitinib, or drugs like it, could therefore become part of humanity's arsenal against emerging infectious diseases. Given the rush to develop novel anti-Covid-19 therapies, the authors did not test baricitinib in an animal model of viral infection, but such experiments could help determine whether antiviral NAK inhibition, anti-inflammatory JAK inhibition, or both are necessary for the drug's putative efficacy. If baricitinib indeed does show efficacy via both mechanisms, it would validate NAKs as bona fide drug targets and elevate the importance of discovering other drugs that provide dual antiviral and anti-inflammatory properties.

As the Covid-19 pandemic is demonstrating, adversity fosters innovation. Here, the marriage of machine learning and rapid clinical trials provides hope for progress not only in today's fight against Covid-19, but in the ongoing fight against acute and chronic diseases.

We need to take the next step here. The large human trials are happening. These are of a regulatory approval standard. But our team needs to show data in subgroups, and relevant ones like the elderly, and that it's safe. And we need to work further on the mechanism of action. I am speaking to Volker Lauschke at the Karolinska Institute later today about his organoid models, tiny organs in a petri dish, the most stunning perfect mini-systems for study here. We'll try to infect them and see if baricitinib can stop this happening. At the same time, I'm having conversations with Oxford Nanoimager and their enigmatic CEO Bo Zhu and their scientific team. It would be awesome if we could use their super-resolution microscopy to actually visualise this happening at the virus particle level. I hear they even want to use their microscope for testing people.

Unfortunately, Covid cases are needed to run vaccine trials. The leader of the Jenner ChAdOx1 trial says they have little chance of getting an answer as the UK runs out of patients (same thing happening in Japan). That might be a good thing since pigs need 2 doses of the AZN/Jenner vaccine, but the UK study is only testing 1 dose. There is a trial evaluating a prime/boost ChAdOx1 regimen in South Africa, but that just started.

Unsurprisingly, China has been accused of hacking US and other vaccine efforts.

One study using influenza networks suggests 8.7 million Americans were infected in March alone. Also in the US, insurers aren't required to pay for Covid-19 testing, according to the guidance just released.

Then there's African track and trace technology. It must be better than the French one, which detected about a dozen cases in a month! Several African countries have been rolling out tools to aid contact tracing. Nigeria is planning to deploy. The service achieves contact tracing by leveraging Bluetooth and device GPS location technology. As you move around, it anonymously logs all the Bluetooth devices you come in contact with up to 8 metres, keeping details of distance, duration of connection and exact location of connection. When a citizen is confirmed with Covid-19, the data is transmitted to the CDC administrative tool. The Nigerian CDC then identifies people who have been in contact with the Covid-19 resident and sends them a push notification. Ghana has also rolled out a similar contact-tracing app.

26.06.20

Case rates are trending higher in the US. States across the country have been reporting daily highs for new cases for nearly a week. On Wednesday, the US reported approximately 37k new daily cases, 39k yesterday, surpassing the record two months prior. Broadly, sunbelt and western states are seeing particularly pronounced outbreaks. On Tuesday, Texas on its own reported 5.5k new cases, days after the state crossed the 4k mark for the first time. As the state faces a heavy increase in new cases and hospitalisations, Governor Greg Abbott issued an executive order on Thursday expanding hospital bed capacity while suspending elective surgeries in four counties. Texas, Florida and California are three of the highest Medicare-exposed states, given population size/age demographics.

I don't think there will be more US statewide shutdowns, but I do think diagnostic testing and contact tracing in these key regions are becoming more critical. Should a spike in cases occur in prior hotbed regions such as New York, with the strictest shutdown protocols, greater concern would be justified but that's not happening.

The new case seven-day moving average also continues to climb for a tenth straight day, reaching 33k – also a new high above the previous April peak of 31k. New cases jumped back up in Arizona after

Wednesday's dip to 3k from 1.8k, with the seven-day moving average in new cases up 61% vs a week ago; hospitalisations are up 40%. Total ICU occupancy in Arizona is unchanged from Wednesday at 88% (or 64% including surge capacity). Florida's statewide ICU occupancy rate is 78%, with most cases in cities: occupancy rates are 70% in Miami-Dade County, 80% in Hillsborough County (Tampa) and 86% in Orange County (Orlando).

New tests jumped to a new record high of 647k, vs 502k Wednesday and the previous high point of 605k set last Friday. The seven-day rolling average moves up to nearly 550k. After rising for the past three days, the positive test rate (the proportion of those positive tests versus the proportion of those tested) dropped from 7.6% yesterday to 6.0%. I like this metric. It shows that if you're doing more tests it leads to more people diagnosed. In particular, if the positive test rate goes up and more tests are being done, it simply means that more people are being infected.

Nationally, overall hospitalisation numbers continue to rise, though the inflexion remains more moderate compared to the spike in cases. New reported deaths dropped to 650 yesterday from ~700 Wednesday. Note this excludes 1,854 probable deaths New Jersey retrospectively added to its dashboard, though I include this in the total cumulative count of 118k, which means in five months America has had twice as many fatalities as in the whole of the First World War.

The US still has significantly underinvested contact tracing, with 27–28,000 current contact tracers vs a need for 100,000+ (this is up from about 6,000 pre-pandemic). Without universal mask wearing and the isolation of new cases, we are unlikely to see a significant change in the current dynamics.

Globally, the vast majority of serology surveys have produced results suggesting that ~5% of the population has been infected, a long way from herd immunity. But, are antibodies protective? There has been incremental progress in answering this question, but many unknowns related to the level of protection provided by antibodies and their durability remain. At this point, consensus around the necessary level of neutralising antibodies (NAbs) required to confer protection or whether asymptomatic patients are protected from reinfection have not been reached. Pre-clinical data suggests that non-human primates (NHP) infected with SARS-CoV-2 elicit a protective immune response against a second infection. This data is important as it implies that people who were infected and recovered may be protected against re-exposure. If a vaccine is available in early 2021, the US could achieve herd immunity by summer 2021.

In the App Store and Google Play, research has been done using the search terms 'coronavirus', 'Covid 19', 'Covid-19' and 'novel coronavirus'. They identified 82 apps from 35 different countries.

Of these 82 apps, 32 were within the UK in English. Apps were evaluated using the Systems Wide Analysis of mobile health-related technologies (SWAT) tool in line with the NHS Digital Assessment Questionnaire and were given a score for each category (usability, functionality, ethical values, security and privacy, user-perceived value, design, and content) by independent assessors. Most apps had high scores for usability, functionality, design and information provision. Apps verified by government organisations (e.g. the Government Technological Agency in Singapore) had higher user uptake than unverified apps. For example, the NHS24 Covid-19 app, which scored highest in their assessment, had approximately 2 million users (3% of the UK population), but the NHS app, which scored low on quality assessment, had a twofold increase in new registrations from 56,655 to 200k before it was closed. Similarly, the TraceTogether App, developed by the Singapore government, had over 1 million users (20% of the population). Given that the effectiveness of a contact-tracing app relies on a high level of user uptake, this is disappointing. The practical challenges of using mobile apps for contact tracing include the possibility of false data inputting and the practicality of location tracking to map epidemiology. Contract-tracing apps need stricter policing and monitoring, compared with apps that rely on daily updating of information and present fewer challenging ethical issues.

And just when we thought things couldn't get any worse, it looks like Covid-19 can trigger diabetes. Earlier this month, an international group of scientists established a global database to collect information on people with Covid-19 and high blood sugar levels who do not have a history of diabetes or problems controlling their blood sugars. All sorts of data have already come out. Maybe it directly affects the pancreas. After all, it seems to affect most organ systems.

27.06.20

On a conference call. I didn't realise that Pfizer/BioNTech were proceeding so rapidly with their vaccine; Phase 1 data from the usual non-human primate studies will be out soon, but also healthy volunteers. No evidence of ADE (antibody-dependent enhancement) where the vaccine might make things worse, and they believe clinical outcome data is important and don't want FDA to lower standards. Pfizer plans to start Phase 3 in July to enrol up to 30k subjects and 1:1 randomisation into placebo or vaccine. It will be a global trial, though most enrolment will be in the US. They will have Phase 3 data in September – especially if US cases continue like this – and will discuss with FDA in October, hoping to get approval then if everything goes smoothly. They also said they're more optimistic about manufacturing, which will need a cold chain, and that it's possible to produce hundreds of millions by 2020 (vs the tens of millions stated previously), going up billions next year if there are no issues.

Trump just tweeted: 'Coronavirus deaths are way down. Mortality rate is one of the lowest in the world.' It is true that the seven-day average of daily reported deaths in the US has fallen from a peak in mid-April of around 2,100 a day to 600 a day currently. We will see in the second week of July whether current cases equate to many more deaths, but I suspect not because of better treatments/protocols, the fact that the virus has already killed many susceptible/vulnerable patients, more nursing home residents now treated, and so on. But is the US death rate one of the lowest? Using death rates per 100k, the US currently has had 38 deaths per 100k. Only eight countries have higher rates, two of which are tiny so statistics are unstable, and Belgium clearly reported any 'elderly' death as a Covid death earlier this year:

- San Marino: 124 (44 deaths in a population of 34k)
- Belgium: 85
- Andorra: 68 (52 deaths in a population of 77k)
- UK: 65
- Spain: 61
- Italy: 57
- Sweden: 52
- France: 44

195 countries or other states have lower rates than the US.

28.06.20

The Covid pandemic remains surprisingly predictable at many levels. Opening bars and restaurants and allowing indoor gatherings without face masks was an obviously irresponsible political decision, leading to spiking cases that will likely get worse before they get better, but it's clear to me the deaths won't be anything like they have been. I've heard that some are eyeing ~50k new cases per day as a 'threshold' level beyond which businesses and schools might shut down again. This is not a magic number. Younger people are the primary risk-takers and driving much of the spread; as such, mortality rates remain low.

There are differences between now and the first wave worth noting: awareness is higher, and social distancing and face masks have increased considerably, even if they partially moderate as the economy reopens. Testing has been deployed so the case capture rate is higher. At the peak of Covid fear, cases were around ten times higher than cases detected, which fuelled fear. That won't – and can't – be the case now. The Democratic Party is becoming the face-mask party and the Republican Party is, oddly, becoming the no-face-mask party – over an issue that shouldn't be politicised. The paradox is as more people take more precautions, economic growth could slow.

Serbia had elections in the middle of this, Iceland had them yesterday (telling people to stay 2 metres apart and everyone was given sanitisers/ gloves), today France (second round of municipal elections) and Poland (first round of presidential election) will follow. EU diplomats Friday reached a provisional deal on the criteria to determine which non-EU countries to allow into the bloc when it opens its borders from 1 July; the USA didn't make the cut.

29.06.20

Scott Gottlieb, the former head of the FDA, has a sobering but encouraging thread. Looks like he's basically given up/written off the next six months (reopening was mishandled, he doesn't have faith in NPIs, virus is too widespread) but is confident that vaccines/medicines will solve coronavirus around the turn of the year: '40k infections a day exhausts our ability to test and trace. Local districts won't open schools this fall in the South with spread at the current rate. Businesses will make their own decision to close. To reclaim these opportunities, we must take individual steps to reduce transmission.'

As the UK considers a Leicester lockdown, on *The Andrew Marr Show*, Jeremy Farrar, Director of Wellcome/SAGE member said, 'We're on a knife edge, it's very precarious, the situation, particularly in England at the moment, and I would anticipate we would see an increase in new cases over the coming weeks.'

Undoubtedly, we'll hear a lot about individual events. Zurich health authorities are imposing a ten-day quarantine on almost 300 people who were present at a nightclub after one of them tested positive and had infected others. Switzerland's first superspreader was at the Flamingo Club on 21 June and tested positive on 25 June; five other people who were at the club with him have also tested positive.

30.06.20

The Standing Committee of the National People's Congress of Hong Kong has unanimously passed a new, more restrictive, national security law. Tensions have been rising steadily in the former British colony, which in 1997 was returned to China with the proviso that its citizens would retain their political freedoms and remain freer than communist China. For years now, there have been more and more protests against China's authoritarian regime as it has slowly chipped away at democratic rights, including the right to protest. Hong Kong's arrival at this point was inevitable, but I feel the Chinese government has pushed this now for two reasons: firstly, Covid. As with the protests in America, the authorities do not want large groups to congregate, no matter the cause, as it will only aid in spreading the virus. That said, data has shown that being out of doors, combined with mask wearing, has not led to superspreader events in the US. Secondly, the behaviour of President Trump has made it easy for China to act unilaterally. Trump distrusts nations that are seen as America's traditional allies, preferring to curry favour with the likes of North Korea and Russia.

As I write this, I feel like I'm describing a parallel reality. America has lost both its role and its image as the world's policeman now that we see, almost daily, images of American citizens being taken away in armoured police vehicles. What is the difference between that and Chinese riot police dealing with protestors in Hong Kong? America's moral authority has evaporated during the Trump years. As a result, China knows it can make its move, and apart from some angry speeches in various democratic countries, nothing will happen.

As the saying goes, sometimes it's better to ask for forgiveness than to ask for permission. Only in this case China will not bother asking for forgiveness because it regards these matters as an internal affair. There is also the fact that both scientifically and financially, China is a key player in the fight against the pandemic. Does any country want to alienate it? I have heartfelt sympathy for the people of Hong Kong.

At a news conference last week, the WHO Chief Scientist said that AstraZeneca was probably the leading Covid vaccine candidate, with Moderna not far behind. AstraZeneca Phase 2 human trial results are expected very soon, she noted, and Phase 3 starts are being planned in many countries. She also noted that the Moderna vaccine will go into Phase 3 in mid-July. There are now over 200 Covid vaccines in development, and fifteen of these are in human clinical trials, including several from China.

July

01.07.20

The situation in Hong Kong is worsening. The police are stopping people in the street for displaying pro-democracy stickers on their phones or wearing them on their clothing, sometimes arresting them for breaching national security. Thousands are protesting on the streets, but it all seems futile as no one is coming to help. The police now have the fig leaf of enforcing an actual law to allow them to prosecute, detain and intimidate campaigners.

Masks are becoming an increasingly contentious political issue in the US. Here in the UK, they're not such a political hot potato, but I spoke to an Uber driver yesterday who told me 80% of his passengers don't wear masks. Is this ignorance, laziness or selfishness?

'The danger isn't over and people will be needing face masks for some time to come,' Austrian Chancellor Kurz said. Asked whether Austria, which has seen an upward trend of new infections in recent days, is about to experience a second wave, Kurz said he doesn't like the term 'second wave', and argued the pandemic would go through various phases, 'which will become difficult again at times'.

It doesn't help that Dr Fauci called 2020 a mix of 1918 and 2009. Scientists carrying out routine monitoring of influenza strains in China have found that pigs are widely infected with a virus with the potential to trigger a pandemic. The G4 strain is a genetic blend of three lineages. One of these is the H1N1 virus that caused the 2009 pandemic, which suggests it might be able to adapt for human-human transmission. Influenza viruses frequently jump from pigs to humans, but most do not then transmit between humans. Two cases of G4 infections in humans have been documented, and both were dead-end infections that did not transmit to other people. The likelihood that this particular variant is going to cause a pandemic is very, very low.

The number of dental and eye care appointments is down significantly and likely to remain so for the rest of 2020. Roughly 25% of patients are unwilling to visit either speciality until a Covid-19 vaccine is available.

02.07.20

The US has gone back through its 50k magic number of cases a day, reporting 53k Covid cases on Wednesday, a new record high by far (the previous 44k was set last Friday). The seven-day moving average rises now to 43k, up 5% vs yesterday and 39% vs a week ago. New tests dropped from Tuesday's record high level but remain high at 626k.

An interesting study is looking at frailty. This is being used in clinical decision-making for patients with Covid-19, yet the prevalence and effect of frailty in people with Covid-19 is not known. The aim of the Covid-19 in Older People (COPE) study was to establish the prevalence of frailty in patients with Covid-19 who were admitted to hospital and to investigate its association with mortality and the duration of hospital stay. This large group study showed disease outcomes were better predicted by frailty than either age or comorbidity. Frailty is a really important concept.

Next up, regarding behaviours, individual differences are especially important among teenagers, who may be less likely to present with symptoms even when carrying the virus, and who may experience greater social pressure to avoid limiting social contact with peers. Findings from another study indicate that adolescents' beliefs about the severity of the virus, the extent to which they value social responsibility, their social trust and their prioritisation of their own self-interest over others were independently associated with their news monitoring, social distancing, disinfecting and hoarding behaviour in the days after the US declared Covid-19 a national emergency. These findings are consistent with past research that found that youths were more likely to engage in socially responsible environmental behaviours in historical years when they were more aware of environmental pollution issues. Concerns about social issues may motivate adolescents to act in socially responsible ways, and these findings highlight the potential importance of ensuring that adolescents view the Covid-19 virus as a serious threat in a way that does not encourage hoarding. These efforts may be aided by informing adolescents about potential asynchronies between the effects of Covid-19 on adolescents vs adults. They also found that increased social responsibility values were associated with greater disinfecting, less hoarding and more news monitoring, whereas self-interest values were associated with less social distancing and more hoarding.

03.07.20

In Alabama, there are – incredibly – parties where people can intentionally catch the virus. There are many words one could use to describe this, but 'fascinating' is a safe start. What possesses someone to deliberately encounter a virus that has verifiably killed hundreds of thousands of people in the world and upended all of our lives? Is it hubris? Ignorance? Bravado in front of friends or potential partners? Maybe they've heard that the younger you are the less likely you are to have severe symptoms, so they are going to party anyway. Or do they think the whole thing is a hoax? There's certainly a lot of that garbage going around. I started by describing this activity as 'fascinating'; I will finish with 'idiotic'.

04.07.20

It's upsetting to read that there has been a large increase in the number of domestic child abuse cases here in the UK (haven't seen representative data from other countries). One hospital reported: 'Ten children (6 boys and 4 girls) with suspected abusive head trauma presented for treatment during March–April. Their ages ranged from 17 days to 13 months old.' This figure compares with an average of 0.67 cases a month for the same period in 2017, 2018 and 2019, representing an increase of 1,493% in 2020.

Staying with children, but in a more positive light, I note Norway's Prime Minister Erna Solberg said, 'It's okay to be scared,' in a children-only press conference. Children are obviously less affected clinically by Covid-19 than adults. Nonetheless, children are impacted by the pandemic's indirect effects, not least from separation or loss in their own families. Projections suggest that over a million preventable child deaths might occur due to decreased access to food and the disruption of essential health services. Children risk missing out on growth monitoring, preventive care and timely management of acute disease and injuries. Some children are experiencing reduced access to social service referrals while suffering from increased rates of domestic violence.

Just when I thought 'that' drug was dead, a Detroit healthcare system study shows the controversial anti-malaria drug HCQ helps lower the death rate of Covid-19 patients. They analysed 2,541 patients hospitalised among the system's six hospitals between 10 March and 2 May and found 13% of those treated with HCQ died, while 26% of those who did not receive the drug died. Really need to see this paper. It's too small compared to the larger databases on this too.

05.07.20

'Issues in Catalonia in Europe and Melbourne in Australia with targeted lockdowns occurring...' This one phrase shows the global impact of the virus. It is also the nature of things to come for the summer.

It's notable that Dr Fauci has not been seen in public since 12 June (no doubt Trump thinks he's too gloomy), but he said this week, 'I think it's pretty obvious that we are not going in the right direction.'

When it comes to Spain, we are seeing hugely encouraging baricitinib data in the elderly, where it seems to save lives. We can't easily randomly assign patients to groups, so we are using the next best thing with Pedro Abizanda Soler, which is something called propensity score matching, where every patient who receives baricitinib is matched against those who don't, by criteria such as age, sex and frailty. We can then compare survival. I don't really understand why there aren't more trials looking at elderly patients. Pedro is another fabulous collaborator with whom I just love working. And we're doubling up with Lilly, combining it with data from Milan and simply increasing the power of our observations. Can't wait for the randomised data.

06.07.20

I think we're going to be seeing many weird and wonderful papers in the next few months, some of which no doubt will be completely spurious, but others of which will contain fascinating new information that will stand the time test. New data covered in the *NYT,* with a link to the preprint, talks about a stretch of Neanderthal DNA associated with higher rates of severe Covid-19. The variant is most common in Bangladesh and South Asia. One of the co-authors, Svanta Paabo, said, 'The DNA segment may account in part for why people of Bangladeshi descent are dying at a high rate of Covid-19 in the UK.' I suspect there are other things that could explain that beyond genetics.

A spike in gun purchases during the early months of the coronavirus pandemic contributed to a nearly 8% increase in firearm violence in the US, according to a new paper: that's 776 additional shooting injuries in the US from March through May, the researchers found. The pandemic appears to have inspired Americans to make 2.1 million more gun purchases than under normal circumstances.

Now to vaccines. Clearly, the Oxford team was able to pull ahead in the race for a vaccine because it had already completed safety testing on a similar vaccine candidate in 2019 for MERS. Their vaccine has now entered both Phase 2 and 3 trials in the UK, although decreasing transmission in the UK means efficacy might need to be assessed in other Phase 3 trials later this year in Brazil. Also, the Imperial College team has UK government funding to accelerate its efforts to produce a vaccine using novel self-amplifying RNA technology.

There are many other candidates in the mix. CEPI has invested almost $400 million in Novavax's protein sub-unit vaccine combined with an adjuvant derived from the bark of the Chilean saponin tree. Tough to make, I think.

07.07.20

Due to the high proportion of asymptomatic or mild infections (estimated now to be at 80%), data restricted to laboratory-confirmed cases do not capture the true extent of the spread or burden of the virus or its infection-fatality ratio. Therefore, serological detection of specific antibodies against SARS-CoV-2 can better estimate the true number of infections.

The key finding from these representative cohorts is that most of the populations in the test areas of Switzerland and Spain appear to have remained unexposed to SARS-CoV-2, even in areas with widespread virus circulation. These findings are further supported by the observation that even countries without strict lockdown measures have reported similarly low seroprevalence, e.g. Sweden, which reported a prevalence of 7.3% at the end of April. Thus, any proposed approach to achieve herd immunity through natural infection is not only highly unethical, but also unachievable. With a large majority of the population being infection naive, virus circulation can quickly return to early pandemic dimensions in a second wave once measures are lifted.

As the US prepares to leave the WHO (next year) and the world moves through 12 million cases today, Bolsonaro in Brazil has previously dismissed the threat of the new coronavirus, referring to the virus as a 'little flu,' appearing in public without a mask and encouraging the country to reopen. But after his positive test, Bolsonaro appeared on TV wearing a mask and urged people not to get close to him. His politics have always been extreme, but in the case of the pandemic, his wilful ignoring of the problem has put Brazil in a position second only to the US as a focal point of infections and numbers of deaths. How do we get out of this mess if those in high office refuse to do the basics of social distancing and mask wearing? Answer: vaccines.

I expect Moderna, Pfizer/BioNTech and AstraZeneca all to start US Phase 3 trials before the end of the summer. Each of the Phase 3 studies are expected to enrol approximately 30,000 individuals over the course of about 1–1.5 months, with Moderna and Pfizer expected to start in July and AstraZeneca, at the latest, in August (UK, Brazil and South Africa Phase 3 studies have already begun). Based on FDA guidance, at least 55% vaccine efficacy (i.e. the vaccine prevents 55% of symptomatic infections) is the minimum bar for approval.

09.07.20

Becton Dickinson (BD) announced it has entered into a partnership with the Biomedical Advanced Research and Development Authority (BARDA) to develop new manufacturing lines at its Nebraska facilities. In exchange, BD will provide priority access to the US government for syringes and needles to support mass vaccination. It's valid planning as someone is going to have to produce billions of syringes and needles for billions of doses (unless the vaccine is oral). Best to start making them now. An initial order includes 50 million needles and syringes to be delivered by December 2020, but there's provision for many more for mass vaccination. Each syringe is 15 cents.

One thing seems apparent: as people lose jobs and health insurance, Medicaid enrolment will jump, perhaps by as much as 20% to 30%. This will have profound implications for the drug chain/channel. How will this increase affect retail pharmacies and pharmacy benefit managers (PBMs)? Most states have both fee-for-service and managed care programmes within their states. However, managed care plans accounted for 71% of Medicaid's total dispensed prescriptions in 2018. Managed care's share varies by state. Most pharmacies will benefit from a Medicaid expansion. What's more, some states are re-evaluating their managed care relationships because of new disclosures about pharmacy benefit manager (PBM) compensation from network spreads in Medicaid. The changes in how states operate their Medicaid programmes will increase the number of pharmacies that will benefit.

Pharmacy Benefit Manager (PBM) reimbursement to pharmacies is highly controversial and has prompted various state laws that attempt to ensure that pharmacies are not paid less than their acquisition costs. During 2020, these laws will be subject to new scrutiny by the US Supreme Court governing PBM behaviour, a case called Rutledge versus the Pharmaceutical Care Management Association.

10.07.20

Deaths have been ticking up generally (down a bit in the last 24 hours), hospitals are busy but not stretched, but it seems that excess mortality is both low and will be tolerated. JPMorgan analysed 30 million Chase credit and debit cardholder spending habits and compared them to data from Johns Hopkins University; it found that spending patterns in restaurants have some power in predicting where the virus has spread since then. The level of spending in restaurants three weeks ago was the strongest predictor of the rise in new virus cases over the subsequent three weeks. They also found similar patterns with supermarket spending, but this correlated to a slower spread. High levels of supermarket spending are indicative of more careful social distancing. Data analysed from three weeks ago in New York and New Jersey (now seeing a decrease in cases) showed supermarket spending was up 20% or more from a year ago, and in states now seeing an increase in cases (Texas and Arizona), supermarket spending was up less than 10%.

In New York City, Mayor de Blasio announced that the city would not resume indoor dining at restaurants next week as anticipated. McDonald's had reopened its indoor dining areas in approximately 2,200 of its 14,000 US locations in mid-June and is now reversing course.

While social distancing is essential to keeping new infections at bay, the German health ministry on Wednesday warned that 1.5 metres may not be enough of a distance in closed rooms, especially in small or poorly ventilated rooms where the risk of corona infection from aerosols increases. In Denmark, the health ministry has advised the use of mouthwashes.

Interestingly, the lockdown is saving the lives of animals. Amphibians like frogs and higher animals from deer to elk are no longer being killed on American roads. New data show mountain lion roadkill plummeted 58% after the shutdown. And as for the affection of car front grills for monarch butterflies – hopefully that's over now.

Disasters of many kinds are associated with higher rates of distress and addictive behaviours. To learn more about the effects of the Covid-19 pandemic, researchers surveyed 6,416 Chinese individuals (half men, mean age of 28) on an e-commerce website and other online forums during the week of 24–31 March 2020. Of the respondents, 4.3% scored in the severe internet addiction range, per a validated questionnaire. Almost half of the participants recalled that internet dependence increased from the start of the pandemic. Increased alcohol drinking and smoking since the pandemic began were reported by 32% of regular drinkers and 20% of regular smokers, also by recall. These data are consistent with a study from China on about 70k people. They showed about 30% of respondents exhibited symptoms of depression, anxiety, insomnia and acute stress. The prevalence of mental health symptoms in the present study is consistent with the results of an epidemiological study conducted in early February 2020, among the general population in China, which indicated that nearly 35% of the respondents manifested psychological distress during the Covid-19 outbreak.

11.07.20

The latest drama in the HCQ saga, or should I say debacle, came as President Trump made the extraordinary public call for the FDA to issue a second EUA, following the release of the observational study by the Henry Ford Health System that produced data that appear to bolster

Trump's enthusiasm for the drug. Specifically, the study found that HCQ alone and in combination with azithromycin was associated with a reduction in Covid-19 associated mortality. Trump has not commented on any of the numerous studies in which HCQ failed to demonstrate benefit. Nor has he commented on a range of other studies on other compounds that have produced positive or negative results, with the exclusion of remdesivir. The FDA withdrew its first EUA for HCQ and chloroquine on 15 June, after determining the drugs are 'unlikely to be effective in treating Covid-19'. Lack of trust in the FDA would amplify anti-vaccine messages along with resistance to public health measures such as wearing face coverings in public. It could also have ramifications for global drug developers who view the agency as the gold standard for regulatory approval.

Kazakhstan recorded the second-highest number of new cases within Europe after Russia. Reporting in the largely authoritarian Central Asia states has been unreliable. Turkmenistan has yet to report a single case of Covid-19. Are they very good at keeping people out of the country or very bad at screening their population? Both are possible. The other major nation of Central Asia, Tajikistan, has yet to provide breakdowns to the WHO. Regardless, the health and economic outlook for the region is bleak. These countries have some of the highest ratios of out-of-pocket healthcare spending to total health expenditure in the world, with women in particular having very poor access to healthcare, further obscuring the true numbers of Covid-19 cases.

In India, after the relaxation of a three-month lockdown, cases are surging. Maharashtra, Delhi and Gujarat are among the worst hit states, with the army needed to help overwhelmed healthcare centres. But some of the larger Indian states have yet to witness a substantial rise in Covid-19 cases, so the country is braced for a further rapid transmission of the virus.

In Central and South America, Brazil steals the headlines for the highest number of Covid-19 cases, but Mexico in particular looks very worrying. A letter published today in *The Lancet* describes the Pan American Health Organisation as on the brink of closure because of member states' non-payments, and that in turn will cause a catastrophe.

12.07.20

The UK government has reportedly rejected the chance to join a European Union-run coronavirus vaccine scheme amid concern over 'costly delays'. The bloc is planning to spend £1.8 billion on the advance purchase of vaccines, with member states pooling resources to drive down the cost of buying vaccines. The programme also promises to adjust the EU's regulatory framework 'to the current urgency' in a bid to speed up vaccine trials and eventual production. Business Secretary Alok Sharma does not feel there is 'sufficient assurance' that the UK would receive the number of vaccines it needs if it joins the plan.

Bill Gates called this weekend for Covid-19 drugs to go to those most in need, saying, 'If we just let drugs and vaccines go to the highest bidder, instead of to the people and the places where they are most needed, we'll have a longer, more unjust, deadlier pandemic.' This followed data that emerged that the US had bought up virtually all of the world's stocks of the Covid-19 drug remdesivir.

Our cricket ball study will be published imminently. Good news for sports and children, keeping fit and morale up.

13.07.20

There's a reasonable discussion to be had about how air-conditioning units that recirculate air in rooms and offices should be turned off or used only with open windows because of the risk of spreading the virus. It is feared that any Covid-19 droplets in the air could be transmitted more easily to people in the room, even those who are socially distanced.

A paper showed mobile phone and credit card data helped to identify nearly 250 coronavirus infections linked to a fast-moving outbreak that began in a popular nightclub district in Seoul soon after South Korean nightclubs reopened on 30 April. By late May, officials had tested more than 40,000 people. The effort turned up 246 infections, including several that were 3, 4 and even 5 steps along the transmission chain from club-goers. Technology is one of our best weapons against this virus.

14.07.20

Hospital and death records show that African Americans, Latinos and Native Americans are disproportionately suffering and dying from severe disease; nationwide in America, black people are dying at 2.5 times the rate of white people. But without knowing the race of everyone tested, we can't say whether high death rates among black people in the US and elsewhere (like here) are driven primarily by more exposure and infection, diagnosis at a later stage of disease or a higher risk of severe illness once infected. And just to continue with this thread, the CDC showed additional data that revealed non-white and Hispanic Americans under the age of 65 are dying in greater numbers than white people in that age group. Some have said the reasons for this aren't clear. Others have said African Americans tend to be younger when they have the chronic risk factors – cardiovascular disease, diabetes, obesity, chronic pulmonary disease – most likely to be associated with Covid-19 infection and severe infection. It's been known for decades that the rate of premature cardiovascular deaths is higher in African Americans than white Americans.

'The pandemic is gaining full momentum' in Africa, says John Nkengasong, head of the African CDC. Egypt, Nigeria, South Africa, Ghana and Algeria account for most of the 24% week-on-week increase. On Twitter, he called for 'an aggressive and bold approach' of mask wearing, testing, contact tracing and community response to contain the spread.

India's lockdown has done one thing and one thing only: delayed the dramatic spread without flattening any curves.

In the US, around 58k new Covid cases were reported by state health departments Monday, down from 60k Sunday. But the seven-day moving average continues to climb, now to 60k. New tests increased vs Sunday, and the seven-day moving average is above 700k, an increase of nearly 50% over the past month.

15.07.20

I spoke to Pfizer last night, who are very bullish, commenting on issues that will occur with fill and finish and distribution – and they are already a vaccine company. Further, they could select the best candidate based on four Phase 1 trials.

Many Phase 3 studies fail because of incorrect identification of the dose that best balances safety and efficacy. The dosing regimen for this mRNA vaccine is still under study, and that's about the only criticism here. Can the vaccine multiverse do it again, leading to the reality of a safe, efficacious Covid-19 vaccine for the most vulnerable in the next six months? Side effects like fevers/chills really occurred mainly after the second dose and were mild.

Typically, it's the time of year when US lawmakers and their staff use their power over the government's budget to take on political pet projects (think opposition to genetically engineered salmon and soya milk). But this year, things are different: Democratic appropriators used their so-called 'reports' to rail against the Trump administration's Covid-19 response and saddle federal agencies with a slew of new requirements. Here are a few that stood out:

1) **The WHO:** Appropriators want the CDC to continue working with the WHO despite the Trump administration's formal planned withdrawal. 'The Committee urges CDC to continue to engage with the WHO to address global health issues, including Covid–19, and to continue to use its resources to support essential WHO global health activities.'

2) **Assessing agency failures:** They railed on the FDA's repeated fumbles in approving accurate Covid-19 tests, and now they want the FDA to conduct an independent audit of its Covid-19 response. 'The true tragedy will exist if FDA does not learn from its mistakes as it moves forward,' they wrote, explaining the requirement.
3) **Stockpiles:** They also slammed the Strategic National Stockpile; they want weekly reports on inventory levels for items like ventilators and masks going forward.
4) **BARDA:** They urged HHS to work with the Department of Defence 'to implement a dedicated medical countermeasures programme focused on developing medical countermeasures in months, not years, for previously unknown epidemic pathogens'. They want an update on this new initiative next year.
5) **The drug supply chain:** They are renewing calls for the federal government to decrease its dependence on China and India for the country's drug supply. They're asking the FDA to write a report outlining supply chain 'vulnerabilities', including a list of all finished drugs and active ingredients 'where supply is dependent on a single or limited number of providing countries'.

16.07.20

About Moderna's *NEJM* paper on 45 healthy volunteers, Dr Fauci, whose plain talking seems to have evoked the ire of Trump, said yesterday, 'The hallmark of a vaccine is one that can actually mimic natural infection and induce the kind of response that you would get with natural infection. And it looks like, at least in this limited, small number of individuals, that is exactly what's happening. The data really look quite good, there were no serious adverse events.'

There were 66k new Covid cases in the US reported Wednesday, up from 63k Tuesday, but the seven-day moving average is flat (at 62k) after five days of increases. The moving average is up 18% from a week ago. This is not good.

17.07.20

Political editorial in the *NEJM* on the US leaving the WHO:

Despite the advantage of a long lead time, the United States was inadequately prepared for Covid-19 when it arrived and stumbled through testing and early policy making. And the national response, countrywide, has been inconsistent and often ineffective. At some point there should be a reckoning, an evaluation of why the United States has done so poorly and who is responsible for the tens of thousands of excess deaths and billions of dollars in additional economic damage that have resulted. But today, in the middle of the outbreak, we must take stock of where we are and how we can do better. To do that effectively, we need the WHO. We must not make the mistake of firing the firefighter in the midst of a fire.

Another editorial in the *NEJM* on masks concludes: 'The potential value of universal masking in giving HCWs the confidence to absorb and implement the more foundational infection-prevention practices described above may be its greatest contribution'.

That was my view, but I have also always liked the John Maynard Keynes quote (not 'In the long run we are all dead,' or 'The market can stay irrational longer than you can stay solvent' and not 'Ideas shape the course of history'), 'When the facts change, I change my mind' (later added on the end, 'What do you do, sir?').

I have written a lot on and off regarding masks, and now I think there is the most solid data on their benefits. My view has been that the virus is largely transmitted aerosolised, and masks can 'stop' someone breathing aerosolised particles. But do masks stop infections – not the same thing but a derivative? A Harvard group now presents evidence that universal masking of HCWs and patients can help reduce transmission of infections. However, after the universal masking policy was in place, the proportion of symptomatic HCWs with positive test results steadily declined, from 14.7% to 11.5. Although not a randomised clinical trial, this study provides critically important data to emphasise that masking helps prevent transmission of SARS-CoV-2. Covering mouths and noses with filtering materials serves two purposes: personal protection against inhalation of harmful pathogens and particulates, and source control to prevent exposing others to infectious microbes that may be expelled during respiration. When asked to wear face coverings, many people think in terms of personal protection. But face coverings are also widely and routinely used as source control.

Statewide mandatory mask requirements now cover 64% of the US population, and another 13% are in states where some local governments have mandates, while 23% are in states with no mask requirements.

18.07.20

As the global total passes 14 million, I thought I'd start with the US numbers today since they set a new record for both cases and tests. Mind you, they did that Thursday, too. There were 77k new Covid cases reported by state health departments on Friday, a new high, topping Thursday's record of 71k. This includes a backlog of 5k cases from Texas that are not new, but even excluding that, it's still a single-day high. New tests topped Thursday's record to reach 856k, while the seven-day moving average increased to 768k, which is 17% higher than a week ago and up 54% over the past month. New deaths decreased to 932 Friday from 962 Thursday, but the seven-day rolling average increased further to 727 from 715 Thursday.

I note a new fund to prevent future pandemics has been proposed by the US Senate and another by the World Bank. The pandemic has heightened interest in creating a separate institution dedicated to health security as a way of both addressing the current crisis and preparing for the next outbreak. Some have criticised it, saying this would undermine the WHO by putting more pressure on scarce resources, especially in the current climate.

Regions in the world with the most successful containment to date have approached the pandemic with integrated measures that include cohesive leadership, effective communication, physical distancing, wearing of face coverings, improvements in the built environment, promotion of hand hygiene and support for the staff, supplies and systems needed to care for patients, with testing and contact tracing as cornerstones of the approach. Despite the emergence of some promising therapies and work towards a future vaccine, basic public health approaches remain the best available prevention and control interventions at this time.

A healthy diet, rich in fruits and vegetables and low in sugar and calorie-dense processed foods is essential to health. The ability to eat a healthy diet is largely determined by one's access to affordable, healthy foods, a consequence of the conditions and environment in which one lives. In the US, poor diet is the leading underlying cause of death, having surpassed tobacco use in related mortality.

The biology of the virus continues to be fascinating but perplexing. We can't get SARS-CoV-2 to infect pulmonary organoids, i.e. little lungs in dishes, but can get it to infect liver organoids. Maybe the liver is really important here. Volker Lauschke has a great team working on this – Ali Mirazami, Sonia Youhanna and other exceptional scientists. And others are using and setting up baricitinib trials. Marco Falcone from Pisa, Delia Goletti from Rome and Fabrizio Cantini from Prato have all agreed to pool data to increase the power of anything we observe. This is true bench-to-bedside research, but it started with a computer, then moved to the bedside, and now we're doing laboratory studies alongside it in parallel.

19.07.20

It seems that the race for vaccines has got mixed up in the low-level cyber warfare between Russia and the West. A UK government report details recent Tactics, Techniques and Procedures (TTPs) of the group commonly known as 'APT29' to steal vaccine secrets, which Russia obviously denies. This report provides indicators of compromise as well as detection and mitigation advice. The introduction reads:

> The UK's National Cyber Security Centre (NCSC) and Canada's Communications Security Establishment (CSE) assess that APT29 (also known as 'the Dukes' or 'Cozy Bear') is a cyber espionage group, almost certainly part of the Russian intelligence services. The United States' National Security Agency (NSA) agrees with this attribution and the details provided in this report. The United States' Department of Homeland Security's Cybersecurity and Infrastructure Security Agency (DHS CISA) endorses the technical detail and mitigation advice provided in this advisory. The group uses a variety of tools and techniques to predominantly target governmental, diplomatic, think-tank, healthcare and energy targets for intelligence gain. Throughout 2020, APT29 has targeted various organisations involved in Covid-19 vaccine development in Canada, the United States and the UK, highly likely with the intention of stealing information and intellectual property relating to the development and testing of Covid-19 vaccines. APT29 is using custom malware known as 'WellMess' and 'WellMail' to target a number of organisations globally. This includes those organisations involved with Covid-19 vaccine development. WellMess and WellMail have not previously been publicly associated with APT29.[1]

20.07.20

There's lots to say on the subject of misinformation as highlighted by Tedros Adhanom Ghebreyesus, the WHO's Director-General, speaking at the Munich Security Conference: 'We're not just fighting a pandemic, we're fighting an infodemic.' Fake news, misinformation, and conspiracy theories have become prevalent and skyrocketed since the beginning of the pandemic. WHO formally began the conversation on the global effects and management of infodemics with its first Infodemiology Conference that convened international experts from diverse scientific and political backgrounds.

Immediate and widespread sharing of medical and other scientific information outside of expert circles before it has been thoroughly vetted can be dangerous, especially in a pandemic. Then one can argue that governments don't make policy decisions solely on the basis of empirical evidence as political interest is key, and the two are frequently at odds. Consequently, incoherent government messaging and reversals in recommendations on the basis of newly emerging evidence, for example on whether masks are protective against transmission, can be misconstrued as incompetence. The outcome is erosion of public trust and a sense of helplessness, the perfect conditions for the spread of harmful misinformation that begins a vicious circle.

Conspiracy theories work because they provide the comfort of an explanation in times of uncertainty and anxiety. Their messaging revolves around core emotions and values and hijacks the mental cues that we use to decide whether the source is legitimate and thus trustworthy. The most pervasive and damaging of conspiracy theories incorporate grains of truth. But who benefits from this misinformation? *Firstdraft* identifies three aspects: financial gain, political gain and experimental manipulation.

The anti-vaccination industry is a notable example of the first: a report from the Centre for Countering Digital Hate shows that wellness and nutritional supplement companies are major backers of and directly profit from anti-vaccination campaigns. In 2011, the CIA orchestrated a fake Hepatitis B vaccination campaign in the neighbourhood in which it suspected Osama bin Laden was hiding: Abbottabad, Khyber Pakhtunkhwa, Pakistan. The CIA's goal in cleverly pursuing this drive was to obtain Osama bin Laden's family DNA samples. It won't surprise you to know that Dr Afridi, who led this, is regarded as a traitor in Pakistan while being hailed as a hero in the US.

If you think the misinformation problem might be bad in the US, let's look at a diametrically different country, Pakistan. The CIA's botched fake vaccination drive, which was revealed to Pakistanis in 2011, deepened the existing distrust of the polio vaccination campaign among certain Pakistani people. In 2012, a resurgence of polio cases appeared in Peshawar, Karachi, and in the Federally Administered Tribal Areas along Pakistan's border with Afghanistan, washing away the eradication progress of the early 2000s. Ever since the CIA's operation, the Taliban and other Islamist militant groups have reinforced growing distrust of vaccines with anti-Western rhetoric and utilised anti-vaccination sentiment as a tool in their anti-Western messaging. HCWs are still killed, labelled as 'Western spies'.

In late 2016, primarily in response to the US presidential election, certain social and search companies, the ones we know, began to acknowledge the need to counter misinformation on their platforms. They focused primarily on political disinformation and protecting elections. In March 2019, the platforms started addressing vaccine-related misinformation. Facebook announced its new efforts to tackle vaccine misinformation globally on 7 March 2019.

On 21 March, Instagram announced that it would begin blocking anti-vaccine hashtags. YouTube also said that it would prevent the monetisation of videos that contained vaccine-related misinformation. Earlier in the year, Pinterest purposefully disabled searches for vaccines, preventing users from accessing related information when they search for the term on its platform: 'Despite an expressed commitment toward limiting vaccine misinformation, content online from both the Pakistani government and social platforms, one of the most pernicious outbreaks of vaccine-related misinformation in Pakistan's history occurred soon after this on April 22, 2019, well beyond the Bin Laden issue.' The videos were posted as part of a pre-planned conspiracy against the polio eradication campaign.

I could go on with countless (as far as I can tell) other videos in which people tell reporters in front of a Peshawar hospital that some children had died after being vaccinated. However much junk this is, the spread of misinformation about the polio vaccine caused mass hysteria in north-west Pakistan. On 22 April alone, concerned parents brought a total of 25,000 children to the three hospitals of Peshawar. HCWs have been killed over this, and distrust runs deep.

In other news, I am getting hold of lots of longitudinal patient samples to see if we can predict who will become sick, though I note there's quite a bit of work that's been published on this already. Gary from Lilly, along with his trusted lieutenant Jonathan Sims, both marshalled by the formidable Anabela Cardoso, are forging ahead with this. Am glad we have the Lilly statisticians here to interpret all of this.

22.07.20

Thought it was interesting to read today that earlier this month the UK government opted out of the EU purchasing deal and has agreed a deal to get 'early access' to 90 million doses of Covid-19 vaccine. This included deals with BioNTech/Pfizer for 30 million doses, with AZN for their mRNA vaccines, with Valneva for 60 million doses of inactivated whole virus vaccine and with AZN for a million doses of treatments containing Covid-19 neutralising antibodies for people who cannot receive vaccines, such as immunocompromised patients and those with cancer. This is in addition to 100 million doses of the AZN vaccine. With these deals the government has said that the UK could have access to enough doses to vaccinate priority groups such as frontline health and social care workers or people with an increased health risk. Don't worry, I had to look up Valneva: they make VLA2001, a cell-based, highly purified inactivated vaccine candidate against the SARS-CoV-2 virus, developed using the same manufacturing platform as Valneva's Japanese encephalitis vaccine.

Comparing the vaccines crudely, AZN/Oxford appears to have an edge on safety, looking at adverse events, whereas it lags on antibody production. But interestingly, all three programmes show some level of drop-off, which raises questions around durability if antibody response is in fact the key efficacy measure. But then again, after natural infection, we've seen no reinfection, ever.

In terms of vaccine production, the latest from Moderna is that they expect to be able to produce between 500 million to 1 billion vaccines annually by the end of the year. Covid-19 vaccine pricing remains a topic of debate, with a potentially broad price range emerging from an implied $2.8 per dose (AZN) to $10.4 per dose (Sanofi/GSK), to a price similar to an existing vaccine such as Prevnar ($202 list price; Pfizer/BioNTech), though both Moderna and Pfizer have indicated a $30–40 price point.

23.07.20

It seems very unlikely one can get Covid twice, or impossible, which is very good clinical news for vaccines, which have a clinical end point. I see on this point that the US government 'placed an initial order of 100 million doses for $1.95 billion and can acquire up to 500 million additional doses of Pfizer's vaccine. Americans to receive the vaccine for free, consistent with the US government's commitment for free access for Covid-19 vaccines. Pfizer and BioNTech remain on track to begin an anticipated Phase 2b/3 safety and efficacy trial later this month, seek regulatory review as early as October 2020, and manufacture globally up to 100 million doses by the end of 2020 and potentially more than 1.3 billion doses by the end of 2021'. So this makes the cost $20 per shot.

Thank you *Daily Star* for the headline about playing with balls, following our paper 'Sports Balls as Potential SARS-CoV-2 Transmission Vectors' being published in *Public Health in Practice*. *The Times* was so much more boring with 'Ball Is not a Vector of Disease'.

24.07.20

A quiet day, more of the same really. Some good papers coming through, but they are saying things I have already said or alluded to. Lots of papers are being retracted, too, for being grossly inaccurate or misleading. There's a paper on 5G technology and the induction of Covid-19 in skin cells. The paper suggests that 5G waves can spontaneously generate coronaviruses in skin cells. Yet, there is nothing in this article that proves this extraordinary claim. It is absolute rubbish and trash, not even junk, as junk can be kept for another day, and trash is thrown out (thus the use of the term junk DNA).

25.07.20

Up to half of stealthy spreaders 'feel fine' on Saturday night, but by the time they come down with the tell-tale cough, fever and fatigue on Monday, they've potentially infected multitudes. As for the people who never feel ill, it's unclear how contagious they might be because researchers have a hard time documenting their transmission. The CDC estimates asymptomatic cases are 75% as infectious as symptomatic ones, but the agency cautions that this is based on a murky understanding of what's known as 'viral shedding', in which people unknowingly release contagious virus into the atmosphere. Perhaps asymptomatic people don't carry as much virus to begin with, or their immune systems behave like those found in bats. These theories could shed light on research showing asymptomatic individuals have a weaker immune response overall and produce fewer antibodies.

I note that neurologic complications in the longer term are common in patients from China, many of whom ended up needing antidepressants.

A poll from the Netherlands revealed that almost three months after the first symptoms of the virus, more than 9 in 10 people reported having problems with simple daily activities.

A truly strange side effect of lockdowns: the lack of human activity during lockdown caused human-linked vibrations in the Earth to drop by an average of 50% between March and May 2020. This quiet period, likely caused by the total global effect of social distancing measures, closure of services and industry and drops in tourism and travel, is the longest and most pronounced quiet period of seismic noise in recorded history. This study uniquely highlights just how much human activities impact the solid Earth, and could let us see more clearly than ever what differentiates human and natural noise. The relative quietness allowed researchers to listen in to previously concealed earthquake signals and could help us differentiate between human and natural seismic noise more clearly than ever before. Who knew a pandemic could help geology?

27.07.20

Harvard conducted a survey of more than 5,800 small businesses between 28 March and 4 April 2020. Several themes emerged. First, mass layoffs and closures had already occurred just a few weeks into the crisis. Second, the risk of closure was negatively associated with the expected length of the crisis. Moreover, businesses had widely varying beliefs about the likely duration of Covid-related disruptions. Third, many small businesses are financially fragile: the median business with more than $10,000 in monthly expenses had only about two weeks of cash on hand at the time of the survey. Fourth, the majority of businesses planned to seek funding through the Coronavirus Aid, Relief, and Economic Security (CARES) Act. However, many anticipated problems with accessing the programme, such as bureaucratic hassles and difficulties establishing eligibility.

Something good-ish: the 100th Ebola outbreak in the DRC has officially ended. WHO highlighted the key role of contact tracing, infection prevention through public awareness, access to clean water and promotion of hygienic practices as well as isolating both confirmed patients and suspected cases. These are now also at the core of DRC's Covid-19 response. Even before Ebola, the country's health system was dysfunctional owing to the collapse of the state and the economy, leaving over 70% of the population, including health workers, impoverished.

28.07.20

More evidence that dogs are man's best friend: volatile organic compounds produced during respiratory infections can cause specific scent imprints, which can be detected by trained dogs with a high rate of precision. Eight detection dogs were trained for one week to detect saliva or tracheobronchial secretions of SARS-CoV-2 infected patients in a randomised, double-blinded and controlled study. The dogs were able to discriminate between samples of infected (positive) and non-infected (negative) individuals with an average diagnostic sensitivity of 83% and specificity of 96%.

An Ipsos Mori poll last week showed that 86% of British people think mask wearing is important or essential. The same survey showed that only 28% wore a mask themselves (do as I say, not do as I do) and that 52% of those that wore one (or planned to) did so to protect themselves.

The possibility of home saliva testing as a way to monitor and control the infection is tantalising, and if the trials in Southampton are successful, it will make regular testing of healthcare staff much simpler (and cheaper).

29.07.20

The UK's imposition of a fourteen-day quarantine on anyone returning from Spain has raised concerns about the reality of a second wave of cases hitting southern Europe. In regions that have already been heavily infected and where the virus has died down, there is a growing likelihood that many of the reported new cases are false positives. A government-sponsored paper uses false positive rates on previous RNA virus studies to estimate that false-positive swab tests in the UK may be happening at a median rate of about 2.3% of tests. To put that in context, if every person in the UK was tested, that would be equivalent to 1.5 million people. In early March, when the virus was at its peak in the UK, the only people being tested were very sick individuals presenting at hospitals, so false positives were not significant relative to genuine positives. But today the virus is much less prevalent, and there are lots of precautionary tests being carried out on people with no symptoms or very mild ones.

Now to babies: There are frequent claims that the ongoing pandemic will result in a baby boom. Couples, it is argued, spend more time with each other and, as such, are more likely to procreate (many reading this may have the opposite view!). The empirical evidence for this is sparse. Instead, recent studies focusing on the short-term fertility consequences of natural disasters such as earthquakes and hurricanes find that peaks in mortality are generally followed by birth troughs within a year, whereas studies focusing on a longer timeframe, from one to five years following the event, have unveiled patterns of increasing fertility. Drivers of these medium-term rebounds are the desire of parents to replace lost children as well as structural shifts in expectations on the survival probability of offspring. In the wake of unexpected mortality shocks, fertility may also take on a symbolic meaning as new births become a positive reframing mechanism, signalling a return to normality.

The irreversible nature of childbearing and the substantial costs associated with child-rearing, unemployment and lost income will necessarily reduce fertility. This was the experience of the 2008 Great Recession when overall fertility declined, particularly in countries that had the strongest economic downturns. In addition, a stronger feeling of uncertainty will make couples postpone any long-term investments, children being prime examples, and therefore reduce fertility further. Coping mechanisms for dealing with uncertainty will consequently matter. There is evidence that, in periods with unexpected increases in economic uncertainty, fertility declines less in areas characterised by stronger trust and social capital.

30.07.20

Fascinating article from *The Atlantic* that will resonate with many of us about some of our obsessive cleaning practices. I can relate to this:

> Hygiene theatre builds a false sense of security, which can ironically lead to more infections. Many bars, indoor restaurants, and gyms, where patrons are huffing and puffing one another's stale air, shouldn't be open at all. They should be shut down and bailed out by the government until the pandemic is under control. No amount of soap and bleach changes this calculation. Instead, many of these establishments are boasting about their cleaning practices while inviting strangers into unventilated indoor spaces to share one another's microbial exhalations. This logic is warped. It completely misrepresents the nature of an airborne threat. It's as if an oceanside town stalked by a frenzy of ravenous sharks urged people to return to the beach by saying, 'We care about your health and safety, so we've reinforced the boardwalk with concrete.' Lovely. Now people can sturdily walk into the ocean and be separated from their limbs. By funnelling our anxieties into empty cleaning rituals, we lose focus on the more common modes of Covid-19 transmission and the most crucial policies to stop this plague.[2]

There were 64k new Covid cases reported by state health departments Wednesday, up from 59k Tuesday – but increases over the course of the week are typical. And the seven-day moving average continues to recede, declining 1% vs the prior day again and down 4% vs a week ago. The peak was six days ago. Deaths in the US: new deaths increased to 1,460 Wednesday – the highest number since May.

31.07.20

A total of 39% of US adults reported using disinfectants and other cleaning products in potentially harmful ways as they tried to prevent infection. Data shows that following Trump's comments, a spike in calls to US poison control centres reporting exposure to cleaning products occurred, so the CDC commissioned an online survey. There were 60% that said they cleaned or disinfected their home more frequently to prevent SARS-CoV-2 infection, but many did so in unsafe ways: 19% used bleach on food such as fruit or vegetables, and 18% reported using household cleaning products on their skin. There were 10% who reported misting their body with a cleaning or disinfectant spray, 6% that reported inhaling vapours from cleaning or disinfectant products, and 4% said they drank or gargled with diluted bleach, soapy water or other cleaning or disinfectant solutions. In fact, 25% of all the survey participants said using cleaning products or disinfectants caused adverse effects such as irritation of the nose, sinuses, skin and/or eyes as well as dizziness, light-headedness, headache, nausea and/or breathing problems.

Those who didn't use the products safely were more than twice as likely to say they had an adverse reaction, compared to other respondents. Although most respondents said they knew how to safely clean and disinfect their homes, the survey revealed serious gaps in knowledge. To curb unsafe practices, the researchers wrote that prevention messages about SARS-CoV-2 should provide specific recommendations for hand hygiene and cleaning high-touch surfaces. They emphasised that it's necessary to always follow directions on the products' labels. This is hysteria, enhanced by the poorly chosen words of the leader of a nation. Words have consequences, and these are the consequences.

Deforestation and wildlife now. It is clear that over the course of a century, two new viruses per year have spilt from their natural hosts into humans. The MERS, SARS and 2009 H1N1 epidemics, and the HIV and Covid-19 pandemics testify to their damage. Tropical forest edges are a major launchpad for novel human viruses. Edges arise as humans build roads or clear forests for timber production and agriculture. Humans and their livestock are more likely to contact wildlife when more than 25% of the original forest cover is lost, and such contacts determine the risk of disease transmission. Pathogen transmission depends on the contact rate, the abundance of susceptible humans and livestock, and the abundance of infected wild hosts. Contact rates vary with the perimeter (the length of the forest edge) between forest and non-forest. Deforestation tends to create checkerboards, whereupon one sees a maximum perimeter at a 50% level of forest conversion. Thereafter, the abundance of domestic animals and humans rapidly exceeds that of wild animals, so although we expect transmission to decline, the magnitude of any resultant outbreak is higher.

Habitat fragmentation complicates this because it increases the length of the perimeter. Roadbuilding, mining and logging camps, expansion of urban centres and settlements, migration and war, and livestock and crop monocultures have led to increasing virus spillovers. Hunting, transport, farming and trade of wildlife for food, pets and traditional medicine compound these routes of transmission and closely track deforestation. For example, bats are the probable reservoirs of Ebola, Nipah, SARS and obviously the virus behind Covid-19.

The clear link between deforestation and virus emergence suggests that a major effort to retain intact forest cover would have a large return on investment even if its only benefit were to reduce virus emergence events. The largest-scale example of directed deforestation reduction comes from Brazil between 2005 and 2012. Deforestation in the Amazon dropped by 70%, yet production of the region's dominant soy crop still increased. How much of this now has contributed to the pandemic, and spillover from animals to humans?

August

01.08.20

It is now apparent to me that there are enough vaccines far enough down the line in terms of trials that at least one (and probably multiple) will be available by year end. As discussed previously, there have been moments in the history of vaccination when genuine concerns have arisen around it – like the events in Pakistan. But the anti-vaccination hysteria, particularly in America, is breathtaking in its intensity and ferocity.

I suspect a lot of the disinformation is created by groups working out of Ukraine and Russia. For the cost of a laptop and Wi-Fi connection, it is possible to generate revenue on a website (presumably called something like 'thundereaglepatriot.com') or sow discord and chaos. Either way, those goals have been achieved.

When Edward Jenner invented the smallpox vaccine in 1796, he used the milder virus of cowpox to inoculate against the far more dangerous disease. He did this to save lives, not to kill people of colour or to bolster the coffers of the East India Company, or for any other sinister reason. He saw a disease that regularly killed thousands and thought he had a solution. Some of his methods would be seen as unethical today, such as proving the efficacy of the vaccine by deliberately exposing vaccinated individuals to the highly dangerous smallpox virus. Thankfully, it worked. There's data that showed similar techniques in Africa years before to vaccinate people too.

In 1998, an erroneous connection was made between the MMR jab and autism. The bad data were very quickly debunked by the scientific community, but a clinical paper cannot compete against a newspaper in terms of reaching the general public. The genie was out of the bottle, and even to this day, there are people who think that vaccines – any vaccine –

will cause autism. My favourite piece of misinformation is that the new vaccines are a way for the government (or Bill Gates) to track individuals. It was the same issue with track and trace. If this is true (which it isn't), why is anyone scared of the government knowing where you shop for groceries? How is that going to help national security or destroy your confidence in the government? Of course, this is not what's happening. The people who won't have a vaccine because of fears of being tagged are more than happy to scroll through alt-right Twitter accounts on their mobile phone, a device designed to let your phone company know where you are. If you're that worried about being tracked, throw away your phone, laptop and satnav.

Today, however, the mistrust of vaccines is, it seems, wilful. 'I've got a feeling' or 'I've heard from somebody' beats clinical data every time on social media. The problem is that clinical trials aren't sexy. Science rarely gives clear-cut, headline-friendly answers. Critical analysis is vital. Just because something sounds good doesn't make it true. The likes of the BBC or CNN are obliged to get the facts right, and they apologise when they get them wrong. However, starting with the opinion programmes on Fox News and going all the way down to dubious anti-vaccination groups on Facebook, they have no such obligations. They are an echo chamber for disinformation where conspiracy theories mutate and reproduce. For the sake of public safety, they should be classified the same as radicalisation sites (because they are, it's just a different flavour of extremist ideology) and shut down.

02.08.20

The offer to employees at the state-owned oil giant was compelling: be among the first in China to get a vaccine. The employees at PetroChina could get one of two vaccines 'for emergency use' to protect themselves when working overseas as part of China's ambitious infrastructure programme. They would effectively be guinea pigs for testing the unproven vaccines outside the official clinical trials. The offer was backed by the government. It stressed that data from clinical trials showed that the products, both made by Sinopharm, were safe. It did not mention the possible side effects or warn against the false sense of security from getting a vaccine that regulators hadn't approved. The unorthodox move to test people separately from the normal regulatory approval process reflects the formidable challenge facing China as it enters the vaccine race. Chinese companies are rushing to get as much data as possible on their vaccines to prove they are safe and effective. In China, they are selectively testing their vaccines on small pools of people like the PetroChina employees – an approach that does not count toward the regulatory process but could bolster their own confidence in the vaccines.

Inspiring stories about the bravery and resilience of HCWs in the fight against Covid-19 are touted in news coverage around the world. However, little attention is paid to the factors that undermine global efforts to protect frontline HCWs. A group now reports findings of a study in which demographic data, medical histories and symptoms of Covid-19 were gathered from the general community and frontline HCWs in the UK and the USA. Frontline HCWs were at increased risk for reporting a positive Covid-19 test, compared with the general community, after adjustments for the likelihood of receiving a Covid-19 test (HR 3.40). HCWs were additionally asked to report week-by-week availability of personal protective equipment (PPE) and the results of any Covid-19 tests they underwent. Although they acknowledged the limitations of their study, the increased risk for Covid-19 identified among HCWs who reported inadequate PPE (hazard ratio – the chance or hazard of getting it versus someone else without PPE is 1.31, i.e. 31% more) is concerning. In May 2020, the American Nurses Association surveyed 14,328 nurses to understand their experiences related to the availability of PPE. 45% of nurses reported PPE shortages, 79% were encouraged or required to reuse PPE, and 36% reported reusing N-95 masks for five days or longer.

03.08.20

A paper on a computer model of the cruise ship outbreak found that the virus spread most readily in microscopic droplets light enough to linger in the air for several minutes. Again, a reminder about the importance of mask wearing in indoor settings. The safe return of students to residential colleges demands an effective monitoring strategy. Results from a modelling study suggest that a highly specific screening test that can easily be administered to each student every 1 to 7 days and that reports results quickly enough to permit newly detected cases to be isolated within hours, would be required to blunt the further transmission of infection and to control outbreaks at a justifiable cost.

Obtaining an adequate supply of testing equipment will be a challenge. On a college campus with 5,000 enrolees, screening students alone every two days will require more than 195,000 test kits during the abbreviated term. It seems that frequent testing is a temporary answer, even at lower accuracy.

Next, the UN Population Fund (UNFPA) predicts there could be up to 7 million unintended pregnancies worldwide because of the crisis, with potentially thousands of deaths from unsafe abortions and complicated births due to inadequate access to emergency care. Similarly, Marie Stopes International (MSI), which works in 37 countries, predicts that the closure of their services would result in up to 9.5 million vulnerable women and girls losing access to contraception and safe abortion services in 2020. That disruption could result in as many as 2.7 million unsafe abortions and 11,000 pregnancy-related deaths.

04.08.20

Madonna. It was pointed out to me that the queen of pop's latest reinvention came this week in the form of a video posted on Instagram that shared a CoV conspiracy theory with her 15 million followers. She claimed a vaccine existed but was being concealed. 'They would rather let fear control the people and let the rich get richer and the poor get poorer.' Instagram blurred the video, captioned it 'false information' and linked users to a page debunking the bogus claim. Later, it deleted it. So ended another skirmish between celebrity, truth and the pandemic, an ongoing battle that pits fame against science and public health. Shame, as I quite like her music.

A few days earlier it was the turn of Lewis Hamilton to skid into trouble by sharing an anti-vaxxer post that suggested Bill Gates was lying about vaccine trials. There are so many incredibly ridiculous statements out there, which, equally incredibly, people buy into.

The vulnerability of food supply chains differs widely across food systems, depending on the priority they are afforded and on their structure. There are four key features:

1) Governments worldwide have placed a high priority on ensuring that staple foods can be moved to consumers. Global supply chains for staple foods appear to have held up reasonably well so far, with relatively few cases of substantial supply disruptions even in countries with strict social distancing requirements. Evidence from China shows that such disruptions can be reduced by creating 'green lanes' that exempt transport, production processes and distribution of agricultural inputs and food products as well as movements of food sector workers from Covid-19 lockdown measures.

2) Labour-intensive 'traditional' value chains (mostly in developing countries) are more affected than capital-intensive 'modern' food value chains (mostly in high-income countries or in richer parts of low- and middle-income countries).

3) Even modern food supply chains and systems can be seriously affected. In the US and Europe, more than 30,000 workers in food processing plants have contracted Covid-19, causing meat processing plants to close or slow production. The closure of passenger aviation has seriously disrupted supply chains of specialised products that rely on air freight, such as high-value horticultural exports from Africa.

4) The pandemic has affected public food distribution systems; for example, schools closing under India's national lockdown resulted in the suspension of school feeding programmes – one of the country's largest safety nets. School closures are depriving many poor children of publicly provided meals. Farmers and other suppliers have found difficulty finding market outlets to replace institutional outlets such as restaurants and schools, resulting in substantial wastage of milk and other nutrient-rich foods.[3]

05.08.20

Now, as any parent knows, young children are extremely efficient at catching and passing on respiratory infections. This intuition is backed by a raft of scientific evidence that was greatly bolstered during the 2009 H1N1 influenza pandemic. Many studies demonstrated the crucial role that children played in the spread of this virus. When faced with the prospect of a devastating pandemic of Covid-19, it was natural that policymakers decided to close schools to try and slow or prevent transmission. UNESCO estimated that more than 60% of the world's students have had their education disrupted by national school closures during the Covid-19 pandemic (I know mine have).

But, it has become increasingly apparent that, compared with influenza and most other respiratory infections, children seem to be largely spared in this pandemic. If infected, children typically have mild disease. This comparative lack of severe disease changes the benefit-to-cost ratio associated with closing schools: most children, if infected, will only get very mild disease, but at the cost of all children suffering as a consequence of school closures. Yet, at the population level the benefits of closing schools might outweigh the costs if children play a key role in transmission to others. In this respect two studies just out are interesting. First, a study of transmission in schools and early childhood education and care facilities in New South Wales, Australia, during the early part of the epidemic. During much of this period educational facilities were formally open, although attendance rates dropped precipitously in schools in mid-March: 27 primary cases were identified (56% staff), and 1,448 close contacts were identified. Nearly half of these close contacts were tested virologically or serologically, yet only 18 secondary cases were identified. These very low rates of infection need to be interpreted with caution because mitigation measures were in place: most educational facilities were closed briefly after case identification, and close contacts were expected to home quarantine for fourteen days.

Nevertheless, the results do align with findings from a similar study from Ireland, also done during the early part of the epidemic, in which confirmed cases (3 adults and 3 children) attended schools. No secondary cases were documented as arising from the paediatric cases.

06.08.20

Trump repeated that he believes coronavirus will 'go away' despite his top public health expert, Dr Fauci, warning that it could take most of 2021 or longer to get the pandemic under control and that it is 'unlikely' the virus can ever be eradicated.

Super cool genomic analyses revealed that northern California experienced a complex series of introductions of the virus, deriving not only from state-to-state transmission but also from international travel by air and ship. The study highlights the importance of being able to rapidly test and trace contacts of positive cases to enable swift control.

There have been several attempts to predict mortality from Covid-19 in the UK, including the calculation of age-based case fatality rates and relative risk (RR) of mortality. In a *Lancet* paper they wrote that 'roughly speaking, we might say that getting Covid-19 is like packing a year's worth of risk into a week or two'. In response to these predictions, some doctors decided to calculate the excess mortality in the Oxford Royal College of General Practitioners (RCGP) Research and Surveillance Centre (RSC) cohort. The RCGP RSC cohort has been recruited to be nationally representative, and the mortality data for the cohort align well with those from the UK Office of National Statistics (ONS). Between weeks 2 and 20 of 2020, they looked at 4.41 million individuals for 0.36 years) and discovered 17,130 deaths.

Based on background mortality for the same period in 2019, they would have expected 6,069 deaths for this period had the Covid-19 pandemic and lockdown not happened. The resulting absolute excess risk (the difference between observed and expected deaths, divided by person-years at risk) was 702.9 per 100,000 person-years. For comparison, the ONS estimate for mortality in the UK population for the entirety of 2018 was 902 per 100,000 person-years. As measured by the RCGP RSC data, excess mortality rose steadily from week 13 to a peak between weeks 15 and 16, after which a steady decline was observed. Around weeks 20–22, cohort mortality merged with the background or expected mortality. They conclude that in about a third of the year, the excess risk amounted to three-quarters of the deaths they might have anticipated in the whole of the previous year.

07.08.20

As promising as vaccines may seem, they can't help patients who are already infected with the virus. The world still lacks a Covid-19 cure that can speed up recovery, prevent complications and reduce the risk of death. Remdesivir helps in some cases, but it's expensive, scarce, difficult to make and mainly cuts the duration of hospitalisations as opposed to mortality. Dexamethasone is cheap, but isn't enough to save every patient's life, either; it helps about a quarter of ventilated patients. Blood thinners can reduce the risk of coagulation and eliminate some complications, but they're not a Covid-19 cure by themselves. Obviously, I like baricitinib. Formerly known as EIDD-2801, now acquired by Merck, the MK-4482 drug was at the centre of the Rick Bright whistle-blower complaint controversy in mid-May. Bright was removed as head of the BARDA in mid-April, worried about the potential side effects of EIDD-2801 as some studies suggested it could cause harmful mutations. Merck has now said it would conduct 'large pivotal studies' involving the drug, without disclosing any results from previous phases of human trials.

Russia today isn't pretty when it comes to Covid. With close to 1 million cases, the government reports only 15k deaths, but who knows the truth? Two people I know in Moscow, who have had 'terrible' symptoms, have repeatedly tested negative. And, in scenes akin to the Cold War space race, Russian officials recently turned heads by indicating the country plans to license a Covid-19 vaccine by 10 August, start mass production in September and initiate a vaccination campaign by October. Apparently, the scientists working on it injected themselves to 'rush it through'.

Re our baricitinib study: I am getting really exciting organoid and super-resolution microscopy data with my collaborators. Amazingly, we're finding some very important things. First, the virus activates clotting genes in the liver, explaining how it causes blood clots. Baricitinib blocks this. Second, it seems to be safe in elderly patients and save lives. Third, we can see the virus infecting the liver organoids and baricitinib blocks this. This is the first time we've ever seen a virus infecting cells and the effect of a drug. It's pretty exciting! What's more incredible is the pure biology and the cleverness of it. It seems that SARS-CoV-2-induced cytokine storm lowers the drawbridge in cells. It upregulates and activates the ACE2 receptor that the virus needs for cell entry. And again, baricitinib can block this. We need to present all of this alongside the clinical data. The best thing about this is the support of a super committed, hard-working team with a 'can do' attitude. Most of this is perspiration, not inspiration, after all. And it's so cool to stitch multidisciplinary teamwork, connecting disciplines like natural language processing to cytokine levels and human trials, microscopy and ordinal scales (the scale telling you how sick patients are from 0, completely well, to 8, which is dead).

08.08.20

A fascinating piece in *The Lancet* on 'The Cummings Effect'. On 22 May 2020, the usual UK tabloids published details of how Dominic

Cummings had broken lockdown rules by travelling 260 m to a family estate with his wife (who had suspected Covid-19) and child. Although some other officials and senior figures had also broken the lockdown rules, this transgression was the first not to be immediately followed by an apology and resignation. The event prompted media condemnation, with concerns about transparency, accountability and equality, and many scientists spoke out about the effect of Cummings' actions and the damage being done by the government's defence of Cummings in undermining essential public health messaging. It is only now, however, with the benefit of hindsight provided by systematic data, that we can see these negative effects in stark detail. New analyses of 220,755 surveys from 40,597 individuals in England, Scotland and Wales, completed between 24 April and 11 June 2020, as part of UCL's Social Study, show that these events specifically undermined confidence in the government to handle the pandemic.

Starting on 22 May 2020, there was a clear decrease in confidence in England, a decline that continued over the following days. Analyses of data from Google Trends showed that public searches of Dominic Cummings' name peaked three days later when he gave a televised statement. This peak coincided with the steepest decline in confidence in government. To ascertain whether this decrease in confidence was a result of the Cummings events (a 'Cummings effect'), they carried out analyses using two types of comparisons. First, they compared the responses of people living in England to those of people living in Scotland and Wales who were asked to rate their confidence in their own devolved governments. There was no evidence of a similar large decrease in confidence in the governments there. Second, using data from questions identical in format to those about confidence in government, they compared confidence in the health service to cope with the pandemic, and confidence that access to essentials (e.g. food and medication) would be maintained during the same time period. There was no evidence of a decrease in confidence in the health system or confidence in acquiring essentials during the same time period.

09.08.20

Dr Tedros Adhanom Ghebreyesus, Director-General of the WHO, asked Donald Trump to reconsider his decision to withdraw from the organisation. 'The problem is not about the money. It's not the financing that's the issue. It's actually the relationship with the US that's more important and its leadership abroad,' he said. The WHO said yesterday that most Covid-19 cases are now among people aged 64 and younger, with an increasing proportion of cases appearing in young adults, teenagers and children. Better testing and detection of mild cases partially explains the demographic shift, but 'a rise in risky behaviour after easing of public health and social measures' is also to blame.

Africa has passed 1 million confirmed cases, but global health experts fear the actual number is much higher, and cases are simply not being caught due to inadequate testing. Still, many African nations have successfully joined forces to gather tests and supplies, and to deploy contact tracers. India has become the third country, after the US and Brazil, to record 2 million cases of Covid-19. It recorded its second millionth case just twenty days after crossing the 1 million mark – faster than either of its predecessors.

Meanwhile, New York Governor Cuomo announced his long-awaited decision about school reopenings. Schools across the state will be allowed to resume in-person learning this autumn as long they're in an area where the average proportion of coronavirus tests coming back positive is lower than 5% (most parts of the state, including New York City, home to the country's biggest school district, which currently has a positivity rate below 1%).

10.08.20

On 3 August, 'Eat Out to Help Out' was launched by Rishi Sunak as a government initiative to build confidence in people returning to restaurants. The British public's response is clear. It was along the lines of: 'The government is going to subsidise me eating out? I'm in!' And I can now say that I, too, have helped the British economy by going out last night to a very nice restaurant near me. It was strange having the waiter approach us with a mask on, but I could tell by the creasing around her eyes that, despite the utilitarian unconventionally coloured black mask, she was smiling a greeting. The food was good, we helped a local family-run business, and the government co-funded it. All a little bizarre, but I'm going to say this is a good news story.

11.08.20

Obvious evidence from the twentieth century demonstrates how the broad uptake of immunisation can eliminate or reduce the risk of infectious disease outbreaks. Smallpox has been eradicated from the globe, and polio has now been eliminated from most countries. The likelihood of harm from seasonal pathogens such as influenza has also been reduced. Something I am hearing is that if the effects of the coronavirus are thought to be less serious, then risky behaviours might resume, ensuring the pandemic endures. An approved vaccine will likely avoid the need for compliance to social distancing and masks, etc., which are effective against the spread of the virus. What we have right now is a collection of animal data, immune response data and safety data from early trials including similar vaccines for related but different diseases.

Senior FDA leadership, including the commissioner, has written a piece on vaccines that they call in oak solid language, 'Unwavering Regulatory Safeguards for Covid-19 Vaccines'. Even under normal circumstances, vaccine development is a challenging endeavour that carries significant financial risk due to the high rate of failure at each stage of the development process. To expedite the development of a Covid-19 vaccine, the US government launched OWS in May 2020. This endeavour is compressing what can sometimes be a decade-long development process into a matter of months through up-front financial commitments that focus resources and lower the risk of innovation. The completion of Phase 1 trials for several vaccine candidates in July 2020 and enrolment for Phase 3 trials are massive milestones. Still, the emphasis on speed has provoked public anxiety about the safety and effectiveness of vaccines developed on expedited timelines. Among the concerns are that the regulatory standards for approval will be lowered under political pressure for a vaccine.

While, historically, the agency has not prospectively recommended numerical end point estimates for licence approval, the FDA believes recommending a baseline for performance is necessary to provide confidence that broad distribution of a potential vaccine could offer immunity to the majority of the population. Next, to achieve population-wide immunity, a Covid-19 vaccine would need to be widely deployed. It is therefore critical that the data derived from nonclinical and clinical studies clearly demonstrate that the vaccine is safe and effective for widespread use. Also acknowledging the need for broad use, the FDA recognises that the pandemic has disproportionately affected many populations and strongly recommends that investigators ensure sufficient representation of racial and ethnic minorities, older adults and individuals with medical comorbidities in the clinical trials. The inclusion of diverse populations, including older individuals, in trials is necessary for a comprehensive assessment of product safety and effectiveness and to properly inform clinical decision-making.

12.08.20

Vladimir Putin said that a coronavirus vaccine developed by the Gamaleya Research Institute has been approved for use in the country, but there are concerns it has not yet been properly tested on humans. Putin said that receiving the vaccine would be voluntary (his daughter had it and had fevers, apparently) and that teachers and HCWs would be prioritised over others. While the president claimed that the vaccine has 'gone through all necessary tests', Svetlana Zavidova, executive director of the Association of Clinical Trials Organisations, warned of the risk stemming from a hurried vaccine approval, denouncing Moscow's move as 'Pandora's Box'.

US numbers are still easing. European case numbers are higher but local in nature; hospitalisations and mortality data are better, and activity is still improving. More vaccine testing and debate over the effectiveness of face masks. In the US, the number of daily cases (usually <50k but yesterday a fair bit higher, but it was Tuesday) continues to fall and hospitalisations ease further.

13.08.20

For more than 100 years, research has documented that African American and Native American individuals have shorter lifespans and more illness than white persons. Hispanic immigrants initially tended to have a relatively healthy profile, but with increasing lengths of stay in the US, their health tends to decline. A black infant born in the US is more than twice as likely to die before their first birthday, compared with a white infant. In adulthood, African Americans have higher death rates than whites for most of the leading causes of death.

Compared with white people, African Americans have higher rates of uninsurance and underinsurance. Segregation of healthcare also contributes to racial disparities in healthcare, with access to primary care and especially speciality care physicians more limited in communities of colour. Covid-19 testing centres are more likely to be in well-off suburbs of predominantly white residents than in low-income neighbourhoods that are predominantly black. The advice to obtain testing through a primary care clinician limits access to testing for people who lack one. We know the rate of hospitalisations and mortality is 2–4 times higher in ethnic minorities than in white people. In the UK, this trend first came to public attention during media reports that showed the first eleven doctors who lost their lives to Covid-19 were all from BAME communities. Following this, various analyses have been published, with one showing that of 106 fatalities in health workers, some two-thirds (63%) were in BAME people. The figure was 94% for doctors and 71% for nurses, with the average reduced with the inclusion of other HCWs (55%). The UK's Intensive Care National Audit and Research Centre shows on ITU, one-third of patients were from non-white ethnic groups; ethnic minorities make up only 13% of the population as a whole.

Reasons include but are not limited to mistrust, close contact, comorbidities, including diabetes/hypertension and obesity, maybe low vitamin D levels and perhaps some genetic factors. One study shows

African American respondents were 3.5% more likely than white respondents to report being infected with Covid-19, and knowing someone who tested positive for Covid-19 was more common among African American respondents. Knowledge of transmission routes was lower in this group too.

But African Americans are less likely to be able to telecommute and more likely to work in the service sector and use public transportation than other racial/ethnic groups (23% among African American individuals versus 15% among Hispanic individuals and 7% among white individuals). Strikingly, knowledge and behaviours were closely related; groups in which behaviours put people more at risk for disease were also groups in which knowledge of appropriate behaviours are weakest.

Regardless of all this, as we strive to overcome the social and structural causes of healthcare disparities, a strong editorial implores the healthcare community to recognise the under-representation of minority groups in clinical trials. The slow realisation of this was probably yet another ingredient to fuel a sense of injustice, and the tinderbox was lit with George Floyd's death.

14.08.20

In the US, daily cases are growing at around 1%, with major hotspots slowing. Texas hospitalisations dropped to their lowest levels in six weeks as Houston reported an R0 rate of just 0.87. California also reported better news, with its governor declaring the state is 'turning the corner on this pandemic'.

Trump argued the case for schools to fully reopen by hosting an event with teachers, parents and researchers who argued for in-person learning. In Europe, Germany recorded its biggest daily increase in infections in more than three months, and Switzerland's Health Minister described the situation in the country as 'fragile' as it delayed by one month its planned resumption of big sporting and entertainment events of 1,000 or more people. As the French Health Minister said that France would never offer a vaccine to its population that hasn't passed Phase 3 trials, Russia dismissed concerns over its vaccine as 'absolutely groundless'.

In the UK, Greater Manchester Police cautioned students getting their A level results against holding parties to celebrate after the UK reported more than 1,000 daily cases for the third time in a week.

Elsewhere, India's outbreak has become one of the fastest growing in the world, with over 60k cases per day. Surely they're reaching herd immunity? Its death toll grew to the fourth largest globally, behind the US, Brazil and Mexico. In China, two patients who recovered from the virus months ago tested positive again, raising concerns about the virus' ability to linger and reappear. These add to what is described as a 'growing list' of 'virus reactivation' anecdotes among recovered patients, but I note the real journals are not reporting peer-reviewed evidence of this. China also warned of the danger of imports after a sample taken from the surface of chicken wings imported from Brazil was found to contain the virus.

And all the time, my collaborators and I are producing more and more data that lead me to believe that not only will the patient trials of baricitinib work nicely, but it will be approved and save lives. It's only one piece of a jigsaw, but I think important, and the use of AI so rapidly can serve as a guide for future drug development.

15.08.20

With Russia approving its junk vaccine (I call it this because, unlike other vaccines that are doing clinical trials and publishing findings around them, this vaccine has nothing – basically Putin has said 'Trust me, it works' and that's it), China is racing ahead too, but with published science, albeit nothing published from Phase 3 trials. Keep in mind that the RNA sequence of the SARS-CoV-2 genome was made public on 10 January 2020. In *JAMA*, the China Biotec Group now reports results from an interim analysis of data for a SARS-CoV-2-inactivated virus vaccine plus adjuvant. It looks ok and at least we can see data. If we see Sputnik's data I may change my mind.

17.08.20

A further population-based study that surveyed 4,351 adolescents and young adults aged 13–24 years has highlighted how the effects of vaping might now be colliding with the risk of Covid-19. Those reporting the use of e-cigarettes only or dual-use with tobacco were at a 5- or 7-times increased risk, respectively, of a Covid-19 diagnosis when compared with non-users. Dual users within the past thirty days were also at an increased risk of having Covid-like symptoms. Given the known damage to the lungs in such cases, the finding of an increased risk of a Covid-19 diagnosis in those who vape is pertinent. Preliminary evidence has also suggested that nicotine might upregulate the ACE2 receptor, the point of SARS-CoV-2 viral entry, and work is underway to study the effects of vaping on this receptor.

For many adults, the pandemic has been a time to stop smoking, and according to a study from Action and Smoking for Health, PHE recommends e-cigarettes as an option to aid quitting. However, surely the precautionary principle should be adopted to mitigate potential damage to the lungs and susceptibility to infection in the Covid-19 era? Smoking cessation services should focus on traditional aids to quitting while the level of evidence on long-term safety and a possible interaction between Covid-19 and e-cigarette use remains uncertain.

18.08.20

In the US, state health departments reported 37k new Covid cases Monday, down from 42k Sunday and the lowest number since 29 June. And this includes an expected backlog of 5.2k cases in Dallas County; excluding that, yesterday's total would be the lowest since 22 June. The seven-day moving average continues to decline (though the pace remains slower due to backlog reporting) in Texas today and in California (15k backlog) and Florida (4k) over the past week. The rolling average is down 3% vs a week ago, while hospitalisations (more indicative of current transmission rates) are down 10%.

Statewide mask requirements are in force for 75% of the US population, while 20% are in states where some localities have mandates and 5% have no requirements. Most states (two-thirds of the population) are leaving decisions on in-person, remote or hybrid learning for the new school year up to the local school or health district.

19.08.20

There has been debate surrounding the timing of manufacturing capacity build-out and vaccine dose delivery ahead of pivotal data expected September–November. AstraZeneca/Vaccitech is arguably ahead on this metric, leveraging an increasingly broad manufacturing network, expecting to supply the UK with 100 million doses (30 million doses by September), the US with 300 million doses (100 million doses by October) and the EU with 400 million doses (first deliveries by the end of 2020).

The news flow around supply deals between vaccine manufacturers and the US and other governments provides a window into pricing dynamics. Manufacturers will be paid ~$10 to $15 per vaccine dose. Several states have proposed legislation addressing Covid vaccine administration in an effort to expand authority to administer vaccines. Both New York and New Hampshire introduced bills authorising licensed pharmacists (or under supervision) to administer a vaccine. That said, given the stricter storage and handling requirements for Covid vaccines, physician offices or hospitals could accommodate volumes when compared to other traditional sites where flu vaccines are being administered (i.e. retail pharmacies, employer sites, schools).

The US is seeing daily case growth declining further as infection rates in all major hotspot states fall below the five-day/fourteen-day moving averages. In Europe, new infection counts are rising in 9 out of the 10 countries they are tracking, with France up 47%, Germany up 43%, the UK up 25%, Italy up 34%, Austria up 83%, Denmark up 80%, Belgium up 12%, Netherlands up 28% and Switzerland up 44%.

The durability of antibodies after infection in those who have recovered from Covid-19 remains a subject of ongoing debate, with implications for both herd immunity and vaccine durability. Based on the current literature, including the inability to reinfect monkeys and no decently documented human reinfection, I believe prior concerns around a short-lived immune response are misplaced and expect neutralising antibodies will persist at high enough levels for at least a year (the current data suggest stable levels through at least six months). The NHS is performing the SIREN study to follow HCWs and answer these questions, but I doubt we'll have data any time soon.

20.08.20

A piece of post-mortem news: it shows SARS-CoV-2 RNA was found in 38 (60%) of 63 patients' kidneys. The presence of SARS-CoV-2 RNA in the kidneys was associated with older age and an increased number of coexisting conditions. Furthermore, SARS-CoV-2 RNA was associated with a reduction in patients' survival time, obtained by calculating the time interval between Covid-19 diagnosis and date of death. These findings support a potential correlation between extra-respiratory viral tropism, disease severity and increased risk of premature death within the first three weeks of disease. Baricitinib is excreted unchanged through the kidneys. Let's see if it helps here.

21.08.20

Covid-19 has struck mink farms in the US: the US Department of Agriculture (USDA) confirmed the virus had infected the mammals and they are killing them all, but they add, 'There is currently no evidence that animals, including mink, play a significant role in spreading the virus to humans. Based on the limited information available to date, the risk of animals spreading SARS-CoV-2 to people is considered to be low. More studies are needed to understand how different species may be affected by the virus that causes Covid-19, and whether animals may play a role in the spread of the virus.'

22.08.20

Dr Fauci has authored a paper in *Cell* talking about how we got to Covid-19 and describing lots of global pandemics. The paper lays out the myriad of global conditions that enabled Covid-19 to bring the planet to its knees, but points out that this is really nothing new. The paper itself describes how genetic mutations can make diseases more or less dangerous and infectious over time. For instance, it points out that the common cold used to cause deadly epidemics before evolving into a far milder disease.

Then there's also a paper studying breast milk from 18 infected, lactating women, showing that although SARS-CoV-2 RNA was detected in one milk sample from an infected woman, the viral culture for that sample was negative. This data suggests that SARS-CoV-2 RNA does not represent a replication-competent virus and that breast milk may not be a source of infection for the infant.

Now insurance: More than 40 million people in the US filed for unemployment insurance between March and May 2020, but official statistics may understate the true extent of job disruptions. Widespread layoffs amid the pandemic threaten to cut off millions of people from their employer-sponsored health insurance plans.

Before the Affordable Care Act (ACA) was implemented in 2010 in the US, so-called Obamacare, people who lost their jobs had limited choices for health insurance. Newly disabled people could apply for Medicaid if their savings and assets were low enough for them to qualify for Supplemental Security Income, or they could enrol in Medicare after receiving two years of benefits from Social Security Disability Insurance. For adults without a disability, many states' income cut-offs for Medicaid were well below the poverty line, and only people with dependent children could apply. An individual private insurance market existed, but without insurer regulations, such as guaranteed issue, community rating, actuarial-value standards and coverage of essential health benefits, plans were skimpy, excluded people with pre-existing conditions and were often unaffordable. Married people who lost their jobs could potentially switch to their partner's employer-sponsored insurance (ESI) plan.

Overall, there was a 6.0% net reduction in loss of coverage after a job loss in the post-ACA period when compared with the pre-ACA period. These results indicate the critical role that the ACA will play in alleviating coverage losses related to the Covid-associated recession, in keeping with findings from other recent reports.

24.08.20

French Health Minister Véran insisted a new nationwide lockdown is 'not a working hypothesis', arguing the situation is different than it was during the first wave. 'The virus is circulating four times more among people younger than 40 than among those older than 65; young patients have fewer medical complications, and the country has ramped up its testing capacity. But authorities must prevent the virus from spreading from young people to the older generation at all cost. The risk is that, after gently removing the lid from the pot, the water will boil again.' His Italian counterpart Roberto Speranza also ruled out a new lockdown, despite an uptick in infections.

Indeed, mortality rates from Covid-19 remain low, including when compared to other common causes of death, and will likely decline further while control measures are maintained. However, the important difference between Covid-19 and all these other risks is the issue of urgency. Cancer, cardiovascular disease, dementia and road traffic accidents will not increase exponentially if we don't tackle them immediately.

In the most comprehensive study of Covid-19 paediatric patients to date, Harvard researchers provide critical data showing that children play a larger role in the community spread of Covid-19 than previously thought. In a study of 192 children and young people aged 0–22, 49 tested positive for SARS-CoV-2, and an additional 18 had late-onset Covid-19-related illness. The infected children and young people were shown to have a significantly higher level of virus in their airways than hospitalised adults in ICUs for Covid-19 treatment. Transmissibility or risk of contagion is greater with a high viral load. And even when children exhibit symptoms typical of Covid-19, like fever, runny nose and cough, they often overlap with common childhood illnesses, including influenza and the common cold. This confounds an accurate diagnosis of Covid-19, the illness derived from the coronavirus. They note that although children and young people with Covid-19 are not as likely to become as seriously ill as adults, as asymptomatic carriers or carriers with few symptoms attending school, they can spread infection and bring the virus into their homes.

Last night at a Trump press conference, the president, Alex Azar (HHS) and Stephen Hahn (FDA) said they were granting approval to a convalescent plasma to treat Covid-19. This was a surprise considering that most data are from single-arm studies. When it comes to treatment it's very difficult to determine what works. Can't believe the FDA is looking at non-randomised data like this. There are way too many biases. Wouldn't know where to begin. Why, oh why, are they doing this? They are meant to be the gatekeepers of data, the Cinderella organisation of standard practice, and they're going against this. Against, I thought, everything they themselves promulgated so fiercely in previous decades.

Trump claimed that convalescent plasma was 'safe and very effective', and had been 'proven to reduce mortality by 35% … a tremendous number'. I have no idea where that figure comes from. I give in with the FDA. 35% in comparison to what exactly? The studies he's referring to are not randomised.

25.08.20

A case of distinct reinfection has been published:

> The confirmation of reinfection has several important implications. First, it is possible that herd immunity may not eliminate SARS-CoV-2 if reinfection is not an uncommon occurrence, although it is possible that subsequent infections may be milder than the first infection as for this patient. Then, Covid-19 will likely continue to circulate in the human population, as in the case of other human coronaviruses. Reinfection is common for 'seasonal' coronaviruses 229E, OC43, NL63, and HKU1. In some instances, reinfection occurs despite a static level of specific antibodies. Second, vaccines may not be able to provide lifelong protection against Covid-19. Furthermore, vaccine studies should also include patients who recovered from Covid-19.

Lots of papers on how less privileged people are more likely to be infected and to die. The alarming inequalities in American society became obvious to me during my time at Johns Hopkins Hospital in Baltimore, though the local community received the best medical care in the world there. I can't fix this, but I can make sure I help drive the change I want to see in my own society and do my best to support medicine in under-represented communities. Paper after paper is showing ethnic minorities do worse and are more likely to contract Covid-19 with so many factors at play.

26.08.20

The British government currently does not recommend that students wear face masks in school, despite advice from the WHO, which recommends that all students aged 12 and older wear them. However, that could change as schools in the UK are set to reopen. 'We'll look at the changing medical evidence as we go on. If we need to change the advice, then of course we will,' Johnson said. His statement comes after Scotland announced it would recommend that all students wear face masks 'in corridors and communal areas' at school.

Acute anxiety, including colloquially called 'anxiety attacks' or 'panic attacks', was monitored because of its higher prevalence relative to other mental health problems and the fact that it can lead to other mental health problems (including depression). It is triggered by outside stressors and is socially contagious. Using Google Trends, a group monitored the daily fraction of all internet searches (thereby adjusting the results for any change in total queries) that included the terms anxiety or panic in combination with attack (including panic attack, signs of anxiety attack, anxiety attack symptoms) that originated from the US from 1 January 2004 through to 4 May 2020. Raw search counts were inferred using Comscore estimates. They compared search volumes after President Trump declared a national Covid-19 emergency on 13 March 2020 with expected search volumes if Covid-19 had not occurred, thereby taking into account the historical trend and periodicity in the data. Internet searches indicative of acute anxiety spiked early during the pandemic but have since returned to typical levels, perhaps because Americans have become more resilient to the societal fallout from Covid-19 or because they had already received whatever benefit they could from searching the internet. Interesting thought.

27.08.20

Speculation that there will be a vaccine FDA advisory committee meeting on 22 October. Yesterday Moderna presented safety and immunogenicity data in older patients (age-stratified: 56–70 and 71+ years old) at the Advisory Committee on Immunisation Practices (ACIP) meeting. The safety profile looks to be generally consistent across all age groups.

More than 2 in 5 US residents report struggling with mental or behavioural health issues associated with the Covid-19 pandemic, including anxiety, depression, increased substance use and suicidal thoughts, according to the CDC. Nothing new then. It also notes that certain groups are disproportionately affected by Covid-19-related stresses, including younger adults, African Americans and Hispanics, essential workers, unpaid caregivers for adults and those receiving treatment for pre-existing psychiatric conditions.

In rural Bangladesh, a group of randomly selected mothers of 3,016 children were invited to participate in a study, 2,424 of whom provided consent. 2,414 of 2,417 mothers were aware of and adhering to the stay-at-home advice. 2,321 of 2,417 mothers reported a reduction in paid work for the family. Median monthly family income fell from US$212 at baseline to $59 during lockdown, and the proportion of families earning less than $1.90 per day rose from 5 (0.2%) of 2,422 to 992 (47.3%). The mothers' depression and anxiety symptoms increased during the lockdown. Among women experiencing emotional or moderate physical violence, over half reported it had increased since the lockdown.

28.08.20

There is a credit-card-sized assay now from Abbott that can be used with a nasal swab (meaning there is no need to go to facilities with reference labs), which can get results in 15 minutes (vs 1–3 days). In terms of the detail for BINAX-NOW:

- Pricing at $5 means it is very accessible vs the likes of Quidel and Becton Dickinson, which charge $20 and require an instrument.
- Volumes are far higher than expected at tens of millions in September, 50 million per month from October (vs 3.5 million for ID-NOW, which they also make).
- Sensitivity (true positive) of 97.1% and specificity (true negative) of 98.3%, albeit sample size <70 for both.
- A free mobile app that will generate a 'health pass' upon a negative test.
- This is a lateral flow test that functions similarly to a pregnancy test and is an antigen test, not antibody or PCR.

Variations in the immune response to SARS-CoV-2 could explain why men are more likely to be hospitalised and die than women. A group studied the immune responses of 98 men and women infected with SARS-CoV-2. All had mild to moderate symptoms. The researchers noticed that male participants' typical immune response to infection differed from that of female participants, which could explain the more severe disease often observed in men. The team found that, in general, men had higher levels of certain inflammation-causing proteins known as cytokines and chemokines circulating in their blood than women. We've been studying those.

29.08.20

Moncef Slaoui, scientific head of OWS, has written an opinion piece in the *NEJM*. Some summary points:

- He describes it as a partnership between the Department of Health and Human Services (HHS), the Department of Defence (DOD) and the private sector. 'The partnership grew out of an acknowledged need to fundamentally restructure the way the US government typically supports product development and vaccine distribution.

The initiative was premised on setting a "stretch goal" – one that initially seemed impossible but that is becoming increasingly achievable.'

- OWS's role is to enable, accelerate, harmonise and advise the companies developing the selected vaccines. The companies will execute the clinical or process development and manufacturing plans, while OWS leverages the full capacity of the US government to ensure that no technical, logistic or financial hurdles hinder vaccine development or deployment.
- OWS selected vaccine candidates on the basis of four criteria: a) preclinical efficacy; b) the potential, with our acceleration support, to enter large Phase 3 field efficacy trials this summer; c) based on vaccine-platform technologies permitting fast and effective manufacturing, developers had to demonstrate the industrial process scalability, yields and consistency necessary to reliably produce more than 100 million doses by mid-2021; d) use of one of four vaccine-platform technologies most likely to yield a safe and effective vaccine against Covid-19.
- The OWS strategy relies on a few key principles: a) a diverse project portfolio that includes two vaccine candidates based on each of the four platform technologies to mitigate risk; b) OWS will maximise the size of Phase 3 trials (30,000 to 50,000 participants each) and optimise trial-site location by consulting daily epidemiologic and disease-forecasting models to ensure the fastest path to an efficacy readout. Such large trials also increase the safety data set for each candidate vaccine; c) OWS aims to harmonise the trials and end points.
- Of the eight vaccines in the OWS portfolio, six have been announced and partnerships executed: Moderna and Pfizer/BioNTech (both mRNA), AstraZeneca and Janssen (both replication-defective, live-vector) and Novavax and Sanofi/GSK (both recombinant-subunit-adjuvanted protein). These candidates cover three of the four platform technologies and are currently in clinical trials. The remaining two candidates will enter trials soon.

My view is markets, including the US, the UK, the EU, Russia, India and China, will have access to limited quantities of a coronavirus vaccine by the end of this year, which would be reserved for HCWs and vulnerable populations. Winning the 'vaccine race' may provide redemption to embattled leaders, but vaccine nationalism will continue to supersede international cooperation in 2020. Despite a new agreement on vaccine access, many developing countries will be excluded from most of the first wave of vaccine availability. Even in developed markets, rollouts could be delayed for scientific reasons (issues related to clinical trials, immunity and scale-up) or for social reasons (vaccine hesitancy and misinformation), complicating the picture this year and next. There will be equitable distribution eventually.

30.08.20

What does SARS-CoV-2 actually want? What's its aim? Where do we begin to answer questions like this? The molecules of life are lifeless, yet life has a molecular basis. Molecules come together to make complex structures like viruses, and they can even come together to make cells. Remarkably, at a certain point, cells come together to make a conscious life form. Perhaps humans are different: the philosopher John Locke defined a person as, 'A thinking intelligent being that has reason and reflection and can consider itself as itself.' It would seem to follow that individual persons are something like states (of mind) and thus are not beings after all, contrary to Locke's original definition. Clearly that's well beyond a virus, let alone most creatures that roam the planet.

For about 100 years, the scientific community has repeatedly changed its collective mind over what viruses are. First seen as poisons, then as life forms, then biological chemicals, viruses today are thought of as being in a grey area between living and non-living. They cannot replicate on their own but can do so in truly living cells and can also affect the behaviour of their hosts profoundly. The categorisation of viruses as non-living during much of the modern era of biological science has had an unintended consequence: it has led most researchers to ignore viruses in the study of evolution. Finally, however, scientists are beginning to appreciate viruses as fundamental players in the history of life.

It is easy to see why viruses have been difficult to pigeonhole. They seem to vary with each lens applied to examine them. The initial interest in viruses stemmed from their association with diseases; the word 'virus' has its roots in the Latin term for 'poison'. In the late nineteenth century, researchers realised that certain diseases, including rabies and foot-and-mouth, were caused by particles that seemed to behave like bacteria but were much smaller. Because they were clearly biological themselves and could be spread from one victim to another with obvious biological effects, viruses were then thought to be the simplest of all living, gene-bearing life forms.

Their demotion to inert chemicals came after 1935, when Wendell M. Stanley and his colleagues, at what is now the Rockefeller University in New York City, crystallised a virus, the tobacco mosaic virus, for the first time. They saw that it consisted of a package of complex biochemicals, but that it lacked essential systems necessary for metabolic functions, the biochemical activity of life. Stanley shared the 1946 Nobel Prize in chemistry – not in physiology or medicine – for this work.

Further research by Stanley and others established that a virus consists of nucleic acids (DNA or RNA) enclosed in a protein coat that may also shelter viral proteins involved in infection. By that description, a virus seems more like a chemistry set than an organism. But when a virus enters a cell (called a host after infection), it is far from inactive. It sheds its coat, bares its genes and induces the cell's own replication machinery to reproduce the intruder's DNA or RNA and manufacture more viral protein based on the instructions in the viral nucleic acid. The newly created viral bits assemble and, voilà, more virus arises, which also may infect other cells.

These behaviours are what led many to think of viruses as existing at the border between chemistry and life. More poetically, some have said that with their dependence on host cells, viruses lead 'a kind of borrowed life'. Interestingly, even though biologists have long favoured the view that viruses were mere boxes of chemicals, they took advantage of viral activity in host cells to determine the nucleic acids code for proteins; indeed, modern molecular biology rests on a foundation of information gained through viruses.

Molecular biologists went on to crystallise most of the essential components of cells and are today accustomed to thinking about cellular constituents – for example, ribosomes, mitochondria, membranes, DNA and proteins – as either chemical machinery or the stuff that the machinery uses or produces. This exposure to multiple complex chemical structures that carry out the processes of life is probably a reason that most molecular biologists do not spend a lot of time puzzling over whether viruses are alive. For them, that exercise might seem equivalent to pondering whether those individual subcellular constituents are alive on their own. This myopic view allows them to see only how viruses co-opt cells or cause disease.[4]

A thought-provoking piece in *The Economist* touched on similar themes. 'We humans are lucky to survive ninety years. Oak trees may live a thousand years, mayflies, in their adult form, a single day, but they are all alive in the same way. They are made up of cells that embody flows of energy and stores of information. Their metabolisms make use of that energy, be it from sunlight or food, to build new molecules and break down old ones, using mechanisms described in the genes they inherited and may, or may not, pass on.'

In viruses the link between metabolism and genes that binds together all life to which you are related, from bacteria to blue whales, is broken. Viral genes have no cells, no bodies, no metabolism of their own. The tiny particles, virions, in which those genes come packaged are entirely inanimate. An individual animal or plant embodies and maintains the restless metabolism that made it. A virion is just an arrangement of matter. The virus is not the virion. The virus is a process, not a thing.

It is truly alive only in the cells of others, a virtual organism running on borrowed hardware to produce more copies of its genome. Some bide their time, letting the cell they share the life of live on. Others immediately set about producing enough virions to split their hosts from stem to stern.

'The virus has no plan or desire. The simplest purposes of the simplest life – to maintain the difference between what is inside the cell and what is outside, to move towards one chemical or away from another – are entirely beyond it. It copies itself in whatever way it does simply because it has copied itself that way before, in other cells, in other hosts.' The molecules of life are lifeless, but viruses, like life itself, have a molecular basis. And if molecules assemble to make a cell, at what point do the cells themselves assemble that they become conscious?

That is why, asked whether viruses are alive, Eckard Wimmer, a chemist and biologist, offers a yes-and-no response. 'Viruses,' he says, 'alternate between non-living and living phases.' He should know. In 2002, he became the first person in the world to take an array of non-living chemicals and build a virion from scratch, a virion that was then able to get itself reproduced by infecting cells.

The fact that viruses have only a tenuous claim to being alive, though, hardly reduces their impact on things that are indubitably so. No other biological entities are as ubiquitous, and few as consequential. The number of copies of their genes to be found on Earth is beyond astronomical. There are hundreds of billions of stars in the Milky Way galaxy and a couple of trillion galaxies in the observable universe. The virions in the surface waters of any smallish sea handily outnumber all of these. It is a general principle in biology that in terms of individual numbers, herbivores outnumber carnivores; in terms of the number of species, carnivores outnumber herbivores. Viruses, however, outnumber everything else in every way possible.[5]

This makes sense. Though viruses can induce host behaviours that help them spread, such as coughing, an inert virion boasts no behaviour of its own that helps it stalk its prey. It infects only that which it comes into contact with, and as for SARS-CoV-2, that inert circle of life, based on 'real life', continues.

31.08.20

A surprising, inexpensive tool is available to us. Saltwater costs pennies; other products with antiviral activity cost just a few pennies. One study from Germany found Listerine, iso-betadine and Dequonal mouthwashes to be most effective against three strains of SARS-CoV-2 of eight commercially available products. One small RCT of nasal irrigation and saltwater gargling showed a shorter illness, 35% reduction in infecting other members of the household and reduction in viral shedding for common colds. Even gargling with chlorinated tap water reduced respiratory infections in a study in Japan. Another small study from Malaysia showed a better reduction of virus with iodine or essential oils compared to water or no treatment.

There are many questions about this approach. Can the viral load be reduced enough through gargling and/or nasal washes to be a worthwhile preventative? Which product is most effective? Would some combination be better? How much contact time is needed? Would putting these compounds in chewing gum or lozenge to prolong contact be more effective? What effects do these antiseptics have on the oral and gut flora (microbiome)? Do we need nasal washes, mouthwashes or both? What side effects might appear beyond tooth staining and rare allergic reactions?

September

01.09.20

It is worth calling out countries that have not reported a single case of Covid-19. The two most dubious candidates are Turkmenistan and North Korea – authoritarian states that still deny the pandemic has spread within their borders. The rest are all island nations located in the South Pacific, which may well have avoided infection.

In the light of the HCQ debacle: On Sunday, FDA Commissioner Stephen Hahn told *The Financial Times* that he would potentially fast track a Covid-19 vaccine before clinical trials are done if it was 'appropriate'. He claimed politics were not part of that decision, saying, 'This is going to be a science, medicine, data decision.' Former FDA Commissioner Scott Gottlieb on CBS's *Face the Nation* criticised the statement, noting, 'I don't know what is meant by saying before the Phase 3 trials are completed. These Phase 3 trials are event-based trials, meaning that they're going to start to read out data after a certain amount of events accrue in the clinical trials. And those events are people getting Covid infection. And so as the trials progress, if we start to see lower rates of Covid infection in the active group, the group that receives the vaccine versus the placebo group, the group that hasn't received the vaccine.'

And why not! I mean, Putin said about the Russian vaccine, 'I know that it works quite effectively, forms strong immunity, and I repeat, it has passed all the needed checks.' He claimed that one of his daughters had been given the vaccine. Members of the Russian elite have reportedly also received doses of the vaccine since April. The chief of the Russian Direct Investment Fund, Kirill Dmitriev, has said that a Phase 3 trial will start in August and will involve thousands of people in Russia, Saudi Arabia and the UAE. The vaccine could then be distributed as early as September.

The approval of a vaccine without large-scale testing has caused concern, and researchers have called for the results to be published for scrutiny and for further trials to take place before the vaccine is rolled out to the public.

A US regulatory review of the numerous Covid-19 vaccine candidates will occur under intense clinical, economic and political pressure. In early August 2020, Trump predicted that a vaccine could be available before election day. Less than a week later, Russia claimed to have developed its own vaccine and was beginning widespread administration without completion of the large-scale testing that Western countries routinely require, bringing efficacy-risk questions to even wider public attention. Acknowledging the pressure the FDA faces on this front, its leadership has stated that no vaccine would receive formal approval unless it met the agency's published standards – as per the above – again and again.

As with drugs, the efficacy and safety of a vaccine is not binary. Each will fall along a gradient and be subject to varying definitions over time. In its June 2020 guidance document, the FDA established its expectation that an approved vaccine would reduce the occurrence or severity of disease in at least 50% of recipients, a standard similar to that for annual influenza vaccines, but that criterion could change. If the pandemic surges further, should a vaccine be approvable if it prevents infection in a lower proportion of people? What if the vaccine substantially reduces the severity of illness but not in half of recipients?

The FDA also cited the possibility of less conventional approaches. One approach would allow 'accelerated approval' of a vaccine based only on antibody levels or another biochemical marker rather than actual clinical outcomes. This could occur if 'additional understanding of SARS-CoV-2 immunology, and specifically vaccine immune responses that might be reasonably likely to predict protection against Covid-19, is acquired'. For many years, the agency has shown increasing willingness to approve medications based on their capacity to affect surrogate measures such as laboratory test results, rather than demonstrating an effect on clinical disease. Such approvals have been made for drugs with extremely limited patient outcome evidence in oncology and muscular dystrophy, among other conditions. Some have argued that extreme clinical need warrants backing away from the FDA's historical standards requiring clinical benefit. This trend coincides with increasing political popularity of the libertarian 'right to try' movement for medications, which advocates that patients should be able to access treatments not approved by the FDA. This approach was likely reflected in the presidential reasoning about unproven Covid-19 treatments: 'Try it; what do you have to lose?'

Alternatively, the FDA has noted that it could implement an EUA to make a Covid-19 vaccine available even before its full evaluation is completed. This would have seemed implausible but for the agency's issuance of another Covid-19-related decision in March. In the context of the president's persistent advocacy for HCQ, the agency issued an EUA to make millions of doses available for this purpose. That decision was eventually rescinded but led to considerable use of the drug, which continues, and the widespread misperception that the FDA had 'approved' HCQ for this use.

Standards for efficacy and safety must be high for any product designed to be administered to millions of healthy individuals in the hope that it will prevent illness in a fraction of them. The calculus is particularly challenging when such infection is often asymptomatic, sometimes mild, but in some cases severe or fatal. The stakes are significantly higher if the decision must be made at a time when the public is experiencing increasing anxiety over the pandemic, by a federal agency under the jurisdiction of a president facing an imminent election who is not known for his understanding of or respect for scientific rigour. The public is not likely to focus on subtle distinctions between antibody levels and clinical end points, or on the difference between emergency authorisation and full FDA approval. An October EUA based on suggestive surrogate markers may give rise to an unjustified sense of 'mission accomplished', a risky strategy for the nation.

The approval or emergency authorisation of any Covid-19 vaccine will just mark the start of a second, equally crucial phase: its deployment across an enormous population. This will be the largest vaccine launch to take place in a period of unprecedented 'vaccine hesitancy' by the public. In one large recent survey, only 44% of 34,269 respondents said they were willing to get a Covid-19 vaccine. If an approved vaccine reduces disease risk by 50% and is used by less than half the population (as occurs each year with influenza immunisation), it is unlikely to achieve the herd immunity that many anticipate from a product expected to 'reopen the country'. If premature authorisation leads to overestimation of its effectiveness, or failure to anticipate a serious adverse effect, either misstep could damage the already delicate trust many people in the United States have in immunisation programmes. The resulting damage to public acceptance could represent a dangerous adverse effect of any vaccine programme, potentially undercutting all the excellent science and expense that preceded it.

02.09.20

A paper in *JAMA* shows administration of systemic corticosteroids like dexamethasone, compared with usual care or placebo, was associated with lower 28-day, all-cause mortality in critically ill patients with Covid-19. Some doctors think baricitinib is like an elaborate steroid, but this doesn't take into account its antiviral and other effects. In some ways because it affects so many cytokines via blocking the JAK-STAT pathway I think it will also end up better than the anti-interleukin-6 drugs like Actemra. If you knock down interleukin-6, from what I can see the beauty of nature compensates and upregulates other dangerous cytokines in a feed-forward loop. And you can't beat nature. We're coming to this conclusion on our Zoom calls across the world.

Up until now, it has been unknown how well cell phone location data portray social distancing strategies or if they are associated with the incidence of Covid. A large US study found that greater reductions in cell phone activity in the workplace and retail locations, and greater increases in activity at the residence are associated with lesser growth in Covid-19 cases. Some of the factors associated with changes in cell phone activity are intuitive. For example, reductions in workplace activity and increases in residential activity were higher in counties and on days where/when there was a greater number of new cases, and thus there was likely a higher perceived risk of infection. Perhaps the most important observation of this study was that a decrease in activity at the workplace, transit stations and retail locations, and an increase in activity at the place of residence was associated with a significant decline in Covid-19 cases at 5, 10 and 15 days. The immediate implication of these results is that it supports the use of cell phone data as a measure of adherence to stay-at-home advisories and may act as a prognostic measure that may help to identify areas at greatest risk for more rapid growth of the epidemic.

And one for People for Ethical Treatment of Animals (PETA) to get angry about, or maybe not: monkey shortage is affecting research. This is, firstly, and obviously, due to the clinical trials of Covid-19-related drugs that have created an extraordinary demand for monkeys. Secondly, this coincided with a massive drop in supply from China, which provided 60% of the nearly 35,000 monkeys imported to the US last year. And finally, these pandemic-related events are exacerbating pre-existing monkey shortfalls. Doctors and researchers are not monsters; we don't want to experiment on monkeys, but with a global pandemic that is killing hundreds of thousands of humans, the lives of monkeys can save millions of human lives. It's cold, hard logic, and the trials are being done for the greater good, although right now there's a problem with supply.

03.09.20

Time to consider the very public and well-documented windfall of financial support from Washington DC. The lead (from a timing standpoint) research efforts have been afforded billions of dollars in a combination of research and product procurement funding. This cash infusion is reliant on successful data, but irrespective of what occurs, beginning as early as the third quarter of this year, it is hard to foresee a scenario that would afford more than a select handful of vaccines from having longer-term relevance. Government purchase advances are up to $10 billion across less than ten programmes. Not only has Washington pre-purchased vaccines that it will then distribute to providers/clinicians, but it has also directly funded R&D efforts across the board. Given warp speed timelines and clear rhetoric from politicians relating to the importance of a near-term vaccine, 2020 may be an anomaly rather than a trend.

This is not to say that BARDA and the WHO (to name a couple) will pull the plug on financing these aforementioned programmes, but we would expect this first wave of vaccine buy-ins to be highly monitored at least several months post broader immunisation. That takes us out to what we would estimate to be a year from now. At that point perhaps Washington will write additional cheques, but to points touched upon earlier, price/shot costs will probably be adjusted lower. In the meantime, material government funding updates will be less fast and furious, leading to more of a news vacuum on this topic alone. Furthermore, it is now consensus that at least one vaccine will be approved prior to the November election, and thus the surprise factor may not be as overzealous if this were not the case.

On the therapy side, it is worth watching the progress out of Regeneron, Merck, Pfizer, Roche, GSK, AstraZeneca, Novartis, Lilly, Alexion and others, including a host of small biotechs like Synairgen, developing therapies for the treatment of Covid-19. Over the past couple of months nearly all the attention with respect to drug development has been on vaccines, but non-vaccine approaches that are aimed at helping patients fight coronavirus if/when it is contracted are interesting. To me, Regeneron followed by Lilly are ahead for their antibodies, though they need to be infused intravenously.

Interestingly, the National Institutes of Health released a missive undercutting the FDA's EUA of convalescent plasma, an escalation of an extraordinary public disagreement between federal agencies. Thankfully, the main question surrounding the treatment is whether it works, not whether it's safe. But this feud could erode public trust in any future coronavirus treatments and vaccines, potentially for good reason. An NIH panel of experts reviewed the existing evidence on convalescent plasma, including the FDA's analysis, and determined that 'there are currently no data from well-controlled, adequately powered, randomised clinical trials that demonstrate the efficacy and safety of convalescent plasma for the treatment of Covid-19'. Although it said that serious adverse reactions to convalescent plasma are rare, the panel wrote that it's still unknown whether the treatment makes patients more susceptible to reinfection.

04.09.20

Excess deaths are hard to measure. Between March and April, EuroMOMO's tracker showed tens of thousands more deaths than expected, about 25% higher than the official Covid-19 deaths figure. Infections were slipping under the radar because of a lack of testing and because different countries counted deaths in different ways, excluding deaths occurring in care homes, for instance. It has been nearly impossible to get a true sense of how countries were faring. So, researchers, journalists and politicians turned to calculations of excess deaths. Rather than getting bogged down by cause, the metric compares all deaths in a given week or month with the deaths that statisticians predict would have happened in the absence of the pandemic, usually as an average over the previous five years. More sophisticated versions model how a population is ageing or how it is changing as a result of immigration and emigration, although these additions can make it tricky to compare countries.

Some analyses of excess deaths, such as a 30 July report released by the UK ONS, standardise their mortality rates to control for differences in the age structure of populations between different countries. Because officials can register the occurrence of a death relatively quickly if they are not logging the cause at the same time, these statistics can be compiled much faster than can cause-specific data. Nature gathered figures from several databases maintained by demographers, as well as from trackers run by *The Financial Times* and *The Economist*. Although the coverage is not universal, it lists 32 countries (largely in Europe) and 4 major world cities; it includes many nations with major outbreaks and comprises about two-thirds of the official Covid-19 death toll up to the end of July. A *Nature* analysis shows that there are huge variations in excess deaths between countries. In the US and Spain, about 25% and 35%, respectively, of the excess death toll is not reflected in official Covid-19 death statistics. But in other places, the mismatch is much greater, such as in Peru, where 74% of the excess deaths are not explained by reported Covid-19 deaths. And some countries, such as Bulgaria, have even experienced negative excess deaths during the pandemic so far, meaning that, despite the virus, fewer people have died this year than expected.

05.09.20

It's staggering to see published Russian peer-reviewed science in a decent journal, for me anyway. The Gamaleya Research Institute of Epidemiology and Microbiology in Russia have now presented findings from two Phase 1/2, non-randomised, open-label studies of formulations in *The Lancet*. The researchers enrolled 76 healthy adult volunteers into the two studies, most of them male soldiers. The primary outcome measures of the studies were safety and immunogenicity (antigen-specific humoral immunity). Adverse events were mostly mild, with the most common adverse events being pain at the injection site, hyperthermia, headache and muscle and joint pain. Serious adverse events did not arise in this small cohort. Both formulations of the vaccine were immunogenic in all participants. In Phase 2, 85% of participants had detectable antibodies at fourteen days after the priming dose, rising to 100% by day 21, with substantial titre rises after the boosting dose. How does this really compare with Western vaccines? If we compare the Russian vaccine to other datasets, it is similar to the AstraZeneca/Oxford vaccine, but it's less efficacious compared to other vaccines like Pfizer/BioNTech, Moderna and Novovax, but it's dangerous to compare across datasets.

A *BMJ* piece states:

A post-viral tsunami is hitting our health services right now, yet in the UK it doesn't even seem to be on the national agenda. There have been 28 rapid reviews and guidance on Covid-19 this year, but their guidance on the chronic fatigue syndrome/myalgic encephalomyelitis is 13 years-old. There is little evidence in the UK of a coordinated response that is truly multidisciplinary, involves organisations such as the ME Association and includes patients.

Society is acknowledging the 'long haulers' but part of the picture is missing. What about people less privileged than us articulate middle classes mobilising ourselves, writing to MPs and talking to journalists? What about the minority groups, the single parent households, people on zero hours contracts, where long convalescence is not an option? These people are trying to navigate an illness that bites back like a demon if you overdo it, batters you physically and mentally and leads you to doubt your own sanity. Pushing themselves because they have no choice will lead to further illness, suffering and distress. They are being left behind.

This stuff is real. People are ill. Doctors need to stop diagnosing this as anxiety. We have messed up before, let's not do it again with long-term Covid-19 illness.[6]

07.09.20

The Speaker of the House of Commons, Lindsay Hoyle, said yesterday he'd spoken to the NHS about the prospect of regular tests, having decided that lawmakers can't get about their work wearing masks in the chamber. 'To be quite honest with you, I'd like to do it daily, not weekly.' Glad to hear the bar will stay shut. UK cases have risen yesterday to 3k per day, the highest increase since 22 May.

Now the *New York Times* states, when it comes to contact tracing, the virus' pervasiveness along with major lags in testing have rendered the system almost pointless. Great piece in *The Atlantic* today regarding contact tracing too:

> Contact tracing, the last two-thirds of health wonks' 'test-trace-isolate' mantra, was supposed to get us out of the pandemic. It's meant to work like this: Let's say Aunt Sally tests positive for Covid-19. A tracer working for the local public health department calls her and asks for her contacts – anyone she's spent more than 15 minutes with recently – and asks her to self-isolate. Then the tracer calls those 'close contacts' of Aunt Sally's and asks *them* to self-isolate too. The tracer doesn't tell Aunt Sally's contacts that she is the person who tested positive, only that someone they were in contact with did.
>
> In the United States, this whole process is failing, allowing Aunt Sally to continue roaming about town, infecting others and spreading Covid-19. There is no national contact-tracing programme in the US, and contact tracers who work for the 40 local health departments in areas with the most coronavirus cases have reached just a fraction of the patients who have tested positive, an investigation found earlier this month. In Maryland, 25% of those called by contact tracers don't pick up. At one point in Miami, contact tracers were able to reach only 17% of the infected...
>
> Some of these numbers might not be totally accurate in the long run. For instance, some health departments might count a person who picks up a contact tracer's second or third call, instead of the first, as a nonresponse. But even giving US health departments the benefit of the doubt, response rates here are far lower than those in other countries. Less than 1% of sick people fail to respond to contact tracers in Iceland; in New Zealand, 86% of people contacted by tracers respond within 48 hours. 'The US contact-tracing effort has been a dismal failure, compared with many of its peer countries,' says Lawrence Gostin, a professor of global-health law at Georgetown University.
>
> Contact tracers are not to blame. Tracers tend to be relatively low-paid, civic-minded workers who make calls relentlessly in an attempt to rescue the nation from a ruthless pandemic. But they're struggling ... there are too many cases to track.[7]

Many countries seem able to recruit an army of contact tracers as part of a 'test, track, and trace' strategy; that's what happened after the recent Beijing market outbreak and it was swiftly brought under control. In the UK and the US, for example, certain volunteers have signed up for online classes on the concepts and methods that have served South Korea, Singapore and Taiwan throughout the pandemic. But whereas the systems in the latter countries rely on downloadable digital technologies, UK and US faith is being placed in humans. By the end of July 2020, more than half a million people had enrolled for a free online Covid-19 contact-tracing course offered by Johns Hopkins, and around 20,000 people had been recruited as contact tracers in the UK.

Communication techniques are a key part of this training. Clarifying signs and symptoms and explaining local guidelines to contacts is mostly script-based and eminently teachable. But to have a meaningful impact, the tracer needs to establish rapport with the contact, which requires tact, patience and empathy, qualities that are less readily teachable.

Particularly in the UK, concerns have been expressed that the training falls short of what is needed to quell the fear and anxiety of people who are being asked to divulge very personal information. Governments thus face a stark reality: tracers' inability to persuade contacts to take precautions may prove costly in terms of illness and death.

08.09.20

Last week saw new infection counts rising week on week in most European countries. These include the UK up 46%, France up 34%, and Italy up 6%, the Netherlands up 30%, Switzerland up 13%, Austria up 10% and Belgium up 3%. Another Spanish data restatement increased the severity of its second wave, and French cases have hit 46.8k – the most severe of the entire outbreak. Both France and Spain are clearly seeing second waves, whereas for now Germany seems to be under control. *The Times* refers to a 'fear that Britain is losing control' as the daily case number reached 3,000. Overall rates of death and hospitalisations remain low across Europe and the UK, suggesting second waves are less lethal, but rates are starting to creep up in Spain and France. A report in *The Sunday Times* also focused on the fact that second waves in Europe have been less lethal, ascribing the trend to: 1) new infections now being among a younger demographic; 2) advances in medical understanding of the virus; and 3) masks and social distancing that may have reduced the viral load transmitted.

Elsewhere, India has now overtaken Brazil as the country with the second-highest number of cases (4.2 million), with daily rates hitting 90k+ over the weekend. India now sits between the US at 6.6 million cases and Brazil at 4.3 million cases. In the UK, Foreign Secretary Dominic Raab confirmed that the testing policy for incoming travellers was under review, with tests eight days after travellers arrive in Britain being considered to cut quarantine requirements. At the same time, home antibody tests have gone back on sale in the UK after months of wrangling over a regulatory ban.

In the US, the R0 is 0.97 (vs 0.95 last week), while the epidemic doubling time is 100 days (vs 110 last week). State health departments reported 27k new Covid cases Monday, down from 33k Sunday and the lowest number in our database since 22 June. But note the Labor Day holiday likely affected reporting and included many no reports. The seven-day moving average dropped again vs the prior day, but is still flat vs where it was a week ago at around 40k.

09.09.20

AstraZeneca's vaccine trial has been put on temporary hold to investigate a case of transverse myelitis in a UK participant. We don't yet have enough data, which is why the trial is on hold, to get the info and establish causality. Timing: was this present with symptoms pre-vaccine? Did the subject have Covid too or develop this when he got Covid? I think it's well described the complication of vaccines, especially oral polio (not an adenovirus and it's live-attenuated). Transverse myelitis is an inflammation of both sides of one section of the spinal cord. This neurological disorder often damages the insulating material covering nerves (myelin). Transverse myelitis interrupts the messages that the spinal cord nerves send throughout the body and is a bit like multiple sclerosis, but it tends to be a one-off event that gets better. Viruses can trigger it, as can vaccines, but we usually don't know the cause. It typically affects 1 in 250k people.

We do not know if this could be a case of antibody-dependent enhancement (ADE), i.e. making a viral infection worse, since transverse myelitis and Covid have also been well described, but the individual is likely to recover.

10.09.20

A 'smart city' is being built in China to cope with a future pandemic. Each flat in Xiong'an has a large balcony and self-sufficient supply garden, lots of vegetables, digital technology, etc. Very few countries can come up with a solution like this.

Deutsche Bahn, a German railway company, has also released a study to demonstrate that taking a train does not come with a high risk of coronavirus infection as long as passengers abide by the rules. According to the study, employees who generally have close physical contact with customers, such as those checking tickets and serving food, were less likely to have been infected than those who work in relative isolation, such as the conductors. Of the 1,100 employees tested for antibodies between 29 June and 3 July, a mere 1.3% of those with close physical contact and 2.7% of those working alone received a positive result. Not sure this convinces me, but hey ho.

The UK's first iteration of a contact-tracing app was based on a centralised model, which caused the approach to be criticised as being inefficient, possibly illegal, and incited public outrage and cost millions.

Norway's contact-tracing app, also based on a centralised model, has been discontinued because of privacy concerns and potential human rights violations. Now, a new consortium for sharing symptom data proposes a federated approach to storing peoples' health data in which the data are aggregated for de-identification.

The WHO reports the worldwide circulation of the influenza virus to be much lower than expected for this time of the year. This low circulation of the influenza virus could be matters of both reassurance and concern, warns WHO. The decreased circulation of the virus is likely largely attributable to the mandatory physical distancing and hygiene protocols implemented to curb the spread of Covid. However, the potential impact of altered infection testing priorities, healthcare personnel capacity and health-seeking behaviours during the pandemic should not be ignored. One way to prepare for a possible double epidemic is to ramp up the testing capacity for both Covid-19 and seasonal infections. For example, the WHO National Influenza Centre at Westmead, New South Wales, Australia, continued to test for other respiratory viruses throughout the Covid-19 pandemic. By June, it had done twice the number of tests it usually would have done. What was interesting was that they actually had negligible cases of influenza and respiratory syncytial virus compared to previous seasons. Combination testing for both Covid-19 and influenza could also be beneficial as a single sample could be used to distinguish the two infections in patients presenting with similar symptoms.

11.09.20

Global cases and deaths have been stable, but are not declining as conditions in South East Asia, Latin America, South Africa, Russia and a few Western European countries are worsening. US cases have been declining in recent weeks and deaths have started to drop as well after rising through most of June and July. In the past three days, cases averaged around 27k and deaths were 0.4k. Despite better US trends, local restrictions continue. In the Netherlands and Ireland there have been negative noises regarding testing capacity being under strain and how long it takes to get results. The Public Health Agency in Sweden has warned that while the level of new infections in the country is low and stable, European travel is still rather risky.

In the UK, confirming new restrictions on social gatherings, Boris Johnson suggested normal life is unlikely to resume before the spring as he said the government was working on an 'Operation Moonshot' mass-testing plan for tests that can give results in less than 20 minutes and prove people are negative, rather than testing for being positive. Chief Medical Officer Chris Whitty prepared people for up to six months of tougher rules by suggesting 'the period between now and spring is going to be difficult'.

Sweden has registered its lowest rate of positive virus tests yet, despite testing being ramped up to record levels. Of 120k tests, only 1.3% identified the virus vs 19% at the peak of the pandemic. Famed for its relaxed policy to virus control, one health official suggested Sweden was benefitting from widespread immunity, and the latest results were a vindication of its strategy.

Different SARS-CoV-2 strains haven't yet had a major impact on the course of the pandemic, but they might in future. This shows 'closed' and 'open' conformations of the spike protein on SARS-CoV-2, which binds to receptors on human cells. A common mutation seems to make the protein favour open conformations, which might mean the virus can enter cells more easily.

Compared with HIV and influenza, SARS-CoV-2 is changing much more slowly as it spreads, but one mutation stands out. D614G has rapidly become the dominant SARS-CoV-2 lineage in Europe and has then taken hold in the US, Canada and Australia. D614G represented a 'more transmissible form of SARS-CoV-2'. One paper used the word 'alarming'.

12.09.20

As UK cases are consistently, for five days, under 2k per day, Austrian Chancellor Sebastian Kurz saw fit today to remind everyone that tough weeks lie ahead when he tweeted, 'We have often emphasized that the summer was comparatively good and that light can be seen at the end of the tunnel. But fall and winter will be very challenging. Many don't believe it yet, but it's getting serious again.' Meanwhile, in France the number of new infections has reached a record level of around 10k per day. This marks the highest number in France since the beginning of the pandemic. The previous record high was reported at the end of March, with around 7.5k new cases in a day.

And apparently, former Italian PM Berlusconi would have died of the disease had he caught it in the spring, according to his doctor: 'The viral load in Berlusconi's nasopharyngeal swab was so high that this would certainly not have had such a happy outcome in March or April as it does now.' (Some might say the correlation is poor.)

13.09.20

My cytokine work has been published today in the *Journal of Allergy and Clinical Immunology*, or *JACI* for short, led by a team collaborating between Imperial, Italy and Lilly to describe the differences in cytokines in nearly 200 blood measurements per sample between healthy individuals and mild, moderate, severe and fatal Covid and compare treatment effects. We can predict ahead of time who will end up on ITU by measuring interleukin-19, though it's not very easy to measure. Some of the results almost seem gobbledygook to me, but it adds to the evidence that we can predict who will become sick. The profiles are really different between healthy, mild, moderate and severe cases.

A dysregulated immune response, a cytokine storm and cytokine-release syndrome are some of the terms used to describe the over-exuberant defence response that is thought to contribute to disease severity in certain people who become seriously ill with Covid-19. A holy grail of Covid-19 research is the ability to assess a person's immune response, to pinpoint early the individuals who have mild symptoms but who are on track to develop the intense defence response that is associated with severe disease. This is important because there is a broad spectrum of clinical disease in people infected with SARS-CoV-2: some infected individuals can be asymptomatic, whereas others are at risk of dying and require hospitalisation in an intensive care unit and use of a ventilator to breathe. Identifying those whose dysregulated immune-response signature predicts the development of severe disease would enable them to be monitored more intensively to minimise disease progression.

We found that levels of several molecules that promote inflammation, immune-modulatory molecules termed cytokines and others, were higher in all of the people who had Covid-19 than in the healthy controls, providing a 'core' Covid-19 signature. Severe disease was characterised by prolonged elevation of many of these molecules, whereas the levels of most of them subsided in people with moderate disease.

What have we learnt from this report, and what still needs to be done? It is clear from this and other studies that the immune response in hospitalised patients with severe Covid-19 is characterised by lymphopenia and the expression of molecules associated with ongoing inflammation, whereas these same molecules are expressed at a lower level in people with mild or moderate disease. Differences in immune responses between the different categories of disease severity are even more evident when people with very mild or subclinical disease are included in the analyses. A key next step will be to analyse samples from people with extremely early signs of Covid-19.

In a limited series of patients who were sampled frequently, confirming reliability and reproducibility of our assays, we demonstrated that intervention with baricitinib attenuates circulating biomarkers associated with the cytokine storm.

14.09.20

Some thoughts today on the efficacy of masks, but first there is an end in sight to the pandemic, though people need to hang on a little longer, Italy's Health Minister Roberto Speranza said in an interview. 'We need to maintain distancing, wear masks and wash our hands,' Speranza added, saying this would not last forever but likely just through the fall and winter. He also laid out what his country's healthcare system could look like with reforms boosted by EU money. 'The key word is proximity: the first place where people are cured should be in the home. We have one of the oldest populations in the world and the numbers of chronically ill patients are increasing, and they aren't treated in hospitals,' Speranza said. Also, any roll-out of a coronavirus vaccine will, by necessity, be based on partial data.

Might the use of masking not only help reduce the severity of disease and ensure that a greater proportion of new infections are asymptomatic? If this new-ish hypothesis is borne out, universal masking could become a form of 'variolation' that would generate immunity and thereby slow the spread of the virus in the US and elsewhere as we await a vaccine.

One important reason for population-wide facial masking became apparent in March, when reports started to circulate describing the high rates of SARS-CoV-2 viral shedding from the noses and mouths of patients who were presymptomatic or asymptomatic, shedding rates equivalent to those among symptomatic patients.

Universal facial masking seemed to be a possible way to prevent transmission from asymptomatic infected people. The CDC therefore recommended on 3 April that the public wear cloth face coverings in areas with high rates of community transmission, a recommendation that has been unevenly followed across the world. Past evidence related to other respiratory viruses indicates that facial masking can also protect the wearer from becoming infected by blocking viral particles from entering the nose and mouth.

Epidemiologic investigations conducted around the world, especially in Asian countries that became accustomed to population-wide masking during the 2003 SARS pandemic, have suggested that there is a strong relationship between public masking and pandemic control. Recent data from Boston demonstrate that SARS-CoV-2 infections decreased among HCWs after universal masking was implemented in municipal hospitals in late March.

Recent virologic, epidemiologic and ecologic data have led to the hypothesis that facial masking may also reduce the severity of disease among people who do become infected.

And Lilly has released the ACTT-II data results. Amazing news. It works – the primary end point was reached! It started with computer servers at BenevolentAI and has now been used in thousands of patients and is safe and effective. We have to file with the FDA now. Study investigators noted an approximately one-day reduction in median recovery time for the overall patient population treated with baricitinib in combination with remdesivir versus those treated with remdesivir alone, but for the sicker people it reduced hospital stays from eighteen to ten days. This finding was statistically significant. Recovery was defined as the participant being well enough for hospital discharge, meaning the participant either no longer required supplemental oxygen or ongoing medical care in the hospital, or was no longer hospitalised at day 29. The study also met a key secondary end point comparing patient outcomes at day 15 using an ordinal eight-point scale ranging from fully recovered to death. I'm a bit surprised it's the sicker people, just before needing ventilation, where baricitinib works best: in those with an ordinal scale of 6, which means pretty sick. This was exactly the situation with our fabulous four from Milan. Now to speak to the regulators. It's such a well-conducted study.

15.09.20

Clearly, the infection picture continues to worsen across Europe (particularly in France), with the exception of Germany and Italy where, so far, the outbreak remains under control. Rates of deaths and hospitalisations remain low but are continuing to pick up in Spain and France. New infection counts rose week on week in almost all countries: the UK up 68%, France up 20%, Germany up 12% and Italy up 7%, Denmark up 102%, Austria up 85%, the Netherlands up 57%, Belgium up 44%, Switzerland up 16% and further restatements from Spain make interpretations more difficult, i.e. everywhere is doing a Sweden like it was in early summer (but doing a Sweden in October is probably worse than doing one in the summer).

Meanwhile, in Asia, there are pockets of better news, with the likes of South Korea saying it would relax social distancing rules for two weeks as the number of confirmed virus infections tapers.

For me, the most frightening thing about getting Covid is the possibility of getting myocarditis, inflammation of the myocardium heart muscle, because I don't know what it means for the long term. Myocarditis is a significant cause of sudden cardiac death in competitive athletes and can occur with normal ventricular function. Recent studies have raised concerns of myocardial inflammation after recovery from Covid-19, even in asymptomatic or mildly symptomatic patients. This has to be a concern going forward.

16.09.20

Ireland introduced new coronavirus measures as part of a national 'Plan for Living with Covid-19'. But there is extra concern about a surge in cases in the capital. Additional restrictions will be imposed in Dublin on home visits, indoor gatherings and care home visits, while wet pubs in the capital will remain closed. 'It shows how we can limit the impact of the virus, while keeping our schools open, protecting and expanding employment, reopening services and supporting social and cultural activity,' said Prime Minister Martin.

German Health Minister Jens Spahn dismissed the suggestion that Germany might make vaccinations compulsory. 'We need 55–60% of the population to be vaccinated,' he said. Spahn added that Germany doesn't intend to hoard vaccines. 'I'm happy to give other countries in the world some of the vaccines we've been contractually assured if we find in the end that we have more than we need.' Spahn said he assumes there will be a vaccine for large parts of the population next year. Bordeaux and Marseille have announced strict new measures to limit public gatherings to ten people or fewer.

The top journal *Science* published an incredibly political editorial entitled 'Trump Lied about Science', which surprised me:

When President Donald Trump began talking to the public about Covid-19 in February and March, scientists were stunned at his seeming lack of understanding of the threat. We assumed that he either refused to listen to the White House briefings that must have been occurring or that he was being deliberately sheltered from information to create plausible deniability for federal inaction. Now, because famed *Washington Post* journalist Bob Woodward recorded him, we can hear Trump's own voice saying that he understood precisely that severe acute respiratory syndrome coronavirus 2 (SARS-CoV-2) was deadly and spread through the air. As he was playing down the virus to the public, Trump was not confused or inadequately briefed: he flat-out lied repeatedly about the science to the American people. These lies demoralised the scientific community and cost countless lives in the United States. Over the years, this page has commented on the scientific foibles of US presidents. Inadequate action on climate change and environmental degradation during both Republican and Democratic administrations have been criticised frequently. Editorials have bemoaned endorsements by presidents on teaching intelligent design, creationism and other anti-science in public schools. These matters are still important. But now, a US president has deliberately lied about science in a way that was imminently dangerous to human health and directly led to widespread deaths of Americans. This may be the most shameful moment in the history of US science policy.

In an interview with Woodward on 7 February 2020, Trump said he knew that Covid-19 was more lethal than the flu and that it spread through the air. 'This is deadly stuff,' he said. But on 9 March, he tweeted that the 'common flu' was worse than Covid-19, while economic advisor Larry Kudlow and presidential counsellor Kellyanne Conway assured the public that the virus was contained. On 19 March, Trump told Woodward that he did not want to level with the American people about the danger of the virus. 'I wanted to always play it down,' he said, 'I still like playing it down'. Playing it down meant lying about the fact that he knew the country was in grave danger.[8]

Am not sure medical journals should be so political. Whatever anyone's views, there's something about journals being so partisan I don't like.

17.09.20

Lilly's results of their neutralising antibody to treat Covid-19 are out, and it has broader significance. LY-CoV555 treatment should incrementally bode well for vaccines in the big picture as it highlights the importance of high antibody titres or levels in reducing and combating Covid-19 infection. It seems important to have high antibody levels and memory T-cells ahead of an infection, ready to go before the infection happens, rather than getting dosed with a treatment after infection and when symptoms are already happening.

Overall, I am positive regarding these therapeutics, but they are likely to be expensive and hard to give as they're intravenous. More importantly, they bode well for vaccines, i.e. neutralising antibodies work.

European Commission President Ursula von der Leyen said, 'Vaccine nationalism puts lives at risk. Europe stepped up' to lead the global coronavirus response in her State of the Union speech yesterday. However, she also called on the bloc to give the EU greater powers over health, which currently is largely a member country competence. 'It is crystal clear: We need to build a strong European health union. It is time to do that,' she said. One of her key proposals is creating a European agency to help the EU better respond to such emergencies. She also called for international cooperation in the search for a vaccine, saying, 'Vaccine nationalism puts lives at risk'.

18.09.20

As global cases top 30 million, the WHO warned of alarming rates of global transmission, warning against quarantines for less than 14 days.

As AstraZeneca's trial remains paused in the US, Moderna held a virtual R&D day and provided additional transparency into the statistical considerations underlying the interim and final efficacy analyses of the Phase 3 Covid-19 vaccine. The major vaccine studies have similar statistical designs for good reason and they're event driven, based on Covid-19 plus one or two symptoms depending on the vaccine. I wonder what information we'll get, if at all, regarding asymptomatic transmission. Think we'll need viral loads for that. Even hospitalised patients don't want repeated nasal swabs.

US state health departments reported 43k new Covid cases Thursday, up from 40k Wednesday. The recent inflexion continues with the seven-day moving average up for a fourth straight day.

19.09.20

The US, India and Brazil account for more than half the world's cases, and the WHO warned that a 'very serious situation' is unfolding in Europe. Weekly cases now exceed those reported in the March peak, and although this partly reflects more effective testing, some see an alarming rate of transmission. With the important disconnect between new cases and hospitalisations and deaths, which may reflect the decline in the average age of those being newly infected, in the UK over 10 million people are now living in local lockdowns. Residents will be unable to socialise outside their households or support bubbles, and hospitality venues, including bars and restaurants, will close by 10 p.m.

BioNTech is buying a German manufacturing site with capacity to produce 750 million vaccine doses a year, more than doubling the amount the company can produce. The EU has agreed to buy up to 300 million doses of the Sanofi/GSK vaccine, having previously made a deal with AZN for up to 400 million shots of its vaccine.

A slew of studies from around the world have reported a disturbing trend: since the pandemic started, there has been a significant rise in the proportion of pregnancies ending in stillbirths, in which babies die in the womb. Researchers say that in some countries, pregnant women have received less care than they need because of lockdown restrictions and disruptions to healthcare. As a result, complications that can lead to stillbirths were probably missed. The largest study to report a rise in the stillbirth rate, based on data from more than 20,000 women who gave birth in nine hospitals across the country, was Nepal. It reported that stillbirths increased from 14 per 1,000 births before the country went into lockdown to stop the spread of the coronavirus in late March, to 21 per 1,000 births by the end of May – a rise of 50%. The sharpest rise was observed during the first four weeks of the lockdown, under which people were allowed to leave their homes only to buy food and receive essential care.

The study found that although the rate of stillbirths jumped, the overall number was unchanged during the pandemic. This can be explained by the fact that hospital births halved, from an average of 1,261 births each week before lockdown to 651. And a higher proportion of hospital births during lockdown had complications. The researchers don't know what happened to women who didn't go to hospital or to their babies, so they cannot say whether the rate of stillbirths increased across the population.

In normal times, the WHO recommends that women be seen by medical professionals at least eight times during pregnancy, even if the pregnancy is judged low risk, to detect and manage problems that might harm the mother, the baby or both. Much of the risk of stillbirth can be averted if women sleep on their side from 28 weeks' gestation, stop smoking and notify their midwife or doctor if their baby is moving less. The last trimester of pregnancy is particularly important for regular health checks, but women are typically monitored for risk factors such as restricted foetal growth and high blood pressure throughout pregnancy. When the pandemic hit, professional bodies for maternity health providers recommended that some face-to-face consultations be substituted with remote appointments to protect women from the coronavirus. But healthcare workers can't take someone's blood pressure, listen to their baby's heartbeat or do an ultrasound remotely.

20.09.20

Spoke with Rishi Sunak to exchange views regarding lockdowns. It's much like talking to my friends and colleagues: half want to stay in and isolate, half want to continue as normal, and half want a hybrid of the two. Yes, I realise how that adds up, or doesn't. We're guided by science, I am sure, by SAGE groups and so forth, but I'm pretty sure all the Chancellor can do is pay for it, or work out how to. How many of us knew the word 'furlough' last year?

I have spoken before about the efficacy and bizarre controversy around mask wearing. However, there is a growing trend of what I shall call 'mask fails'. There are two types:

1) Wearing the mask over the mouth but allowing the nose to protrude from the top. Why bother wearing it? This method has all the effectiveness of not wearing a mask. Do these people not realise they can breathe through their nose with a mask on? One comment I heard graphically illustrates the point: A man wouldn't put on his underpants but allow his penis to hang out over the top. It's a fair analogy.

2) The chin support. I think this could be people forgetting to put their mask back over their mouths, but I've seen a growing number sitting on the train or wandering around a shop with their masks diligently covering their chins, presumably ensuring none of the aerosol particulates we produce 3 centimetres below our mouths are caught. Again, why go through the motions of putting on a mask and then fail to use it? Ultimately it begs the question, how hard is it to wear a mask?

Thomas Hobbes wrote that the best prophet is the best guesser. We really aren't so good at predicting the future. Humans have a problem with this. A deep one. Rousseau wasn't wrong to say that when things are truly important, we tend to believe something that's wrong, rather than nothing at all. We want to feel like we're on some kind of power walk down the yellow brick road into the future, but really, we're tapping our canes through smog on some cracked pavement. This isn't deliberately poetic (not even haiku-esque, way too many syllables). We know so little of the biology of SARS-CoV-2, though how do we know when we can say we know something? We all want an authoritative voice giving us direction (believe me, I could do with more than one right now), someone who calmly knows the future, but it's hard. I've made so many mispredictions. I realise now the only real effect of temperature is the way it changes our behaviour and forces us inside, where transmission occurs, or outside. And in the US and elsewhere, unlike the UK, when it's hot out paradoxically many people go inside where it's cool and air-conditioned.

21.09.20

Today we reached the grim milestone of 200,000 Covid deaths in America. This is more than all US combat deaths in the First World War, Vietnam and post-Vietnam wars combined. This is a truly terrible toll, with little sign of an end.

Drug overdose deaths in the US also increased in 2019, despite a slight decrease from 2017 to 2018; this increase was largely driven by illicitly manufactured fentanyl. The opioid epidemic has also been complicated by increasing use of methamphetamine in combination with opioids. It is likely that the emergence of Covid and the subsequent disruptions in healthcare and social safety nets combined with social and economic stressors will fuel the opioid epidemic. Reports from national, state and local media suggest that opioid-related overdoses are increasing, but the absence of real-time national reporting of overdose-related mortality limits the ability to confirm these reports. Now, two studies report on indicators that reflect the opioid epidemic before and after the widespread emergence of Covid-19 in the US in March 2020: urine drug test results and emergency department visits for nonfatal opioid overdoses.

Researchers reported an increase in the detection of four tested substances in random samples (150k total) of urine drug tests ordered by health professionals nationwide four months before (14 November 2019 to 12 March 2020) and after (13 March 2020 to 10 July 2020) the national emergency declaration. The most noteworthy increases in prevalence were for fentanyl (3.80% to 7.32%) and methamphetamine (5.89% to 8.16%); increases in cocaine and heroin were also noted. Although the large sample size is a strength, there likely was bias in the clinician selection of patients for urine drug testing.

Another study found that the number of cases of nonfatal opioid-related overdose in one emergency department in Virginia increased from 102 cases in March–June 2019, to 227 cases in March–June 2020, whereas the total number of emergency department visits and diagnoses of myocardial infarction decreased during this same period. Patients diagnosed with opioid-related overdose in 2020, compared with 2019, were more likely to be black (63% vs 80%).

Now to the question of causation, which is always a tricky one, as opposed to mere associations or correlations. And causation in medicine, like SARS-CoV-2 causes Covid-19, is so much harder than law (if A happens before B then let's blame A). Covid-19 can't occur without SARS-CoV-2, akin to HIV and AIDS. A more definitive answer to the question of whether opioid use has increased during the Covid-19 pandemic will require linked patient data (before and after Covid-19) to examine changes in an individual's substance use or overdose over time. However, the studies are consistent with the hypothesis that the US Covid-19 epidemic has been accompanied by an increase in substance use with important consequences (nonfatal overdose), with a signal of greater effect among people who are black. Social determinants of health are important drivers of both the Covid-19 epidemic and opioid epidemic in the US. The study also suggests an additional problem: the failure to deliver effective treatment for opioid use disorder even among patients with a symptomatic, life-threatening episode requiring emergency treatment, and even in tertiary care institutions that offer substantial addiction speciality treatment services. The studies suggest that substance use and opioid overdoses in the Covid-19 era may be increasing, consistent with media reports. Conversely, Covid-19 has ushered in the introduction of policies that, if made permanent, have the potential to not only mitigate the effect of the Covid-19 pandemic on overdoses, but also address long-standing structural barriers to accessing proven treatments. There has been an historic failure to deliver effective treatments for opioid use disorder, despite long-standing evidence of efficacy, in the absence of the additional burden Covid-19 has placed on US healthcare infrastructure.

22.09.20

Despite a green light to resume in the UK, AZN's Phase 3 trial remains on hold in the US after a volunteer in the UK developed a condition thought to be transverse myelitis, a rare spinal inflammation disorder, after receiving their second dose of the vaccine. The company has not confirmed the diagnosis, and a document posted by Oxford University last week suggested that the vaccine was not linked to the condition. There are lots of rumours.

The CEO of the Serum Institute in India says that there won't be enough vaccine until 2024 (article in *FT*) to vaccinate the whole world. So that's not good, but I suspect producers will ramp up supplies and manufacturing throughout 2021.

There's lots to think about here. With the passing of Ruth Bader Ginsburg, the balance of the US Supreme Court is in question, as is the state of the Affordable Care Act (ACA). Despite Ginsburg's death and the potential appointment of a more conservative justice, as the ACA has seen some 70 unsuccessful repeal attempts, I am hard-pressed to see it unravelled leaving around 20 million people uninsured on a 'technicality'. Moreover, Republicans themselves may not want a repeal considering there is no replacement plan; the political ramifications of millions becoming uninsured and/or the elimination of pre-existing conditions would be disastrous.

Trump and Mitch McConnell both intend to nominate and confirm a new justice prior to the November election. Of course, this is easier said than done given a number of Republicans indicating discomfort prior to elections and timing extremely tight. In recent history it has taken 50–99 days from nomination to confirmation for Supreme Court justices. It is currently 43 days until the election, and there is no historical precedent for filling a seat this close to an election.

23.09.20

The CDC has changed its mind on how airborne this virus is. It initially added warnings that the virus could spread through the air and encouraged good ventilation indoors. Then the CDC reverted to the previous guidance, saying that a draft version had been 'posted in error'. The U-turn fuels concern about the once world-leading public-health agency.

I note the WHO just announced that countries representing close to two-thirds of the world's population have joined its plan to buy and distribute vaccines around the globe. It also unveiled the mechanism through which it plans to allocate the vaccine as it becomes available, aiming 'to end the acute phase of the pandemic by the end of 2021'.

US state health departments reported 35k new Covid cases Tuesday, up from 31k Monday.

24.09.20

Danish health authorities reported the country's second-highest number of new infections in a single day since the pandemic began (558). Also, Austria's consumer protection association today filed four lawsuits by tourists against the state of Tyrol over allegations that the authorities did not warn of the risk of coronavirus infection early enough. I wonder if there will be more court cases.

In the UK, at PM's Question Time: 'Let's be in absolutely no doubt that the work that this government has done to protect the economy of this country … has been unexampled anywhere else in the world,' the prime minister said, charging Sir Keir Starmer, leader of the opposition, with trying to exploit the pandemic for political gain. 'I think … the cat is out of the bag … because it was [Starmer's] shadow education secretary who said about the present crisis … don't let a good crisis go to waste,' Johnson said, adding that his government was 'taking the tough decisions'.

The WHO has just issued a nineteen-page paper outlining the 'key criteria for the ethical acceptability of Covid-19 human challenge studies'. Among many other things, it says initial studies should be limited to healthy young adults aged 18 to 30, in whom fatal infection rates are currently estimated at about 0.03%. The practical questions range from how to administer the virus, to arranging a secure facility where participants and staff would have to stay for at least four weeks while the trial took place. Then there is the question of what virus to use.

Now for further association versus causation work. A group asked what is the association between the daily wear of glasses and susceptibility to Covid? In a cohort of 276 patients hospitalised with Covid-19 in Suizhou, China, the proportion of daily wearers of glasses was lower than that of the local population (5.8% vs 31.5%). These findings suggest that daily wearers of glasses may be less likely to be infected with Covid-19. Although it is tempting to conclude from this study that everyone should wear glasses, goggles or a face shield in public to protect their eyes and themselves from Covid-19, from an epidemiological perspective, we must be careful to avoid inferring a causal relationship from a single observational study.

Gary at Lilly has even taught me, and you'd think I'd know, that an observational study on baricitinib can't even inform another one when it comes to effectiveness, but it can for safety.

25.09.20

As many countries' cases retest the peak, will deaths follow? Part of the explanation for cases has been an increase in the proportion of global infections occurring in emerging market economies, where case fatality ratios have been lower, probably due to younger populations. In addition, however, there has been a large reduction in fatality rates in the advanced economies. For example, new daily infections in the US's second wave peaked at more than twice the level seen in early April, but fatalities peaked almost 50% lower. Similarly, in advanced Europe (including the UK), new daily infections are now slightly above the peak in the first wave, but daily fatalities remain more than 90% below those seen earlier in the year. Using data from Spain, the UK and the US (three economies where time series for both new infections and fatalities can be obtained by age), 50–75% of the lower fatality rate during the second wave has been due to demographics: essentially a larger share of new cases has occurred in younger individuals for whom Covid-19 has been less deadly. Across the three countries, fatalities are currently occurring at 6% (UK) to 40% (US) of the expected rate based on first-wave characteristics, with 55% (US) to 75% (Spain/UK) of this gap due to changing demographics.

Encouragingly, there is also some evidence that fatality rates have fallen within each age group – probably because of better treatment, higher testing rates, lags, etc., although this looks to be a smaller part of the story. This suggests that the ongoing age distribution of infection will remain the key determinant of future fatality rates.

26.09.20

US data continues to worsen as the number of cases has increased from recent lows, but the death rate remains stable. UK daily cases rose to 6,633 yesterday, from 6,178 Thursday and 4,126 Wednesday – a milestone described by Public Health England as 'a stark warning for us all', though this is daily deaths.

Several European countries have registered a new record of daily infections. Within 24 hours, France registered 16,096 new cases – that's 3,000 more than Thursday. The Netherlands is confirming a record of 2,777 new cases in the past 24 hours and Poland counted 1,587 new infections. Slovakia's 419 new cases mark its third new daily record in a row. The Czech Republic's coronavirus caseload rose to 2,913, the second-highest figure on record. EU Health Commissioner Stella Kyriakides said Europe is at a 'decisive moment' in the coronavirus pandemic as France introduced new restrictions, including an earlier closing time for bars and limiting public gatherings in several cities.

In terms of travel, Hong Kong will require travellers from the UK to submit a negative coronavirus test 72 hours before the scheduled time of departure, while Denmark, Slovakia, Iceland and the Caribbean island of Curacao have been removed from the UK government's list of travel corridors. UK restrictions are now in place for 34 countries or islands, including Spain, France, Portugal, Malta, Croatia, Belgium and the Netherlands. Turkey, Italy and Poland are now in high demand for those wishing to travel. Passengers flying with United Airlines from San Francisco to Hawaii from mid-October will be able to take a test that offers a result within 15 minutes or can opt to receive a test 72 hours prior to flying. Meanwhile, back in Europe, sniffer dogs specially trained to detect Covid-19 have been taking part in a trial in Helsinki. No one knows if they can really do it, and if they can, what are they actually detecting in sweat?

German Health Minister Spahn advised against vacationing abroad because it is 'not necessary'. He said that during the pandemic, it was repeatedly shown that travel returnees in particular spread the virus. That's why 'one should avoid unnecessary trips ... You can also take a vacation at home,' he said.

More than 80% of people in the UK do not follow the rules of self-isolation if they show symptoms or come in contact with an infected person, according to a study by King's College. Only 18.2% of the respondents who had experienced symptoms in the past seven days stayed at home. A majority were also unable to identify the signs of the disease, such as coughing, fever or loss of the sense of smell and taste.

27.09.20

President Trump is suggesting that a vaccine would be ready before the election on 3 November amid growing public uneasiness about the credibility of the unfolding approval process. The more Trump suggests the possibility of an 'October surprise' approval, the more many become concerned about the soundness of the vaccine development and evaluation process. Do the back-to-back statements of the president and industry leaders represent an irresistible force meeting an immovable object? The resolution will be the result of conflicting currents of clinical trial design, immunology, statistics, regulatory policy, economics, public health and politics; two key determinants will be outcome definitions and statistics. The manufacturers' pledge stipulated that any application to the FDA for vaccine approval or an EUA would require data 'demonstrating safety and efficacy through a Phase 3 clinical study that is designed and conducted to meet requirements of expert regulatory authorities such as [the] FDA'.

The American public is already dangerously sceptical of the process of Covid-19 vaccine development. In a poll conducted a few days before the manufacturers' pledge, 78% of respondents said they believed the process was being driven by politics more than by science. This credibility problem will inevitably diminish vaccine uptake, whatever occurs in October.

28.09.20

India passed 6 million cases; today, the world will pass 1 million deaths. US state health departments reported ~35k new Covid cases on Sunday, down from 47k Saturday. And the seven-day moving average flattened again and has been basically flat at 40k for more than a week.

Since the early pandemic, significant racial and ethnic inequities have persisted across the continuum of Covid-19 morbidity, hospitalisation and mortality. Indeed, much has been written, but let's focus on data, including some studies published at the weekend. The CDC has estimated that Covid-19 case and hospitalisation rates are at least 2.5–4.5x higher, respectively, among African American, Hispanic and Native American populations than among white populations. African Americans have died from Covid-19 at more than twice the rate of white individuals.

29.09.20

In Europe, the infection picture continues to get worse across Europe (particularly France at +20% last week), with the exception of Germany and Italy where, so far, the outbreak remains under control; UK numbers seem to be declining rapidly. Merkel has said that local coronavirus infection clusters are going to have to be tackled more swiftly and decisively because 'otherwise we will have 19,200 infections per day by Christmas'.

Rates of deaths and hospitalisations remain low but are continuing to pick up in Spain, France and a bit in the UK. French Health Minister Olivier Veran rejected the idea of a pre-emptive three-week lockdown to enable people to spend Christmas together despite senior doctors warning the French government to do more, given the risk that the health system may soon be overwhelmed.

Interesting that a dozen members of staff on a cruise ship that departed Sunday from Crete with 920 passengers on board have tested positive for coronavirus; all passengers had tested negative for the virus before being allowed to board the ship, but when 150 crew members were tested, 12 tests came back positive. 'They are all asymptomatic … The vessel will most likely return to Piraeus port for repeat rapid Covid-19 tests,' an official at the Civil Protection Agency said.

30.09.20

I note Google Maps will soon show how prevalent coronavirus is in geographic areas with a new colour-coded update. Beginning this week, the maps app will display seven-day averages of new Covid cases per 100k people. The chosen areas will show if cases are increasing or decreasing and be shaded with one of six colours to signify how many new cases were reported. In a blog, Google said the tool shows 'critical information about Covid-19 cases in an area so you can make more informed decisions about where to go and what to do'. Google is pulling data from three sources: Johns Hopkins University, *The New York Times* and Wikipedia. It receives its data from the WHO and other public or government health organisations. Information is available for all 220 countries where the Google Maps app works. The feature will soon be available on iOS and Android versions of Google Maps.

On the medical front, Bloomberg reports that the US government is expected to send 100 million rapid-result tests to states, urging that they be used in schools as a way to help restore the economy. The tests will be a single-use device about the size of a credit card and provide a result within 15 minutes without using any laboratory equipment. Separately, the WHO and non-profit organisations, including the Gates Foundation, said they will help provide access to 120 million of the tests to 133 low- and middle-income countries. Former FDA commissioner Scott Gottlieb said vaccines now in development are likely to be 'partially protective' but won't prevent everyone who is inoculated from being infected.

Signalling its distrust of the Operation Warp Speed (OWS) initiative, California will conduct its own independent review of potential Covid-19 vaccines. There is a document that came online showing the workings behind OWS. It relies more heavily on military leaders with little to no experience in vaccine development than has been previously disclosed. In fact, military leaders outnumber civilian scientists 2:1.

October

New York Mayor Bill de Blasio said fines will be introduced for people who refuse to wear masks, with the Covid-19 test rate in the city also above 3% for the first time in months.

In Britain, Education Secretary Gavin Williamson reassured students that they would be able to return home for the Christmas holidays, saying measures would be put in place to 'minimise the risk of transmission'.

In Europe, Spain is planning new national virus rules that will impose restrictions on Madrid, the hardest-hit region of any in Europe. Germany announced a limit on the number of people at private and public gatherings in areas with high coronavirus infection rates. Malta now has the highest Covid-19 mortality rate in Europe; according to the European Centre for Disease Prevention and Control, it has surpassed Spain to reach 3.6 deaths per 100,000 inhabitants. A public prosecutor's office in Austria has identified four individuals who are being investigated as potentially guilty in the case of coronavirus infections in Ischgl, where a large outbreak occurred last winter. Among those are the mayor of the ski town as well as Landeck District Commissioner; the individuals are accused of having recklessly endangered people through the spread of an infectious disease.

The *FT* reports that Novacyt will supply the UK government with testing equipment and rapid coronavirus tests to be deployed in healthcare settings, while the EU will reportedly sign a second contract for remdesivir. I note for the AZN vaccine, 'Independent safety monitors will conduct their first review of the vaccine's safety and effectiveness after 75 trial subjects become infected with Covid-19, up from the original initial review plan after about 40 infections,' according to a Reuters review of protocol documents issued in July and amended in mid-September.

I know I'm not alone in noticing subtle, and sometimes not so subtle, changes in kids' behaviours and personalities. Millions of other families whose children are cut off from their schools, friends and normal activities are also experiencing similar shifts. We say it's an emotionally hard time, but that misses half of what emotions are. Kids' bodies are being changed as they endure the constant stress and weight of the pandemic.

Mightier.com has a unique view into the change going on inside the bodies of many children. Video games were developed at Boston Children's Hospital and Harvard Medical School that leverage biofeedback to help children develop emotional strength: the ability to take on moments of challenge and frustration with grace. Each game includes a wearable monitor that measures the player's heart rate, which is integrated into the game. As a game gets more challenging, the player's heart rate increases. Children learn they need to take a breath, relax and calm down before they continue; this builds emotional regulation skills and awareness. The data aggregates the story of the pandemic among more than 17,000 children who use the video games for fun while building social, emotional and coping skills.

From July 2019 to July 2020, they looked at heart rate data collected from kids in the first week of playing a Mightier game before the game teaches them strategies to help them manage frustration and keep the heart rate low in gameplay. The change from a historical average of between 90 and 90.5 beats per minute to more than 92 beats per minute is a significant and persistent change. Extrapolated over 24 hours, that represents an extra 2,000 heartbeats per child per day. On a purely physical level, kids' hearts are working a lot harder than they were before the pandemic.

02.10.20

As Trump and Melania test positive for Covid, I feel the news has an air of inevitability about it. He has flouted his own CDC's guidelines for so long it feels like everything was leading to this.

I note that Germany lifted its blanket warning against travelling to all non-EU countries, but at the same time issued new travel warnings for a number of European countries, saying the entirety of Belgium and Iceland, as well regions in 11 other member countries, are at-risk areas. Poland remains Germany's only neighbour that is not on the at-risk list.

There is no end in sight to the state of emergency in Italy as Prime Minister Conte is asking the parliament to extend it until 31 January.

The term 'long Covid' was first used by Elisa Perego as a Twitter hashtag in May to describe her own experience of a multiphasic, cyclical condition that differed in time, course and symptomatology from the bi-phasic pathway discussed in early papers, which focused on hospitalised patients. Just three months later, following intense advocacy by patients across the world, this patient-made term has been taken up by the WHO. Politicians have used it too: UK Health Secretary Matt Hancock explained to a Parliamentary committee that 'the impact of long Covid can be really debilitating for a long time'.

The term 'long Covid' has clearly struck a chord; however, it's not the only term being used to describe persistent symptoms: we've also seen post-acute Covid, post-Covid syndrome and chronic Covid-19. Patients and professionals see 'long Covid' as better able to navigate the socio-political, as well as clinical and public health challenges posed by the pandemic in the coming months.

03.10.20

With the press reporting headline-grabbing stats of high infection rates and second waves approaching March levels in absolute terms, what gets lost is the fact that by comparing infection rates today with those in March, we are not comparing apples with apples. That is, testing rates in March were incredibly low vs today, so in order to understand the virus pathway, we need to amplify the likely true infection rate in March as if testing then had been the same.

Following the recent tightening of restrictions designed to slow the spread of the virus in the UK, concern about the impact of Covid-19 on everyday life has risen to its highest level since the end of May. The ONS reported that 74% of adults were 'very or somewhat worried about the effect of Covid-19 on their lives right now,' the highest proportion since restrictions started to ease in late May.

I think the vaccines will work, and I think they will work well. This is my view because most vaccines confer efficacy >90%. Ones that don't are typically in the context of incomplete coverage of multiple circulating strains (flu, pneumonia, Dengue), and that doesn't appear to apply to Covid-19. There is even an oral Adeno 4/7 viral vaccine that has nearly 99% efficacy.

The earliest data readout without this requirement is Pfizer/BioNTech, where the Pfizer CEO hopes to have statistically significant early Phase 3 data by the end of October. An FDA Vaccines Advisory Committee meeting is scheduled for 22 October 2020. While we may have early data then, it does seem unlikely there will be an EUA before the election.

Including AZN, there should be 300 million Covid vaccine doses manufactured by year-end (predominantly in the US and UK). I continue to expect a material ramp in capacity through 2021, but acknowledge this depends on trial success.

04.10.20

We knew yesterday afternoon (Saturday) that something wasn't right when Trump received an experimental antibody treatment. He reportedly had mild Covid-19 symptoms, including fever and congestion, and he was transferred to Walter Reed National Military Medical Center. Trump, who has now tweeted a video from Walter Reed, says he feels fine. He is 74 and male, both risk factors, and his BMI is over 30 (just), although all you have to do is look at him and wonder if the numbers have been 'tweaked' to reassure the public and make him feel good. He is on a high dose of the strongest statin (AZN's Crestor), high cholesterol being another risk factor (he also takes finasteride for urinary problems).

Three Republican senators, Kellyanne Conway, Bill Stepien and Governor Chris Christie are among others who have tested positive for the virus. The front rows of the Rose Garden event announcing the nomination of Amy Coney Barrett to the Supreme Court have the hallmarks of a superspreader event.

Most think the president's Covid diagnosis is bad for his political prospects. The trajectory of Trump's disease matters a great deal: if this is a relatively mild case and he recovers quickly, that will underscore the view with Trump's supporters that the disease is no worse than a mild case of flu and will allow him to resume campaigning without much impact on the race. If his disease is much worse and he is incapacitated for a longer period of time, we would likely downgrade his odds further as a prolonged period of serious disease underscores his greatest weakness in this campaign – his response to the coronavirus – and would make it very difficult for him to mount a comeback from where he is today. The mechanics of the US government are unlikely to be affected by this diagnosis, but the constitution creates a clear process for the vice president to take over if the president is incapacitated, and the Republican National Party would likely make Pence the nominee if Trump were to pass away, but there is some question as to how the Electors in the Electoral College would handle this situation if it arose.

CDC guidelines recommend that Trump isolate for at least ten days from symptom onset; that would put him back in the White House during the second week of October. He could be back on some version of the campaign trail by the second half of October, but symptoms can persist for weeks or months as in long Covid. This happened to Boris Johnson when his symptoms got worse and then slowly better over the course of a month. Contrast this with Jair Bolsonaro in Brazil, who was diagnosed but had very few symptoms and used his quick recovery to argue the illness wasn't that bad.

Mitch McConnell is focused on getting Amy Coney Barrett to the Supreme Court. She has been meeting with senators all week. This could become harder if other senators, like Mike Lee, catch Covid. The second presidential debate is likely to be cancelled or modified by the Commission on Debates; Biden will not want to be exposed to Trump and this was meant to be a town hall format, so there is no way to ensure that everyone can be safe. The election date can't change without an act of Congress, and this is unlikely.

Stimulus talks are ongoing. If anything, Trump's diagnosis makes Pelosi dig in further as she senses increased desperation from the administration to get a deal. The Senate can't pass the House bill. The rising risk is one where a deal is announced 'in principle', but then nothing is agreed and the gap between the two sides remains too big to bridge. Does Biden suspend his campaign out of a sense of fairness even as internet and television ads continue? What happens to votes cast for Trump if the Republicans are forced to replace him? What happens at the state level is more complicated than what happens within the parties. There are different state rules, and there would likely be legal challenges as to whether or not the votes automatically go to Pence. Some states have laws that bind the Electors to the winner of the popular vote in that state, and some states have clauses that specify what happens if a candidate is replaced late in the game. As a practical matter, Trump votes would be treated as votes for the Republican ticket, but the mechanics of the Electoral College would come into play and matter a great deal.

Prominent scientists have signed the Great Barrington Declaration, which calls for individuals at significantly lower risk of dying from Covid-19 – as well as those at higher risk who so wish – to be allowed to resume their normal lives, working at their usual workplaces rather than from home, socialising in bars and restaurants, and gathering at sporting and cultural events. The declaration claims that increased infection of those at lower risk would lead to a build-up of herd immunity. No doubt we'll see the opposite kinds of declarations from those opposed.

05.10.20

Following his drive-by in an SUV outside the hospital, Trump suffered two oxygen dips. He may have been wearing a mask during the stunt, but what about the Secret Service inside his bulletproof limo? He knowingly put those men and women in harm's way… for the sake of a photo opportunity? Really?

As testing has become more widespread, we've learned that, like the president, most infected people will have the disease in a mild form and recover without any specific treatment. The natural history of the disease is such that those who are going to get very sick will generally do so in the first seven to ten days. There are always exceptions, but these are rare and depend on both host factors and bug factors.

It's important to remember that at age 74, the president, like most people, will recover. But when looking at the mortality curves related to age, it becomes obvious that they rise substantially with the years. Compared to 18–29-year-olds, people aged 64–74 have five times the rate of hospitalisation and a ninety-times higher risk of death. Remember Pope John Paul II's doctor said he was getting better every day, till he died.

The president's medical team confirmed he had started a course of remdesivir shortly after diagnosis. More concern was felt when it was revealed that he had been given an experimental antibody treatment. This cocktail is a combination of two antibodies directed against a key protein of SARS-CoV-2. Is there any data showing that the cocktail works and is safe? Experiments with both golden hamsters and rhesus macaque monkeys intentionally infected with SARS-CoV-2 showed that the cocktail could reduce viral levels and disease pathology.

Regeneron, the maker of the cocktail, earlier this week presented preliminary data from its ongoing clinical trial in people who tested positive for SARS-CoV-2 but were asymptomatic or, in the most extreme cases, had moderate disease, a group that would, at first blush, appear to me to mirror Trump's current condition. No serious safety concerns surfaced, and the treatment reduced the viral load and shortened symptomatic disease in patients who did not have SARS-CoV-2 antibodies at the trial's start. It's unclear whether the treatment can prevent severe disease, but there were hints that it might.

Why did the president receive the higher dose of the antibodies? Likely out of 'an abundance of caution' by his medical team, says George Yancopoulos, the co-founder and chief scientific officer of Regeneron. Is the president receiving any other Covid-19 treatments? A statement released Saturday by the president's physician said that in addition to the antibodies, Trump 'has been taking zinc, vitamin D, famotidine, melatonin and a daily aspirin'. That wording leaves unclear whether he was taking those substances before his diagnosed infection. Notably, the statement does not indicate whether Trump was or is taking hydroxychloroquine, the antimalarial he controversially pushed.

In a poll of >1,000 adults in the US, 65% agreed with the statement 'If President Trump had taken coronavirus more seriously, he probably would not have been infected.' Predictably, 90% of Democrats agreed with the statement, but so did 50% of Republicans. The poll also revealed a lack of faith in Trump's statements on Covid-19: 55% said the president has not been telling the public the truth about the coronavirus, with 34% saying they believe the president's statements; 11% were unsure.

06.10.20

Trump has left the hospital and appeared unmasked on the White House balcony in a very strange, quasi-messianic scene. He was clearly breathing heavily and said, 'Don't be afraid.'

After concentrating on just one man for a few days, let's go back to the macro view. The WHO has said that 1 in 10 of the world's population could have been infected so far in this pandemic. This is twenty times the number on the Hopkins' tracker (35.5 million).

In Europe, French infections have fallen for the first week in twelve, and infection counts suggest the EU second wave could be close to peaking. Hospitalisation and death rates remain materially better than the first wave. The countries with the increases are the UK up 6%, Germany up 18%, Italy up 32%, the Netherlands up 36%, Belgium up 23% and Austria up 10%. In France, infections fell by -6%, Denmark by -18% and Switzerland by -2%. The fall in France and the slowdown in the UK could suggest lockdowns are working as hospitalisation rates remain low, although still rising.

The government in the UK is said to be considering a three-tier lockdown system for England involving pub closures and bans on social contact. European Commission President von der Leyen revealed that she is isolating after being in contact last week with someone who later tested positive. Paris Mayor Hidalgo announced the city would be put under restrictions as of today to fight its recent surge in new infections.

As fatalities continue to rise above 1 million, we've also seen the virus move up to 20th in the list of the 'worst' pandemics in history. To move up an additional place on this measure, global deaths would need to reach ~1.4 million. To get into the worst 15, it would need to rise to 5 million. I really hope we do not, and doubt we will, get there. The worst ever, the Black Death (1347–51), killed approximately 42% of the global population on typical estimates. When comparing Covid-19 to pandemics through history, it's clear that the world's medical facilities are far superior today, and people are healthier. So, it's quite probable that this virus would have been more deadly through previous centuries. But would it have spread as fast?

The flu season is rapidly approaching in the northern hemisphere, and researchers are acutely focused on the potential impact influenza may have on the Covid-19 pandemic. There have been several case studies published on the outcomes of a limited number of patients with Covid-19 and documented co-infections. At this point, the potential spread of influenza in the next few months could force governments to reimpose a range of mitigating strategies to protect at-risk populations and ensure the availability of necessary hospital capacity.

As if on cue, scientists are criticising the Great Barrington Declaration. Take a very simple example of a grandparent looking after a school-age child, highlighting one household member (the child), who would not be expected to suffer much from Covid-19, who would attend a large gathering with other young people on a daily basis, but where the other household member (the grandparent) should be 'protected'. There are no practical details of how this would be done. In fact, this 'Focused Protection' approach is used each year during our annual influenza season, where we vaccinate the vulnerable – elderly and those with comorbidities, including pregnancy and even primary school children who have contact with such vulnerable groups – in an effort to further protect the vulnerable. And if this fails to prevent influenza infection of the vulnerable groups, we have antivirals like oseltamivir and zanamivir that we can give to anyone who has influenza or in whom we even just suspect influenza (as empirical therapy during the influenza season) to reduce the severity of their illness. But we don't yet have these additional 'tools' (the vaccine and antivirals) for Covid-19 to assist with this 'Focused Protection' approach. I fail to see how they will achieve this 'Focused Protection' for these vulnerable groups in any practical, reliable or safe way.

A similar approach may also work for Covid-19 one day. Indeed, a similar vaccination strategy for Covid-19 to that of influenza, targeting the most vulnerable first, would probably be rolled out, but we don't have a Covid-19 vaccine yet, nor do we have a more general-use antiviral treatment. I don't count remdesivir, with no real effects on mortality. But I think the vaccines will work and stop people who have the virus from dying. We've also got the monoclonal antibodies coming from lots of companies now, including Lilly, Regeneron and Roche. I note AstraZeneca is making a one-shot one, and GSK/Vir.

Logistically, how on earth are we to both identify those at risk and effectively separate them from the rest of society? Basing risk primarily upon the risk of death completely ignores the profound morbidity associated with the pandemic, including what we now term long Covid, plus the criteria by which one or more risk factors might predispose toward severe disease remain both uncertain and incredibly diverse – we have only lived with this virus for ten months, we simply do not understand it well enough to attempt this with any surety.

Scientifically, no evidence from our current understanding of this virus and how we respond to it in any way suggests that herd immunity would be achievable, even if a high proportion of the population were to become infected – there's lots of modelling studies and they differ in their herd immunity predictions and thresholds. We know that responses to natural infection wane, and that reinfection occurs and can have more severe consequences than the first, but we don't know that here yet. I'm putting my faith in vaccines to lead us out, but not sure if we'll have data before or after the US election. It will be close.

Then, of course, we have baricitinib as a treatment. Trying to remain objective here. My discussions with the Karolinska Institute and the USA with doctors at Emory and at Lilly are very regular, and even doctors from Asia seem interested in baricitinib. It seems like every day we're getting new data. It's incredible what these organoids in dishes can show, and it's great that my collaborators like Volker Lauschke and Ali Mirazimi are totally data-driven. Those livers in dishes really are miniature model systems, and it's great they're derived from human cells. Have just used sequencing of RNA before and after liver organoid infection to show that the virus turns on all the genes that cause clots, and baricitinib stops this. Haven't seen any clots on patients on baricitinib with Covid-19, and to cap it all off, my team's interrogation of FDA databases of safety events shows next to nothing. It looks more effective and safer than I could have predicted, and Lilly isn't involved with this laboratory work, so we're showing this completely independently of pharma. But we can't seem to infect lung organoids and don't get why. It's a pulmonary disease, after all, or so I thought? And, when we stain the virus for its spike protein, the super-resolution microscopy images aren't nearly as good as when we stain for the nucleocapsid. The calls on this are a bit tense, but the data is the data. You can't argue with it. It just is. And then we just fit in explanations afterwards.

07.10.20

My comments about a quasi-messianic return for Trump seemed to be prophetic as today he has referred to catching the virus as a 'blessing from God'. Certainly, the narrative to his supporters is that beating it proves he's tough, although his followers are far less likely to gain access to a world-class team of physicians and an experimental cocktail of therapeutics, including remdesivir.

08.10.20

A UK study involving random sampling of 36k individuals showed 76.5% of those who tested positive reported no symptoms, and 86.1% reported none of those specific to Covid-19. This is a very elusive bug.

Italy makes masks compulsory outside (cases are over 3,000 per day for the first time since April), and Brussels will close all bars from Thursday for a month. Also, from Friday people can only have close contact with three others (down from five) outside their household. In Denmark, pandemic restrictions will be extended for at least an additional two weeks until the end of the month.

Last night Mike Pence and Kamala Harris met for a vice-presidential debate, which was more civilised than the first presidential one. However, the political discourse has been so degraded that one of the main talking points by the American news outlets was about a fly that sat on Mike Pence's head for 2 minutes.

Today it was revealed by the FBI that they had thwarted an attempt to kidnap the Democratic Governor of Michigan, Gretchen Whitmer. Despite Trump's election focus on 'law and order', he did not comment on the case but chose, instead, to attack her on the same day for failing to ease Covid-19 restrictions, the very issue believed to have triggered the kidnapping plot and an illness he is still recovering from. Really not great.

09.10.20

For me, the main news yesterday was that Lilly provided some further details on our global trial, showing baricitinib works best on those on oxygen. Baricitinib reduces the recovery time and death rate further. This is proper randomised data, the sort we needed for HCQ or convalescent plasma. The sort that's fileable with the FDA.

Now, as US virus data continue to trend higher, suggesting the presence of a third wave, states continue with a variety of local lockdown measures to control the spread. In New York, Andrew Cuomo said businesses and schools in virus hotspots must close by the end of the week as part of what he described as a 'Cluster Action Initiative'.

A further 17,540 people tested positive in the UK, and Scotland recorded 1,000 daily cases for two days (for the first time, with 13.5% test positivity). As a sign of what could happen elsewhere in the UK, pubs in Edinburgh and Glasgow will close for two weeks from today.

The RKI reported more than 4,000 new infections within 24 hours for the first time since the pandemic peaked in April. German Health Minister Spahn also said there is 'hardly any other country in Europe that has managed the crisis as well' as Germany, urging people to make an effort to 'save what we have achieved'.

At Black Lives Matter protests in US cities, most attendees wore masks. The events did not seem to trigger spikes in infections, yet the virus ran rampant in late June at a Georgia summer camp where children who attended were not required to wear face coverings. These events give us hints of the effectiveness of masks at mass gatherings. Researchers also looked at 200 countries that adopted mask use in January and, as of May, had recorded no deaths related to Covid-19. Another study looked at the effects of US state-government mandates for mask use in April and May. They estimated that those reduced the growth of Covid-19 cases by up to 2% per day. They cautiously suggest that mandates might have averted as many as 450,000 cases after controlling for other mitigation measures, such as physical distancing.

We're working with Lilly to present the ACTT-II data, understand the role of steroids here, and get effective drugs to patients. Around 10–20% of patients in ACTT-II in both arms had steroids and many more in COV-BARRIER, the placebo-controlled baricitinib trial. This means when/if we show a benefit, the reality is that the treatments are additive or synergistic, all pieces of a jigsaw that reduces the fatality rate.

10.10.20

Protests against face coverings and social distancing in Europe are becoming violent, I think, for the first time. On Tuesday, a 67-year-old bus driver in Amsterdam was savagely beaten up by a passenger whom he had asked to wear a mask. Yesterday, four men assaulted a train conductor who had made the same request.

The official Covid-19 death toll currently stands at 1.07 million people globally. How does this compare to fatalities from major illnesses in a typical year? Global data from 2017, the last year with full data, highlights where this year's pandemic stands on a relative basis and where it might be by the end of the year. If the increase in fatalities lies between the growth rate seen over the last month and that seen during the local peak in July and August, we will end up with between 1.75 million and 2.3 million fatalities by year end. However, we know from excess mortality numbers from those who report it that in some areas total deaths are as much as 50% higher. Many other nations also underreport, so it's possible an extra million deaths may need to be added to the official global numbers by the end of 2020, but the reality is that we'll never know the exact figure.

11.10.20

The US moves to more than 50k cases per day over the last two days, but one analysis shows that hospital admissions here seem 'less serious now' and are probably levelling off.

Even as the British Medical Association (BMA) has now said people at work should wear masks and, it's also said, as per the WHO, that vulnerable people should be provided with medical-grade masks that protect the wearer as well as preventing transmission. Surgical or medical-grade masks filter more of the droplets that may contain the virus from the air as the wearer breathes. Some studies suggest a single-layer cloth mask filters only about 3% and a triple-layer cloth mask about 60%. A medical mask will stop 86%. The BMA also recommended that people on low incomes and benefit recipients should also be supplied with masks, as should those eligible for free prescriptions or with children eligible for free school meals. With this in mind, it should be noted that masks are widely worn in Japan, where they are common due to allergies caused by pollen.

12.10.20

Fatalities in Spain continue to be the highest in the EU, with 3.6 deaths per 100,000 inhabitants over fourteen days, compared to 3.5 in Romania, 2.9 in the Czech Republic, 2.0 in Hungary, 1.7 in Belgium, 1.5 in France and 0.2 in Germany.

In the UK, the situation will remain very uneven overall. Universities in the south and south-west of England, where coronavirus numbers are still light, may escape the worst effects. The small number of universities able to test most students regularly will perform better than others, and the rate of the infection's increase will clearly slow down as this term progresses. Cities in the north of England are hugely disproportionately affected: Leeds, Sheffield, Manchester, Newcastle and Liverpool, though Nottingham is worst affected. This suggests two things about the outbreak: first, as expected, given the nature of superspreader events, outbreaks at different universities may take very different courses. Second, the outbreak is moving in two directions; that is, it is entering and spreading in universities hosted by cities where Covid-19 had never truly ebbed from its first wave, as well as being brought by the students to those areas. British universities, far more integrated into their host communities than many American colleges, are being affected by the severity of the outbreak around them.

13.10.20

In Britain, scientists warned another national lockdown is a possibility, but Boris Johnson has said he does not believe another national lockdown would be the 'right course' in combating the pandemic; instead, a new, three-tier lockdown system will be rolled out, categorised under medium, high and very high. Most areas in England will be put on a medium-alert level, meaning current restrictions continue, including the 10 p.m. hospitality curfew.

Elsewhere, in China, Qingdao's population of 9 million will be tested for Covid within five days after 12 people tested positive. The number of people diagnosed with influenza in New Zealand during its winter fell by 99.8% due to efforts to tackle Covid.

I was surprised the US purchased AZN's long-acting antibody going into Phase 3 for prevention – 100k doses this year for $0.5 billion. Now some US vaccine distribution points:

- In the US, hospitals in some states are being asked to be ready to administer the Covid vaccine, starting in early November if clinical data comes back positive and emergency authorisation designation is used.
- Retail pharmacies will likely not be able to administer Covid vaccines until Phase 2 (wider availability of supply will require more access points) and when the vaccines have received FDA approval. Phase 2 likely will not begin until late January to late February.
- Within Phase 1, some retail pharmacies may be selected to administer vaccines at nursing homes.
- Within Phase 2, the distribution of the vaccine will largely be to pharmacy chains with >200 stores or chains that are affiliated with buying groups. The size requirements are set to prevent waste (many of the vaccines come in dry ice and are required to be used in a short period of time after being reconstituted).
- Retail pharmacies indicate they expect to make ~$15 net of costs on each Covid vaccine administered.
- CVS & Walgreens Boots are likely to administer 16% of shots in the 2020–21 flu season (CVS = 9%, Walgreens Boots = 7%).
- In terms of distribution, Pfizer will ship direct to providers via UPS.
- McKesson is investing in its capabilities and retrofitting existing trucks to be able to distribute vaccines that are later to come to market.
- Hospitals are making heavy investments in commercial grade freezers and refrigerators to be ready for Covid vaccine administration.
- One of the reasons CDC is limiting which pharmacies/others they can supply is because some bottles have 100 doses and once opened they need to be used in 6 hours so need the patient volume or much will go to waste.
- The Pfizer vaccine will come in a special layered container packed with dry ice, which can hold it at needed temps for up to fourteen days. This can then be shipped directly to providers on more of a real-time basis. Most retail pharmacies have freezers that can hold temps at -20 °C to -30 °C, which will be adequate for future vaccines. I hear UPS is building a freezer farm in Kentucky.

14.10.20

Trump was once again attending crowded rallies where many did not wear masks, himself included, illustrating that he appeared to have learned nothing from his own battle with the virus.

Meanwhile, Africa has reasons to worry. Already, several high-income countries have signed their own contracts with individual companies to buy selected vaccines. The US, for example, has made deals with most manufacturers, as have the EU and UK. We've seen a scramble for access to therapies before. It happened with HIV and H5N1 influenza, and Africa has ended up at the end of the queue every time. Yet, the global economy depends on the continent for its exports of raw materials, food, energy and labour. This experience, and the fact that other infectious diseases will surely emerge, is why Africa needs a coordinated strategy to develop, finance, manufacture and deliver vaccines across the continent. For the past few months, the Africa Centres for Disease Control and Prevention (Africa CDC) in Addis Ababa has been developing this with leaders from the African Union. When antiretrovirals to treat HIV came along, the prices that companies set for these drugs put them out of reach. As deaths in rich countries plummeted, infected people were left to die across Africa. It is estimated that between 1997 and 2007, 12 million Africans died waiting for enough life-saving drugs to reach the continent. The drugs' arrival was largely thanks to the efforts of the US President's Emergency Plan For AIDS Relief (PEPFAR) and the Global Fund to Fight AIDS, Tuberculosis and Malaria.

In 2004, the highly pathogenic avian influenza virus H5N1 re-emerged, prompting fears of an overwhelming global pandemic. Negotiations by the WHO to share and stockpile doses of an eventual vaccine broke down. At one point tensions were so high that Indonesia refused to share H5N1 virus samples that were crucial for surveillance, I am told. The COVAX initiative promises to benefit Africa and many people on other continents. It hopes to offer lower-income countries equitable access to a diverse portfolio of potential vaccines at highly subsidised prices. This international cooperation and solidarity is laudable and essential. As of now, nearly 2 million people were known to have been infected with SARS-CoV-2 in Africa, with around 40k deaths. The World Bank estimates that economic growth in Sub-Saharan Africa will decline from 2.4% in 2019 to between 2.1 and -5.1% in 2020, the first recession in the region in twenty-five years. Africa's population is 1.2 billion, and most vaccine candidates require two doses. The cost of the vaccine and of building systems and structures required for delivery is estimated at between $7–10 billion, according to Africa CDC.

15.10.20

It was good to see Facebook rolling out a new policy yesterday aimed at cracking down on vaccine falsehoods as a growing number of users with neutral views about vaccines appear to turn into vocal opponents. The new policy prohibits formal advertisements that discourage people from getting vaccinated, reversing a years' long trend in which such ads were widely permitted. The site also said it will amplify factual messages from international public health authorities, including the WHO, as well as direct users in the US to locations where they can get a flu shot. It will make anti-vaxxing less prominent in search results. They will not take down anti-vaccine posts entirely, however, and some say this does not address Facebook's most virulent sources of health-related falsehoods: pages and groups. Vaccine misinformation has taken an increasingly strong foothold in those spaces in recent months, with some individuals using them to peddle and profit from falsehoods while flying under the radar of policies designed to police advertisements.

16.10.20

It's one of the pandemic's puzzles: most people infected by SARS-CoV-2 never feel sick, whereas others develop serious symptoms or even end up in an intensive care unit clinging to life. Age and pre-existing conditions, such as obesity, account for much of the disparity. But geneticists have raced to see whether a person's DNA also explains why some get hit hard by the coronavirus, and they have uncovered tantalising leads. Now, a UK group studying more than 2,200 Covid-19 patients have pinned down common gene variants that are linked to the most severe cases of the disease and point to existing drugs that could be repurposed to help. Really interesting stuff, and the genes shown have mechanisms of action that make some logical sense.

Other work shows nose and throat swab PCR testing can miss up to 50% of Covid-19 cases, in part because the virus may have already cleared the upper respiratory tract. But by then, patients may have developed antibodies against the virus. An approach that combines rapid PCR and antibody testing could help physicians quickly diagnose more cases, a recent small study of hospitalised patients with suspected Covid-19 suggested. It's not the best news, but the sample size is small. Definitely needs further research.

17.10.20

In vaccine news, I note Pfizer's CEO published an open letter on vaccine timing. I quote: 'We will share any conclusive readout (positive or negative) with the public as soon as practical, usually a few days after the independent scientists notify us' (that refers to the data safety monitoring board). Pfizer's Q3 is on 27 October, and as the CEO also said, 'We may know whether or not our vaccine is effective by the end of October...' A ton of statistical work I have done suggests that their second interim at 53 events is a much easier bar than the first at 32. Also, Sanofi/Translate Bio's mRNA product elicited high levels of protective neutralising antibodies in mice and non-human primates. The countdown to the first Phase 3 vaccine results is definitely live. I have conviction they'll work well, easily exceeding the 50% bar the FDA has laid down.

The Indian health ministry has begun to recommend traditional herbal remedies to tackle the country's outbreak, dismaying many Indian doctors and scientists. On 6 October, Health Minister Harsh Vardhan released recommendations for preventing Covid-19 and treating mild cases based on Ayurveda, India's millennia-old system of herbal medicine, triggering sharp criticism from the Indian Medical Association (IMA), a group of more than a quarter of a million modern medicine practitioners. The Indian government's push for Ayurveda is in line with the ruling Bharatiya Janata Party's mission to revive traditional medicine. Since 2014, when the Hindu Nationalist Party was elected to power, it has upgraded a government department for alternative medicine to the Ministry of Ayurveda, Yoga & Naturopathy, Unani, Siddha and Homoeopathy (AYUSH) and more than tripled its annual budget to $300 million. Developed by the AYUSH ministry, the Covid-19 advisory includes treatments such as clarified butter applied inside the nostrils, a hot concoction of pepper, ginger, and other herbs and a patented formulation called Ayush-64. The latter, a mixture of four herbs, was developed in the 1980s for malaria by the Central Council for Research in Ayurvedic Sciences (CCRAS), now a body under the AYUSH ministry. Although last week's protocol only recommends the remedies for mild disease, it says moderately and severely ill patients can make an 'informed choice' about using Ayurveda.

While there is some evidence of these sorts of remedies helping with general wellbeing and mental health, there is no evidence that they will stop viral infections. Let's put our trust in the likes of Pfizer and Moderna rather than pepper. A sensible approach has been threatened by the complexity of Covid-19, public demand for progress and the pace and volume of pandemic science. Clinicians and scientists have been led astray as often as uncovering new Covid-19 biology and treatments. An attainable strategy for sensible medicine is required. Some strategic points as follows:

Strategy 1: Medicine Without Magic
Clinicians must first embrace the improbability that a single treatment for severe Covid-19 will be a so-called 'magic bullet'.

Strategy 2: Practice Doing (Almost) Nothing
For most physicians, it is difficult to do (almost) nothing for patients. The list of the experimental therapies proposed for Covid-19 is long, including hyperbaric oxygen therapy and even the administration of thalidomide. The lack of control groups in some recent trials of Covid-19 treatments further highlights the do-something mentality. But there is an alternative: sensible medicine accepts that unreasoned intervention with experimental treatment may lead to more harm than good.

Strategy 3: Elevate Usual Care
Sensible medicine is still labour intensive. For patients with Covid-19 who have acute illness, guidelines include supportive or usual measures like lung-protective ventilation or prone positioning, both of which reduce mortality.

Strategy 4: Focus on High-Quality Evidence
Some clinical research is biased. Even the best research methods, such as randomised trials, can be unreliable. But to be confident that an intervention is effective for Covid-19, many have suggested, requires the reliance on evidence from only the highest-quality randomised trials.

Strategy 5: Think Bayesian
In 2009, *The New York Times* said that 'new treatments are a bit like the proverbial new kid on the block: they have an allure that is hard to resist'. A simple application of the Bayes theorem may help. In essence, if it works, use it; if it's new, does it work better than what's already available?

19.10.20

Politicians seem desperate to avoid full-fledged lockdowns. But if hospitals get overwhelmed, they may have no choice; here that doesn't seem to be happening despite headlines about Manchester. However, in Belgium hospital admissions were up 96% last week, compared to previously, but I note that even now, it's still using only about 20% of its intensive care beds vs Portugal now using two-thirds.

20.10.20

China has reported 19 new imported cases, Argentina becomes the fifth country to pass 1 million cases, Canada reaches 200k cases, even in New Zealand there's a small outbreak, and Ireland becomes the first European country to re-enter a formal lockdown (for six weeks).

One thing I hadn't previously realised was the increase in cyberbullying. An article I read said 28% of 10–18-year-old children in a sample reported having been victims of cyberbullying during lockdown, while 50% reported to have seen others being cyberbullied (bystander role). The younger in age, the more likely they were to have been victims. Overall, 49% of males experienced significantly more frequent cyberbullying since lockdown.

Just under half of the children who said they were victims of cyberbullying (41%) told a parent or caregiver. Under a fifth of the victims (19%) said they told a friend, and fewer than a tenth told a school counsellor (9%) or a teacher or principal (5%). Just under a tenth of the children said they did nothing about it or ignored the problem (8%).

21.10.20

The CDC now reports exactly 300k excess deaths in America. The official figures of Covid deaths are far behind this.

As we wait for the vaccine Phase 3 data from Pfizer/Moderna in the US, and AZN too, a couple of days ago China National Pharmaceutical Group Corp (Sinopharm) became the fifth Covid-19 vaccine developer to report immunogenicity data from elderly volunteers. Sinopharm is developing BBIBP-CoV, an inactivated SARS-CoV-2 virus vaccine. Across the five candidates, neutralisation titres fell by 8.4–61% in the oldest cohorts relative to the youngest, with the two viral vector-based vaccines at either end of the spectrum. Individuals receiving the Ad26-based vaccine, JNJ-78436735, from J&J experienced the least age-related decline, while those receiving Ad5-nCoV from CanSino Biologics experienced the most. Both the J&J and CanSino vaccines were given as a single dose, so it remains unknown how a prime-boost regimen would modify the age effect. Both companies are testing single dose and prime-boost regimens of their vaccines.

Everything in the US, from masks to vaccines, seems partisan. In a recent survey, 58% of the US public said they would get vaccinated as soon as a vaccine was available when asked earlier this month, down considerably from 69% who said the same thing in mid-August. Drill down further, and the new data shows a striking disparity by race. The poll found that 59% of white Americans indicated they would get vaccinated as soon as a vaccine is ready, a decline from 70% in mid-August. Only 43% of African Americans said they would pursue a vaccine as soon as it was available, a sharp drop from 65% in mid-August. The poll was weighted to ensure the sample was representative of the general US population. The survey also asked Americans how the news that Trump had tested positive for the virus might affect their actions. About 40% of Americans said they are somewhat or much more likely to get the coronavirus vaccine once it is available. That response was similar among Republicans and Democrats, with 41% and 44%, respectively expressing this view. At the same time, 41% reported their view on a vaccine hadn't changed even though Trump was infected. Another 19% said they were somewhat or much less likely to pursue an available vaccine.

22.10.20

Both Spain and France passed 1 million cases (as we in the UK will in about ten days), Germany sees >20k cases for the first time, six US states reach record highs, deaths attributed to Covid-19 hit daily records in Iowa, Minnesota, Montana, Kansas, Hawaii and Wisconsin, Reuters found.

As the US AZN trial restarts imminently, a volunteer in Brazil apparently has died, but if you take a sample of 10k adults, you'd expect deaths during a trial for all sorts of reasons; Brazilian media report that the volunteer was a 28-year-old doctor who died of Covid-19 complications. If he's on the placebo arm that's obviously better news for the vaccine. We don't know which arm he is in.

23.10.20

Trump tested negative before the latest presidential debate, and this debate with Biden was far more disciplined, compared to the disastrously petulant first performance by Trump. Trump said, 'We've rounded the corner [on coronavirus], it's going away.' There is absolutely no evidence of this, with numbers continuing to grow, and Dr Fauci has contradicted this, calling the latest statistics 'disturbing'.

24.10.20

The Australian state of Victoria has recorded just 7 new cases of Covid-19 and no new deaths, while the US broke its daily record for new infections. In Europe, the upward trend in new cases continues in most of the major countries. France reached a new daily high of 40,000 cases. UK and Spain are over 20,000 daily cases, Italy reports 15,000, and Germany's daily cases are still volatile, averaging 8,000.

Asia's new cases remain low. South Korea increased slightly to 150 cases per day and Japan continues to report 500 cases per day. India's daily new cases have dropped to 50,000 after trending down for a few weeks. Its daily testing positivity rate also decreased from >10% to around 5%. The current cumulative cases stand at 7.7 million. Brazil now reports 5.3 million cumulative cases and appears to be in its terminal stage of the current wave.

In the past few weeks, there has been a great deal of trepidation among the public about the impact of children returning to school. Children have greater difficulty adhering to physical distancing rules but are believed to transmit the virus less efficiently than adults. Rhinoviruses normally circulate year-round, with seasonal peaks in spring and autumn, and are transmitted in largely the same manner as SARS-CoV-2. Children are the main drivers of transmission of rhinovirus, with subsequent transmission to adults associated with exacerbations of airways disease and hospitalisations.

In Southampton, a group tested adult medical patients admitted to hospital using point-of-care multiplexed PCR testing for a wide range of respiratory viruses, including SARS-CoV-2, from the height of the pandemic. They compared the rate of respiratory virus detection in 2020 with the same period in 2019. There was a drop in the rate of detection of all respiratory viruses, including rhinovirus, following the nationwide lockdown on 23 March. Detection of rhinovirus remained low after the easing of the national lockdown on 10 May, compared with the previous year. Around two weeks after the concurrent reopening of state primary and secondary schools in early September, there was a sharp increase in the number of detections similar to that seen in 2019.

25.10.20

Europe became the second region after South America to surpass 250,000 deaths. Europe now accounts for nearly 19% of global deaths and 22% of global cases. The UK has Europe's highest death toll, followed by Italy, Spain and France. The Polish president tested positive, and riots against restrictions occurred in Naples. The Czech Republic now has 105 ventilators sent mainly by the Netherlands, with 15 from Austria as well as 30 from the EU's rescEU medical reserve, so that the request for 150 ventilators has now been fully met, according to the European Commission.

A primary goal of science is to produce robust and generalisable theories of empirical phenomena. For psychologists, the phenomena of interest are the human mind and behaviour. Both the robustness and generalisability of psychological theories have come into question over the past decade. Experimental findings from some of the most widely known theories in social psychology could not be reproduced, provoking what is sometimes called the replication crisis.

Comparative studies of humans and other species can reveal which psychological theories generalise to other species and which apply only to humans. Now scientists use comparative data to assess the tenets of one prominent theory in social psychology. Socioemotional selectivity theory (SST) posits that humans become progressively more aware of their mortality, and this awareness prompts us to place a greater priority on positive social relationships as we grow older. This theory was tested in chimpanzees and the same phenomenon could be seen. It seems we are not the only species aware of our own mortality and seek to do something about it.

26.10.20

The Spanish government yesterday adopted new restrictions, including a nationwide curfew and the declaration of a state of emergency. The Italian government announced restrictions to run from today until 24 November: bars and restaurants will close from 6 p.m., except to offer takeaway; gyms, swimming pools, cinemas are closed; and homeworking is encouraged whenever possible, while home visits and outings for reasons other than work, study, health and emergencies are discouraged. Attackers threw incendiary devices early yesterday at the Berlin offices of the RKI, and in the UK, the quarantine will be reduced for people who have come into contact with positive individuals from fourteen to either ten or seven days.

India reported its lowest death toll for four months, while Mexico said there had been 193k excess deaths in 2020. China reported 161 new asymptomatic cases and five aides to Mike Pence have tested positive.

The Trump administration's lack of focus on the pandemic was emphasised yesterday when Mark Meadows, the White House Chief of Staff, stated that 'we are not going to control the pandemic'. With this in mind, it's time to review the polls. Similar to previous tracking polls, there is a partisan divide in the top issue for voters. More than half of Republican voters (53%) identify the economy as their top issue. In contrast, the coronavirus outbreak is the top issue for Democratic voters (36%) and independent voters (29%). 14% of Democratic voters continue to identify healthcare as their most important voting issue, compared with 1 in 10 independent voters and very few Republican voters (4%). The pandemic has also slightly shifted voters' healthcare priorities as increasing access to healthcare (18%) now ranks alongside healthcare costs (15%) in the top spots when we ask voters to say in their own words what it means that healthcare is important to their vote. Although healthcare is not currently the top-ranked issue for voters when thinking about their 2020 vote, it has still been prominently featured throughout the campaign. Healthcare policy occupied 20 minutes of the first presidential debate. Interestingly, 41% of September campaign ads aired by Biden mentioned healthcare – only the coronavirus pandemic was mentioned more often (50%). On the other side of the aisle, Trump's campaign ads have most often mentioned jobs (63%), followed by immigration (51%). Senate candidates from both parties have prominently featured healthcare in approximately one-fourth of their campaign advertisements (27% of pro-Democratic ads and 24% of pro-Republican ads).

28.10.20

The *BMJ* has an article on research that shows communities with greater use of social media to organise offline political actions had more public concerns about vaccine safety in a cross-national analysis of social media and vaccine hesitancy. Additionally, foreign disinformation campaigns were found to be significantly associated with declining vaccination rates. The study found that a one-point shift upward in the five-point disinformation scale was associated with a 2% drop in mean vaccination coverage and a 15% increase in tweets containing negative content about vaccines. The study findings were not specific to SARS-CoV-2 vaccines, though the authors emphasise the importance of combating disinformation during the Covid-19 pandemic.

However, an international cross-sectional survey of 1,541 caregivers responsible for the care of a child, recruited from paediatric clinics conducted from March to May 2020, found that 65% had intentions to vaccinate their child against Covid-19. An intention to vaccinate was more common among caregivers with older children, children with no chronic illness (when fathers complete the survey) and caregivers of children with an up-to-date vaccination schedule. The most common reasons supporting the uptake of vaccines were to protect their child (62%), while the most common reason for refusing the vaccine was its novelty (52%).

29.10.20

Unfortunately, we're getting a dose these days of 'that's why you run clinical trials'. Word came that the ACTIV-3 trial being run by the NIH has shown a lack of efficacy for the combination of the Lilly/AbCellera anti-coronavirus antibody (bamlanivimab, LY-CoV555) when combined with remdesivir in hospitalised patients. This is the trial that had been paused earlier this month for 'safety concerns' (I'd heard manufacturing issues, too), but now no more patients will be enrolled at all. A thorough review of the data showed that there were, in fact, no differences in safety between the arms of the trial, with and without the antibody, but there was also no difference in efficacy.

Prophylaxis, i.e. prevention, frankly, might be an easier public health decision than one that relies on very early treatment. After all, most cases of coronavirus resolve, and most people don't end up in the hospital. There really does look to be a gap before any vaccine rollout where the antibodies could help, the key word being 'could'. Might. Maybe. Clarity has been in short supply in 2020.

30.10.20

Merkel faced criticism in the Bundestag: 'The measures we have to take now are suitable, necessary and proportionate,' she said, referring to the closure of bars, restaurants, gyms and cultural venues as well as stricter bans on gatherings, all to come into effect Monday for one month. In what was a very rare occurrence, lawmakers of other opposition parties echoed AfD's criticism, though not their rhetoric.

Austria will decide on more restrictions and a potential lockdown this weekend. Spain and Italy hit daily records for new cases, increasing testing being a part of this but not all of it. The US has passed 9 million cases (test volumes in the last week have moved from 1 to 1.5 million/day). The world is going past 500k confirmed cases per day. Australia cases are at a four-month-low, however, and the small 'outbreak' in China again has dissipated.

31.10.20

As the US presidential election approaches, no single issue, including healthcare and Covid-19, dominates the campaigns; instead, voters cite multiple issues. Two polls from early October show six issues at the top of the voters' agenda: the economy, coronavirus, healthcare, race relations and equal treatment of racial groups, Supreme Court nominations and crime and safety. The top issues for voters differ substantially from those in the 2016 presidential election when the economy and jobs (38%) and national security and terrorism (28%) were the main voter concerns. Healthcare ranked third (11%), followed by immigration (7%). The economy is still a top issue, but it does not stand alone at the top as it did in 2016. Covid-19, which has overtaken problems of the healthcare system, and race have emerged in 2020, replacing national security and terrorism as chief concerns.

When an incumbent president is running for re-election, one of the factors that affect the outcome of the election is the public's evaluation of the job the incumbent president has been doing overall and on issues the public is most concerned about. Currently, as shown, 43% of the public approve of the job Donald Trump is doing as president, while a small majority of 54% disapprove. Majorities disapprove of Trump's handling of healthcare (56%), Covid-19 (58%) and race relations (60%).

Healthcare is ranked among the top election issues by voters in two polls in 2020. In another survey, likely voters who said that healthcare, not including Covid-19, was 'extremely important' in their presidential vote were asked which healthcare issue was most important in their vote choice. High healthcare costs in general, together with high drug costs, were the top issue among healthcare voters (56%). Around one in five healthcare voters said that the problems of the nation's uninsured were the most important issue (21%). There are large differences in the views of Republicans and Democrats on the role of government in healthcare.

November

01.11.20

Some research now shows that self-reports of smell/taste changes are more closely associated with hospital overload and are earlier markers of the spread of infection of SARS-CoV-2 than current governmental indicators. It also shows a decrease in self-reports of new-onset smell/taste changes as early as five days after lockdown enforcement. Anosmia, the technical term for the once relatively unfamiliar loss of one's ability to smell, is now all too common. Cross-country comparisons demonstrate that countries that adopted the most stringent lockdown measures had faster declines in new reports of smell/taste changes following lockdown than a country that adopted less stringent lockdown measures.

They propose that an increase in the incidence of sudden smell and taste change in the general population may be used as an indicator of Covid-19 spread in the population. The analyses reveal strong spatial and temporal relationships between self-reported smell and taste changes and multiple indices of healthcare system stress, such as admissions to ITUs. This is consistent with cumulative evidence showing a high prevalence of chemosensory alterations in patients affected by Covid-19 in Europe. Participants endorsed smell and taste changes only three to four days after their first symptoms. Such early chemosensory estimators may represent a cost-effective and easy way to implement alternative surveillance methods to large-scale virology tests, which are difficult to perform, costly and time-consuming, especially during a pandemic.

02.11.20

Dr Fauci said the US is 'in for a whole lot of hurt ... It's not a good situation. All the stars are aligned in the wrong place as you go into the fall and winter season, with people congregating at home indoors. You could not possibly be positioned more poorly,' he told *The Washington Post*. Remarkably, he said that Biden was 'taking it seriously from a public health perspective'. Trump, he said, was 'looking at it from a different perspective ... the economy and reopening the country'. Unsurprisingly, this has caused outrage in the Trump administration, which has accused Fauci of 'playing politics'.

Nearly half of Slovakia's entire population was tested on Saturday as the country began a two-day testing programme that it hopes will bring the virus under control without further lockdown measures. Of the 2.58 million Slovaks who took the test, 1% tested positive and must go into quarantine. More than 40,000 medics and support teams of soldiers, police, administrative workers and volunteers staffed around 5,000 sites to administer the antigen swab tests. The country, which has a population of 5.5 million, is aiming to test as many citizens as possible except those under the age of 10. The tests that have been purchased by the government include BIOCREDIT Covid-19 Ag (RapiGEN, South Korea) and Standard Q Covid-19 Ag (SD Biosensor, South Korea). Prime Minister Igor Matovič, reading from the package insert for the latter, said the test has a specificity of 99.68% and a sensitivity of 96.52%, compared with PCR tests. Those figures sound impressive, but if the prevalence of the disease is lowered you start turning up lots of false positives, i.e. telling people they have it when they don't.

Israel has started testing a new BriLife vaccine, which is vesicular stomatitis virus (VSV), an animal virus that does not cause disease in humans. During Phase 1, the vaccine's safety will be assessed in the trial on 80 healthy volunteers given a dose of the BriLife vaccine or placebo.

An interesting preprint has been published about a new variant, including a spike mutation. The data is not equally up to date in each country, but it shows a clear uptrend in the prevalence of the new strand in almost all countries in the sample. There are some anecdotes that specific case studies in Norway suggest that the new strain has a higher Rt, but nothing conclusive. However, a study involving more than 5,000 Covid-19 patients in Houston finds that the virus is accumulating genetic mutations, one of which may have made it more contagious.

The scientists noted a total of 285 mutations across thousands of infections, although most don't appear to have a significant effect on how severe the disease is. Ongoing studies are continuing to look at the third wave of Covid-19 patients and to characterise how the virus is adapting to neutralising antibodies that are produced by our immune systems. In summary, if the mutation happens on the spike protein, which causes it to be a very different virus, it won't be able to replicate via the spike anymore; hence it can't spread, and the virus won't survive. If the virus mutates in other regions beyond the spike protein, then the vaccine efficacy won't change at all unless they are all targeting this region.

03.11.20

I have just published a paper in the more-than-respectable *Journal of the National Cancer Institute,* showing in >3,000 patients with Covid-19 and cancer, the death rate was 23%, vs 6% in the control set. Lung cancer patients had >30% mortality and obviously older men did worse. One of my previous PhD students, Hua Zhang at New York University, worked with a team and me to group other studies, so-called meta-analyses, to look at the effects of Covid-19 on different cancers. I hope we can get these patients any vaccine early – before I saw our own data, I couldn't have guessed it was such bad news. Again, this shows the 'power', for want of a better word, of global collaboration and network effects.

The US response to Covid-19 has been dismal, characterised by anti-mask behaviour, anti-vaccine beliefs, conspiracy theories about the origins of Covid-19 and vocal support by elected officials for unproven therapies. Less than half of the people in the US heed health recommendations to wear a mask when out in public. Anti-science rhetoric has consequences. While only 4% of the world's population resides in the US, the US has accounted for 20% of the world's deaths related to Covid-19 and has performed less well than several other wealthy nations. Low science literacy contributes to the denial of science. The relationship between anti-science viewpoints and low science literacy underscores new findings regarding the brain mechanisms that form and maintain false beliefs.

Covid-19 science is complex, and the public is presented with a dizzying array of graphs, statistics and proposed therapies. Also, communications by scientists changed as they learned about the infectivity and virulence of Covid-19, exacerbating mistrust of scientists by some. In 2015, in a survey of 11,000 12th grade students who took the National Assessment of Educational Progress (NAEP) science assessment, only 22% were proficient or better in science, and 40% were rated as having 'below basic knowledge'.

Two-thirds of US adults say they've seen the news sources they turn to most often present factual information that favours one side of an issue in coverage of the election. More than half (56%) say their news sources have published breaking information before it was fully verified, and 37% say their sources have reported made-up news that is intended to mislead. The findings come against a backdrop of broader concern about misinformation. In the same survey, 59% say made-up information that is intended to mislead causes a 'great deal' of confusion about the 2020 presidential election. Many say the same about breaking news that is not fully verified (47%) or factual information presented to favour one side of an issue (42%). Voters who support Donald Trump are about twice as likely as registered voters who support Joe Biden to say that the news sources they turn to most often have reported made-up information that is intended to mislead the public (45% vs 22%). It doesn't help when the FDA approves HCQ and convalescent plasma.

04.11.20

The UK registered the highest daily increase in Covid-related deaths in five months, a further 397 deaths to 47,250. The Tuesday tally each week tends to be higher owing to a delay in reporting deaths over the weekend, but the latest figure is still the highest recorded since 422 people were reported as having died on 27 May. Obviously, there are lags from diagnosis to hospitalisation and hospitalisations to death, but this is bad news.

Europe passed more than 11 million cases as Austria and Greece became the latest countries on the Continent to impose shutdowns. France's daily Covid-19 death toll rose by 854 on Tuesday, an increase unseen since 15 April, while the number of people hospitalised for the disease went up by more than 1,000 for the fifth time in nine days. Hungary will close bars and entertainment venues and impose a nighttime curfew as of midnight and similarly in the Netherlands, too.

The growth of big data and greater analytic sophistication have contributed to the exploration of predictive risk modelling (PRM) in child welfare work, the goal being to use large data sets, usually from child welfare systems, to assess which child, caregiver or community characteristics were associated with unfavourable outcomes for the children.

These criteria would be applied to future children to define their risk potential. A group now reports their work in validating a PRM derived from a database of children reported to Child Protection Services in Allegheny County, Pennsylvania. The authors then validated the algorithm's ability to predict subsequent emergency department visits for injury to a child. They demonstrated that their algorithm was able to classify children at risk for subsequent emergency department visits for injuries but did not demonstrate an association with their control condition.

What about vaccine-induced injuries and no-fault compensation? As of now, there are more than 200 vaccine candidates in preclinical and clinical development, including eleven in Phase 3 trials. We've had some adverse events already such as transverse myelitis, but it looks like the risk/benefits strongly favour the vaccines. Wealthy governments that have invested in vaccine candidates have made bilateral agreements with developers that could result in vaccine doses being reserved for the highest-income countries, a phenomenon known as 'vaccine nationalism', potentially leaving people in poor countries vulnerable to Covid-19.

The response to vaccine nationalism has been the creation of the COVAX Facility, an international partnership that aims to financially support leading vaccine candidates and ensure access to vaccines for lower-income countries. There are 79 higher-income countries that are COVAX members. Their governments will help support 92 countries that couldn't otherwise afford Covid-19 vaccines. But large, up-front financial commitments to manufacturers are only half the solution when it comes to ensuring that companies will be willing to participate in the COVAX mechanism for vaccine distribution. Equally important is offering companies protection against potentially substantial liability should Covid-19 vaccines cause real or perceived injuries to recipients. Manufacturers won't agree to procurement contracts or ship vaccines without liability protection.

For most countries, offering pharmaceutical companies indemnity or complete immunity from lawsuits is constitutionally or financially impossible. Some governments will refuse to make such offers because of basic fairness principles: manufacturers should pay for the injuries their products cause. A solution to this problem involves leveraging two existing no-fault, vaccine-injury regimens and constructing a third regimen under COVAX's authority. Countries could, of course, opt out of these programmes or design their own national or regional compensation systems, but such systems would have to be created fairly quickly. Twenty-four countries and the Canadian province of Quebec have no-fault, vaccine-injury compensation systems for routine immunisations.

05.11.20

The US tallied its highest number of new cases in one day – 103k.

Yesterday voters encountered an array of precautions meant to keep the presidential election from becoming a superspreader event. After a turnout of 67% of the electorate, the biggest since the presidential election of 1900, tensions were running high, as were risks of infection. Masks and hand sanitisers were ubiquitous, of course, as was moaning about masks. Some polling places handed out individual pens for voting, while others cleaned off markers in between each use. Elsewhere, each person was given a plastic glove to wear while handling their ballot. And in a number of states, people too afraid to get out of their cars and stand in a socially distanced line could vote from their cars, as if they were picking up a McDonald's. Despite the safety measures, though, there were sporadic complaints of crowding as well as worries that in some communities hard-hit by illness and joblessness, voting may not be 'top of mind,' as a San Francisco activist put it.

06.11.20

In the US, daily infection rates increased to the highest level on record – 116k – for the second day in a row. Over in Europe, German infection rates hit a new high, and Italy imposed its 10 p.m. to 5 a.m. curfew as the PM referenced the risk of exhausting intensive care capacity again within weeks. In the UK, the CEO of the NHS last night referred to current hospitalisation trajectories, saying that current capacity was sufficient if we included capacity from the Nightingale hospitals, but it would mean even more resources taken away from other non-Covid-19 related emergencies.

Denmark will cull millions of mink being farmed for their fur in order to stop a mutated version of the virus from spreading. I note China has now barred entry to non-Chinese travellers from – among others – the UK, France and Belgium. It has also been announced that China and the WHO will collaborate on determining the source of the virus.

The majority of US states announced their outcomes in the first 24 hours after the presidential election, but hours have turned into days as neither candidate reached the necessary 270 Electoral College votes. The tally stalled at 253 for Biden against 214 for Trump, and all eyes turned to the Rust Belt states of Michigan, Wisconsin and Pennsylvania, where postal votes are being counted under previously unseen scrutiny. Regardless of the election outcome, the US pulled out of the Paris Climate Agreement yesterday.

Ambient air pollution is responsible for more than 5 million deaths annually, deaths caused by heart disease, stroke, chronic obstructive pulmonary disease, lung cancer, diabetes, pneumonia and premature birth. Covid-19-related improvements in air quality translate into fewer deaths from pollution-related disease. The measures to combat the coronavirus have led to an approximately 40% reduction in average levels of nitrogen dioxide (NO_2) pollution and a 10% reduction in average levels of particulate matter pollution over the past 30 days. This effect comes as power generation from coal has fallen 37% and oil consumption by an estimated one-third. Coal and oil burning are the main sources of NO_2 pollution and key sources of particulate matter pollution across Europe. Thus, cleaner air is estimated to have saved 11k lives in Europe in April and 77k lives in China in January and February.

Other avoided health impacts include 1.3 million fewer days of work absence, 6,000 fewer new cases of asthma in children, 1,900 avoided emergency room visits due to asthma attacks. A study has estimated that about 15% of worldwide deaths from Covid-19 could be attributed to long-term exposure to air pollution.

07.11.20

The US daily infection rate continues to accelerate upwards with a record 132k yesterday, beating the 116k record the day before, well over 1,000 deaths per day. Thirty-eight states have seen a notable outbreak in this past week and hospital admissions are now approaching levels seen in the first and second waves. Twitter has permanently suspended an account belonging to former White House chief strategist Steve Bannon after he suggested Dr Fauci and FBI Director Christopher Wray should be beheaded.

In Europe, France's Health Minister Olivier Veran warned, 'If we do not sufficiently respect the lockdown, we will experience a wave that is stronger than the first ... and for longer. The second wave is here and it's violent.' In the UK, Boris Johnson seemed to limit his ability to extend the lockdown beyond the current four weeks by saying he had 'no doubt we will get things open again before Christmas'. Talking up the prospect of rapid mass testing as a 'real way forward through the crisis' he said, 'People will have as normal a Christmas as possible.' The CEO of the NHS was more cautious, saying instead that the four-week lockdown was sufficient only to show whether hospital admissions had levelled off. In travel news, the UK is set to remove the travel corridor from Germany and Sweden.

One of the ways out, other than vaccines, is testing. The FDA and Instructions for Use (IFU) documents outlining the currently approved virology tests are largely unstandardised. As such, there remains an urgent need for a searchable interface allowing exploration of standardised information reported in these EUA and IFU documents in order to gain an improved understanding of the current testing landscape and to galvanise future test development.

The contact-tracing data suggest two important findings regarding transmission: first, there is an increased likelihood of cases infecting contacts of similar ages; and second, children under 14 are active participants in transmission. These findings probably reflect prevalent social mixing patterns in India, but raise concerns about the possibility of enhanced transmission when poorly ventilated, crowded schools reopen.

08.11.20

Virology: An interesting paper shows conclusively to me that the D614G spike mutation makes the virus a little more infectious but doesn't affect neutralising antibody binding, i.e. it should make no difference to vaccines. However, a study involving more than 5,000 Covid-19 patients in Houston finds that the virus that causes the disease is accumulating genetic mutations, one of which may have made it more contagious.

A study from France modelling the effectiveness of public health measures to slow the spread of SARS-CoV-2 (aside from strict lockdown) found that mask mandates and restricting access to public places such as bars reduced the number of new cases per day by 75% and delayed a peak in infections by about two months. However, these measures did not prevent ICUs from becoming full.

Testing: Even if all current EUA tests for the SARS-CoV-2 virus were performed with more than 95% sensitivity and more than 95% specificity, their combined capacities would still fall short of enabling large-scale, ubiquitous temporal monitoring (tens of millions per day).

A cross-sectional study in a university setting in England indicated that universal, repeated self-testing for Covid-19 using PCR was both acceptable and feasible. Staff and student participants were given four PCR swabs to self-administer over two weeks. 76% of participants provided at least one swab, among whom 86% provided all four. Of those who submitted at least one swab, none had a positive test (six participants with one inconclusive result). The mean acceptability score was 4.5/5 (5 was most positive).

Vaccines: A qualitative study investigating the perceptions of vaccine trials among people from ethnic minority and vulnerable communities in the UK found that while there was overall agreement that clinical research was necessary, most interviewees expressed extreme discomfort with the idea of attending a hospital for a vaccine trial. Participants highlighted concerns about fear of contracting Covid-19, lack of support if problems arose and language barriers. Participants also reported suspicion of hidden agendas behind vaccines and expressed the need for transparency and vaccine information that was culturally appropriate.

A study of Twitter messages from multiple countries early in the SARS-CoV-2 pandemic identified a co-occurring 'infodemic': the rapid and widespread dissemination of misinformation or content from unreliable sources. Analysis of more than 100 million tweets indicated that waves of misinformation preceded the rise of Covid-19 infections, but content quickly shifted towards more credible information as infections rose.

Another totally negative HCQ study is looking at a UK cohort already taking the drug.

Player interaction and proximity analysis of four professional rugby matches in which 8 players were retrospectively found to have SARS-CoV-2 suggest that the risk of in-game transmission may be minimal. While video footage analysis and GPS data show the positive players were within 2 meters of other players for up to 316 seconds during 60 interactions, only 1 of 28 identified contacts and 5 of 100 players on opposing teams had positive tests, all of which were eventually linked to either internal club outbreaks or wider-community transmission.

09.11.20

As global cases march through 50 million, the US numbers really do not look good (let's hope for vaccine news this week), and numbers now since Wednesday are consistently >100k (though a bit less yesterday); the number of people hospitalised with Covid-19 rose 14%, deaths up 8% week on week. Never, in the nearly 250-year history of the US, has a president inherited a pandemic on the scale of Covid-19.

There is huge anxiety over ballot recounts and a quite frankly insane level of conspiracy theories over a rigged election, not helped by Trump's refusal to say anything other than how great his numbers are. But it does seem that the Washington machinery will start turning, and America will see Biden inaugurated in January. Biden has won. Hopefully, the transition will be uneventful. I wonder if he still wants the job as he will have to shoulder several herculean tasks, including a massive testing scale-up, restoring the credibility of government scientists and overseeing the eventual distribution of hundreds of millions of vaccine doses. One of the first things he announced in his victory speech Saturday night was that he would be putting together a coronavirus task force as of Monday, composed of 'a group of leading scientists and experts'. Perhaps most daunting in a country plagued by apathy and misinformation is that Biden will need to earn the buy-in of the American public. He will need to reach out to Dr Fauci, and he will need to declare his intention to be an active participant in the WHO and in the world.

The pandemic may have been a decisive factor in Biden's win. In one exit poll, a majority of voters said they favoured pandemic containment measures even at the economy's expense, though only 20% listed the pandemic as their top deciding factor, and one-third of voters said their top issue was the economy. In the campaign's closing weeks, Trump urged Americans to return to their everyday lives and pledged to fire Dr Fauci. Biden, meanwhile, campaigned on choosing 'science over fiction,' said he will ask governors to quickly issue statewide mask mandates and asked Dr Fauci to continue his service in government.

It does look like a virus played a deciding factor in the politics of the world's most powerful nation. Science, nature and politics coalesced in one event.

10.11.20

Well, the news we have all been waiting for: Pfizer reported 90% vaccine efficacy off 94 cases (this may be as good as a 92 vs 2 split), steamrolling, or rather ignoring the first interim in the protocol, which they sensibly chose not to look at until after the election, also probably realising it was too big a risk off small numbers, i.e. they did their first interim at 94 not 32 cases, and there will be no other interims. With more cases that 90% number can go down, or better still up. If the FDA has an Advisory Committee (AdCom) of doctors to advise its decision-making in December they'll have 164 cases in both arms to draw conclusions from, but I don't think they will, and there are no adverse or new safety signals. I think they'll file in the third week of November for an EUA, which will be rapidly granted. They could have done this over a month ago but, interestingly, waited for Trump to lose. They haven't had the over-70s this excited since they discovered Viagra. I note the FDA is still, despite HCQ and convalescent plasma, in the mood to give EUAs: they gave one to Lilly last night for its bamlanivimab antibody treatment.

I think they'll have herd immunity in the US by April. Pfizer's vaccine study enrolled 43,538 volunteers, the companies said, and 38,955 have received their second dose, which means this fulfils the FDA's guidance of waiting two months. About 42% of global participants and 30% of US participants have racially and ethnically diverse backgrounds. Bourla, Pfizer's CEO, said the results mark 'a great day for science and humanity,' in a statement, saying they provide 'initial evidence of our vaccine's ability to prevent Covid-19'. He added, 'We look forward to sharing additional efficacy and safety data generated from thousands of participants in the coming weeks.' Moderna, using similar mRNA technology, will work too, any day. Maybe even better due to their newer lipid nanoparticles.

In summary, this is a very good result. The primary end point of the trial was any symptomatic infection, so the vaccine was able to reduce the odds of people getting Covid with symptoms by 90%, maybe more. This is very promising and comes in ahead of expert expectations (which typically landed in the 70–80% range). Furthermore, if we think about likely efficacy against severe disease, the kind that leads to hospitalisation or death, the vaccine is almost certainly even more effective there (this is true of most, maybe all vaccines). This bodes well.

11.11.20

Technically, if you vaccinate the old and a few others you can eradicate most of the deaths from Covid-19, but it's not herd immunity until you reach the threshold because the virus keeps circulating, right? But what's the threshold? This is a hard one, along with the cross-reactivity. Whatever the threshold is, let's subtract another 10% because that's the number, or thereabouts, who've had it. Europeans and others also have Pfizer and Moderna pre-purchases and options. The question is whether the US gets slightly favoured in distribution or whether it's all scrupulously equal.

Following the logic above and assuming an average vaccine efficacy of 90% and a herd immunity needed of 50%, the United States could theoretically achieve herd immunity by vaccinating the correct set of roughly 80 million adults (31% of the adult population) or by indiscriminately vaccinating 142 million adults (56% of the adult population). The Trump administration pre-purchased 100 million doses from Pfizer and 100 million from Moderna this summer, with options to purchase 500 million more of Pfizer's and 400 million more of Moderna's. The companies have yet to announce exactly who will get priority in the early production runs or what formula they will follow.

Still, it is hard to imagine the US waiting on the sidelines while Canada or Japan sees its orders delivered first. The US government is a major investor in these vaccines via BARDA and is Pfizer's largest customer. The US federal government and the European Commission have the greatest bargaining power with the vaccine makers, but they will also be able to make an ethical case, given the ongoing third wave, that they need the vaccines more urgently than their Asian and Antipodean peers.

12.11.20

The EU secures 300 million doses of Pfizer's vaccine, and Moderna announces they have enough cases for their interim. Russia's Sovereign Wealth Fund (RDIF) said early results from its Phase 3 clinical trial of Russia's coronavirus vaccine, called Sputnik V, showed its efficacy amounted to 92%. The Russian calculation was 'based on the 20 confirmed Covid-19 cases split between vaccinated individuals and those who received the placebo. Currently 40,000 volunteers are taking part in double-blind, randomised, placebo-controlled Phase III of Sputnik V clinical trials, out of which over 20,000 have been vaccinated with the first dose of the vaccine and more than 16,000 with both the first and second doses of the vaccine,' the website said. But using basic maths, I am not sure how one gets 92% from 20 individuals.

The Serum Institute of India, the world's largest vaccine producer, said on Thursday it has made 40 million doses of AZN's vaccine and would soon begin making Novavax's shot. Might the vaccine, in general, be the saving grace for pharma? Democratic presidential candidates always promise to cut drug prices, and polls show the public has no love lost for pharma. But this doesn't seem like the time to kill the golden goose.

13.11.20

In the US, the daily infection rate increased to another record high of >150k cases, meaning new highs in seven of the last nine days, with the hospital census reaching 65k, the highest since April. California, after Texas, has topped 1 million cases. New York's mayor said the city has 'one last chance' to halt a second wave as the infection rate approaches the safety threshold that would force a shutdown of schools.

In Europe, Sweden is now also struggling to contain the infection rate. It has announced the sale of alcohol in bars, restaurants and nightclubs will be banned after 10 p.m. Headlines today refer to the better news that the number of new cases has plateaued or begun to ease in the UK, Germany and France, with smaller countries posting even bigger declines. The UK became the first country in Europe to surpass 50,000 deaths and recorded its own record high, while universities' minister Michelle Donelan said students in England must display 'refined behaviour' for two weeks before they are allowed to return home for Christmas as plans were unveiled for a 'student travel window' to minimise the risk of spreading the virus.

A spokesman for Boris Johnson said he would be happy to receive a vaccine and his deputy chief medical officer said he would urge his elderly mother to be vaccinated. Pfizer's vaccine is expected to be up to seven times more expensive than the jab being developed by Oxford, with ministers hoping the latter could help ease logistical and supply issues. But we're talking about the costs of several cups of coffee so there are many ways to look at it.

Oxford University and PHE said lateral flow tests that can give a result in less than 30 minutes without the need for laboratory equipment are accurate enough for general use. The first published evaluation of the tests being used in pilots showed they picked up three-quarters of cases and 95% of those with the highest viral loads, raising hopes for dramatically cutting infection rates by locating the estimated 500k people currently infected with the disease. Boris Johnson said lateral flow testing was 'very exciting' and 'one of the boxing gloves we hope to wield to pummel the disease into submission...' EU Health Commissioner Stella Kyriakides said Europeans could begin to be vaccinated against Covid-19 in the first quarter of 2021 as a best-case scenario.

14.11.20

Following reports of a new coronavirus strain that mutated in minks and can infect humans, the European Centre for Disease Prevention and Control (ECDC) has conducted an assessment of the situation. 'Due to the large number of infections and possibly due to biological differences between minks and humans, the virus can accumulate mutations more quickly in minks and spread back into the human population,' the agency said. 'If these new ... variants, with lower susceptibility to neutralising antibodies, spread widely in the population it could potentially affect the level of overall vaccine effectiveness of vaccines under development, and that the establishment of a virus reservoir among minks may give rise to problematic virus variants in the future,' it added, urging countries to set up preparedness strategies.

Where are we with animals? In view of the similarities of the new virus with SARS-CoV-1, which caused SARS in 2003, a zoonotic/animal origin of the outbreak was the suspected link to the Wuhan fresh market, where various animals are sold, including fish, shellfish, poultry, wild birds and exotic animals. The finding of cases with onset of illness well before the period observed in the Wuhan market-associated cluster also suggests the possibility of other sources. Although closely related coronaviruses found in bats and pangolins have the greatest sequence identity to SARS-CoV-2, the most likely divergence of SARS-CoV-2 from the most closely related bat sequence is estimated somewhere between 1948–82. Therefore, the true animal reservoir(s) of SARS-CoV-2 is (are) yet to be identified.

In Wuhan, researchers will take a closer look at the Huanan meat and animal market, which many of the earliest people diagnosed with Covid-19 had visited. What part the market played in the virus' spread remains a mystery. Early investigations sampled frozen animal carcasses at the market, but none found evidence of SARS-CoV-2. However, environmental samples taken mostly from drains and sewage did test positive for the virus. 'Preliminary studies have not generated credible leads to narrow the area of research,' it states. Now, the WHO mission will investigate the wild and farmed animals sold at the market, including foxes, raccoons (*Procyon lotor*) and sika deer (*Cervus nippon*). They will also investigate other markets in Wuhan and trace the animals' journeys through China and across borders. The investigators will prioritise animals that are known to be susceptible to the virus, such as cats and mink.

In response to the outbreaks in mink farms, the Dutch national response system for zoonotic diseases was activated, and it was concluded that the public health risk of exposure to animals with SARS-CoV-2 was low. After the detection of SARS-CoV-2 on mink farms, 68% of the tested farm workers and/or relatives or contacts were to be or have been infected with SARS-CoV-2, indicating that contact with SARS-CoV-2 infected mink is a risk factor for contracting Covid-19.

15.11.20

There are precious few signs that the virus is slowing down across Europe, and Greece is shutting schools and nurseries. Is that the right thing to do? A paper shows that during the Covid-19 pandemic (mid-March to October), mental health-related emergency department (ED) visits among children and adolescents decreased in absolute numbers, but increased as a proportion of all paediatric ED visits. The proportion of mental health-related ED visits among all paediatric ED visits for children aged 5–11 and 12–17 years increased by 24% and 31% respectively, compared to the same time period in 2019. Everyone calls it the novel coronavirus. It's hardly novel to anyone now.

During this period, there were initial substantial declines in the overall reported number of children's mental health-related ED visits, which coincided with measures such as school closures, followed by a return to an absolute level similar to the pre-pandemic period. Even larger decreases in overall paediatric ED visits were observed. It is suggested that this reflects that children's mental health concerns were sufficient to drive ED visits at a time when non-emergent visits were discouraged.

A total of 24.2 million children aged 5 to 11 years attended public schools that were closed during the 2020 pandemic, losing a median of 54 days of instruction. Missed instruction was associated with a mean loss of 0.31 years of final educational attainment for boys and 0.21 years for girls. These consequences are especially dire for young children. There is little reason to believe that virtual learning environments can be effective for primary school-aged children. A meta-analysis of 99 experimental studies included only 5 conducted in school-aged children, and they were primarily in 5th through 8th grades. The meta-analysis concluded that 'the mean effect size [for online learning] is not significant for the seven contrasts involving K-12 students'. That so few studies have even been conducted in this age group is also telling.

I note an editorial in the *NEJM* on trying to protect the NHS written by Professor Hunter from Oxford. It ends saying, 'So, as the days shorten, the second wave is breaking on the shores of "the scepter'd isle". The exhausted NHS workforce is being asked to step up again, and despite government edicts to maintain normal services, much of the NHS may again be repurposed as a Covid service. Large-scale deployment of rapid tests in the hands of local authorities may help the exit from lockdown, but new optimism about vaccines is tempered with realism that a mass rollout will take many months. This is likely to be a winter of discontent'. Personally, I am shattered, and was hoping to see the kindness promised in words by so many but am not seeing it at all. Quite the opposite, in fact.

16.11.20

Surges in nursing home-associated SARS-CoV-2 infections occurred in hotspot states during the end of October. Data was collected from 778 facilities in Idaho, Montana, North and South Dakota, Utah and Wisconsin regarding community spread, testing and PPE and staffing shortages. Across the six states, weekly cases among staff members tripled from September to October and cases among residents quadrupled. By the end of the study period, one in five nursing homes reported PPE shortages and one in four reported staff shortages. The authors suggest that mitigation efforts thus far have been insufficient to change the trajectory of SARS-CoV-2 transmission in nursing home communities.

Detection of SARS-CoV-2 in the ventilation system of three linked Covid-19 wards in a Swedish hospital suggests long-distance airborne dispersal beyond droplet transmission. SARS-CoV-2 genetic material was detected in seven of nineteen vent openings within wards, while eight of nine samples obtained from HEPA exhaust filters located several floors above the wards were also positive for genetic material.

Should prisoners be in vaccine studies? After all, the worst outbreaks are no longer occurring in nursing homes or meat-packing plants, but in prisons. Incarcerated populations are especially vulnerable to acquiring infectious diseases like Covid-19 because of factors including overcrowding, confined spaces, high population turnover, poor sanitation and poor access to healthcare. People who are incarcerated are also more likely than the general public to develop complications associated with infectious diseases because of their higher rates of underlying health conditions. The consequences of Covid-19 outbreaks in correctional facilities are disproportionately felt by people of colour; as a result of structural inequities, non-white people are more likely than white people to be incarcerated and are more likely to die from Covid-19. Now, researchers are considering whether incarcerated people should be included in multisite efficacy trials of Covid-19 vaccine candidates after there is some evidence that such vaccines are safe.

Interesting preprint shows at least six months of immunity after being infected by the virus.

17.11.20

By the end of 2021, Pfizer and Moderna supplies alone could vaccinate approximately 15% of the global population (cumulative estimate: Q4 2020 – 0.4%, Q1 2021 – 3%, Q2 2021 – 6%, Q3 2021 – 10%, Q4 2021 – 15%). Allowing for an estimated additional 500 million doses for Russia/China (domestic vaccine manufacturers) could take this to a maximum of 18% by year end in 2021. 'Obviously, the data speak for themselves,' says Dr Fauci. 'This is a very positive result.' He said that next month doses of one or both vaccines will start to be offered to people at the highest risk.

Moderna is expected to file for an EUA shortly. Pfizer is due to do the same by the third week of November. AZN is due to report Phase 3 data by year end, followed by Johnson & Johnson and Novavax in early 2021 and Sanofi/GlaxoSmithKline and Merck in Q1 2021. No idea how Curevac, Inovio or Translate Bio or any of the other 200 on the list can even contemplate competing, let alone recruiting for a Phase 3 trial with a placebo arm. Sinovac Phase 3 will report soon and am much more inclined to believe published data and hope we'll see this sort of information. There are many ways to measure vaccine efficacy, but it's good the trials are focused on infections plus one or two symptoms. I wonder if we'll understand their ability to prevent asymptomatic transmission and infections?

18.11.20

French Health Minister Olivier Véran warned, 'Resuscitation services are operating at 140% of their initial capacity. Now is not the time to let down our guard.' With regard to potential Christmas gatherings, the minister said that 'the conditions under which we will celebrate the holidays at the end of the year depend on the evolution of the epidemic in the coming weeks and on our collective efforts,' adding, 'What is certain is that we will have to be careful because the virus will still be circulating'. Bavarian premier Markus Söder said, 'I have little hope that everything will be fine by the end of November.' David Nabarro, special envoy to the WHO, said, 'There has been quite a resistance by European countries to look eastwards and say "ah, there are lessons in East Asia."'

Denmark's Agency for Patient Safety today announced that a significant number of mink farm employees in the country have been infected with the coronavirus: 'In the past week, we have found over 200 cases of infection among employees at six mink fur farms in Denmark.'

Many of us have been puzzling over the 10 p.m. closure rules, previously in London, now in New York. Was this based on some brand-new evidence that the virus mutates like a gremlin, getting worse at night? I've seen this happen again and again since the start of the pandemic: a new, 'science-based' Covid-19 measure is prescribed, but the science in support of it is either vague or non-existent.

Yet, unsourced rules are everywhere in this pandemic. There was no way for the general public to know, at first, that the recommendation to stay 6 feet apart originated in part from a 3-foot rule determined by decades-old studies of card game players, and that the recommended spacing had been doubled on the basis of research into the spread of the original SARS virus through aeroplane cabins. And what about the widespread rule that each child in school should be allotted 44 square feet of space?

Some pandemic guidelines are even stranger and more mysterious. In an effort to stop people from going out unnecessarily and spreading Covid-19 as winter approached in the southern hemisphere, the South African government prevented the sale of open-toed shoes (unless they were intended to be worn over leggings), on the grounds that any trip to purchase such articles of clothing would be inessential. In a seemingly backward move, the city of Madrid has closed parks but allows some indoor dining to continue. Meanwhile, Canada's chief medical officer recommended that people engaging in sexual activity should wear masks.

19.11.20

Merkel warned that the situation in Germany remains 'very serious,' and Berlin police used water cannons and tear gas to disperse crowds of several thousand people who demonstrated against the government's coronavirus measures.

Reports suggest French bars and restaurants will remain closed until mid-January, but UK figures are looking better despite the latest ONS figures showing virus-related deaths increased 40% in the first week of November to their highest level since May. This was the ninth consecutive week of increases in the number of virus-related deaths and the second consecutive week the figure has surpassed 1,000.

Can't help but be super proud today. The US FDA has given an EUA for baricitinib to treat hospitalised patients with Covid-19. That's 'computer to bench to bedside to FDA' approval in ten months. Wow! Exceptional global collaboration and teamwork. Hard to open any champagne with so much suffering. Standing on shoulders of giants and all that. Four stand out: Joanna, Gary, Mario and Volker – such exceptional people.

20.11.20

Great paper in *Nature Communications*. A group describes a city-wide SARS-CoV-2 nucleic acid screening programme between 14 May and 1 June in Wuhan. All city residents aged 6 years or older were eligible and 9,899,828 (92.9%) participated. No new symptomatic cases and 300 asymptomatic cases (detection rate 0.303/10,000) were identified. There were no positive tests among 1,174 close contacts of asymptomatic cases. 107 of 34,424 previously recovered Covid-19 patients tested positive again (re-positive rate 0.31%). The prevalence of SARS-CoV-2 infection in Wuhan was therefore very low five to eight weeks after the end of lockdown. They do know how to decisively lockdown.

In the US, the number of daily cases reached 183k, the hospital census reached >80k, and the number of daily deaths increased to the highest level since 7 May. Positive tests as a per cent of the total increased to double digits. Oregon added to the growing list of US states tightening lockdowns by ordering non-essential businesses to close and banning social gatherings of more than six people.

In the UK, London is one of nine England regions to report zero excess deaths in the first week of November, suggesting at least some herd immunity, meaning if true that small vaccine uptake in OECD countries will lead to an end to Covid-19 sooner not later. Boris Johnson told MPs that Christmas 'will not be normal', although reports suggest that families in the UK may be able to mix indoors for five days from Christmas Eve as part of a common approach. Tight restrictions may, however, be required both before and after the festive period. The virus doesn't know it's Christmas, and if this goes ahead someone is going to be asymptomatic, hug grandpa and pass on a disease that will kill him. An act of love leading to a loved one's demise.

We know Asia has a toolkit to lock the virus down. The central explanation for South Korea's success in taming the pandemic thus far is its strategy of targeted testing and aggressive contact tracing. Taiwan and China too. That and the willingness of the public, including most religious believers and political protesters, to follow basic precautions.

21.11.20

In the US, daily cases (+200k), hospital admissions (+80k) and daily deaths (+2k) all hit records in the last two days. The trends are becoming an increasing focus for global markets, with inertia over fiscal spending and policy damaging confidence. The CDC gave a 'strong recommendation' not to travel during the upcoming Thanksgiving holiday, although the White House said the annual presidential pardoning of a turkey will go ahead. New York City announced it will close schools, with the city's mayor saying it is 'just a matter of time' until the state orders a halt to indoor dining. Governor Andrew Cuomo warned that the entire city could be placed in the state's orange-zone category, which would also limit outdoor dining and force the closure of gyms and hairdressers.

In the UK, as Boris Johnson continues to debate a new tiering system for after the current lockdown, the UK's hospital bosses have suggested 'Tier 3' restrictions should be the new normal across the country and the lockdown must continue in some areas. They argued even a limited Christmas relaxation risked an 'uncontrollable flood' of cases that could impede hospitals' ability to treat emergency patients.

Former Health Secretary Jeremy Hunt has said everyone should be tested monthly to give them 'freedom passes' to resume everyday activities. He has urged the PM to set an Easter deadline for mass testing through home testing kits even if vaccines are yet to arrive. On travel, Israel, Sri Lanka and Namibia were added to the UK's air corridor list.

22.11.20

Effects of the virus on mental health aren't limited to the Western world. They're everywhere. For example, a research group asked, what were the patterns of, and factors associated with, mental health conditions among the general population during the outbreak in China? In their survey of 60k participants across all 34 province-level regions in China, 27.9% of participants had symptoms of depression, 31.6% had symptoms of anxiety, 29.2% had symptoms of insomnia and 24.4% had symptoms of acute stress during the outbreak. Factors independently associated with negative mental health outcomes included having confirmed or suspected Covid-19, having a relative with confirmed or suspected Covid-19, having occupational exposure risks, living in Hubei Province, experiencing quarantine and delays in returning to work. Clearly, the mental health burden associated with Covid-19 is considerable among the general population. But it's complicated, as illustrated by the fact there is a real-time study from Australia that shows there does not yet appear to be an overall change in the suspected suicide rate in the seven months since Queensland declared a public health emergency. The interplay of local cultural factors here is central, and there's also a coming together in adversity akin to the Blitz spirit.

23.11.20

After all the furore about side effects, AZN announced:

Positive high-level results from an interim analysis of clinical trials of AZD1222 in the UK and Brazil showed the vaccine was highly effective in preventing Covid-19, the primary end point, and no hospitalisations or severe cases of the disease were reported in participants receiving the vaccine. There were a total of 131 Covid-19 cases in the interim analysis.

One dosing regimen (n=2,741) showed vaccine efficacy of 90% when AZD1222 was given as a half dose, followed by a full dose at least one month apart, and another dosing regimen (n=8,895) showed 62% efficacy when given as two full doses at least one month apart. The combined analysis from both dosing regimens (n=11,636) resulted in an average efficacy of 70%. All results were statistically significant (p<=0.0001). More data will continue to accumulate and additional analysis will be conducted, refining the efficacy reading and establishing the duration of protection.[9]

As always, we'll need the publication.

Moncef Slaoui, Chief Scientific Adviser of OWS, which involves the military/private sector, said the first Americans could be vaccinated outside of clinical trials by mid-December. And Slaoui said that if the vaccination distribution and immunisation plan goes well, enough Americans should be vaccinated by 'May or something like that' of 2021 to allow life to go back to normal.

Yet another superspreader event has been publicised, and my review on these is published in the *Journal of Infection*. Today we hear that following a ten-day motorcycle rally in Sturgis, South Dakota, attended by approximately 460,000 persons, 51 confirmed cases of Covid-19 that were directly associated with the event were identified in Minnesota residents, along with 21 secondary cases and 5 tertiary cases. An additional 9 likely event-associated secondary or tertiary cases were also identified. There were 4 patients who were hospitalised and 1 who died. So, was it worth it?

Elsewhere, barracks-style buildings for migrant workers in Singapore were associated with a faster pace of infection when compared to apartment-style housing. The workers were confined to their respective living quarters, where the number of cases of SARS-CoV-2 infection doubled every 1.6 days in barracks-style buildings, whereas the corresponding doubling time for apartment-style buildings was 2.7 days.

We're pooling numerous investigator-led studies on baricitinib, all of our organoid work alongside gene sequencing studies and our super-resolution microscopy. *Science Advances* is going to take this, I'm sure. It's truly cross-disciplinary.

24.11.20

In the US, daily cases reached a new record of 192k on Friday, though a fair bit lower yesterday, and the hospital census continued to climb.

In Europe, on the other hand, the national lockdowns are taking effect and infections fell in eight out of the eleven major countries. Cases in France were down 38% to a two-month low, Italy down 5%, Germany down 1%, Spain down 9% and the UK down 20%. In the other EU countries, Belgian infections were down by 31%, Austria down 15%, and the Netherlands down 3%. Conversely, infections increased in Denmark by 19% and Switzerland and Sweden each by 13%.

As UK cases trend lower, Boris Johnson gave details of the 'Covid winter plan' after it was confirmed that the national lockdown in England will end as planned on 2 December when a tougher three-tier system will take effect. While households will still be banned from mixing indoors in higher-infection areas, the plans are to allow mixing of up to three households for 'a small amount of days' over Christmas. Boris will likely promise to bring back 'normal life' by Easter next year.

25.11.20

A new presidential administration could have a meaningful impact on federal allocation decisions of vaccines to the states. Important decisions are whether more vaccine will be allocated to current hotspots, areas with little protection from the virus or populations where more than 25% have been exposed, as well as how effective IT infrastructure is in the early months of distribution. State vaccine distribution plans have not changed materially since introduced several weeks ago, and most remain focused on vaccinating their most at-risk populations first (medical personnel and nursing home residents). Pfizer's and Moderna's EUA can be expected on 10 December, and vaccinations for the earliest recipients could come in December.

If patients only take one shot, there may be 50% efficacy. It will be harder to deliver the vaccine at high levels to some parts of the US, for instance rural areas and Native American reservations. The impact on pregnant women may actually be entwined in the trials but not explicitly recruited, and elderly people could need a booster shot over time. Antibodies could also wane over time or, if we are lucky, once you have immunity you can never get it again (like measles).

In other news in recent months, most Western governments detected cyberattacks from three nation-state actors targeting seven prominent companies directly involved in researching vaccines and treatments for Covid-19. The targets include leading pharmaceutical companies and vaccine researchers in Canada, France, India, South Korea and the United States. The attacks came from Strontium, an actor originating from Russia, and two actors originating from North Korea that Microsoft calls Zinc and Cerium. The majority of the targets are vaccine makers that have Covid-19 vaccines in various stages of clinical trials. One is a clinical research organisation involved in trials, and one has developed a Covid-19 test. Multiple organisations targeted have contracts with or investments from government agencies from various democratic countries for Covid-19-related work. Strontium continues to use password spray and brute force login attempts to steal login credentials. These are attacks that aim to break into people's accounts using thousands or millions of rapid attempts. Zinc has primarily used spear-phishing lures for credential theft, sending messages with fabricated job descriptions pretending to be recruiters. Cerium engaged in spear-phishing email lures using Covid-19 themes while masquerading as WHO representatives. The majority of these attacks were blocked by security protections built into products.

Cyberattacks targeting the healthcare sector and taking advantage of the pandemic are not new. Attackers recently used ransomware attacks to target hospitals across the United States. Earlier in the pandemic, attacks targeted Brno University Hospital in the Czech Republic, Paris' hospital system, the computer systems of Spain's hospitals, hospitals in Thailand, medical clinics in Texas and Illinois and even international bodies such as the WHO. In Germany, we recently saw the resulting threat to human health become a tragic reality when a woman in Dusseldorf reportedly became the first known death as a result of a cyberattack on a hospital.

26.11.20

As the world moves through 60 million diagnosed cases, in the UK, in a move that will lead to some awkward decisions for families across the country, leaders of the four UK nations agreed that only three households can meet indoors during a five-day Christmas period between 23 and 27 December. As the UK recorded its lowest number of new coronavirus cases in nearly two months, Sadiq Khan said London should be placed on the second tier of coronavirus restrictions when England's national lockdown ends next week, while *The Times* reports that business travellers and tour groups may be exempt from quarantine measures from early 2021.

In Europe, Germany's sixteen regions agreed to extend the partial lockdown until at least 20 December, but to relax it for Christmas and New Year's Eve. President Macron announced plans to ease restrictions from 15 December if infection rates fell further, but nighttime curfews will come into force, public gatherings will be illegal, and restaurants and cafés will remain shut until at least 20 January. Curfew restrictions will be lifted on just two days, 24 and 31 December.

The WHO's chief scientist said people around the world will probably need to take precautions against Covid-19 for the next year as countries vaccinate their populations broadly, while Matt Hancock (the UK's Health Secretary) said there would be a shift to an emphasis on 'personal responsibility' rather than social distancing restrictions after Easter.

Finland has been voted the best European country to live in during the pandemic, according to a Bloomberg ranking. The Nordic country ranked fifth overall, trailing New Zealand, Japan, Taiwan and South Korea.

I note Dr Fauci did a Zoom call with well over several thousand participants in Boston last night, facilitated by two female pastors, to talk about vaccine uptake in historically marginalised communities. Important outreach to be sure.

27.11.20

The Times reported that in the US, 'Thanksgiving will be the "mother of all Covid superspreader events".' Let's see. More than 2,000 deaths were recorded in a single day in the US.

When it comes to transmission, handwashing or using an alcohol-based hand sanitiser after touching frequently touched surfaces is a key strategy, the CDC recommends. A survey of 4,800 US adults who said they had been out in public during the previous week showed 85% of the participants said they always or often washed their hands or used hand sanitiser after coming in contact with high-touch surfaces in public places. However, men and younger adults were less likely than women and older adults to practice proper hand hygiene after touching common objects while out shopping or for other reasons.

A quota-sampled online survey of 788 US adults found that 60% of participants were either definitely willing or probably willing to receive a future Covid-19 vaccine, and 25% were either definitely willing or probably willing to receive the vaccine if it were approved under an EUA. Significant predictors of Covid-19 vaccine uptake intent with and without EUA included high perceived susceptibility to Covid-19, high perceived benefits of the vaccine and scored low on barriers to the vaccine. Willingness to take a vaccine approved under an EUA was more common among respondents who were older and who identified as white race. Uptake intent and willingness to get the vaccine with EUA appeared to be reduced by concerns about rushed vaccine development.

28.11.20

When it comes to tests, the FDA and the scientific community are currently almost exclusively focused on test sensitivity, a measure of how well an individual assay can detect viral protein or RNA molecules. A test that has a high sensitivity is able to correctly identify patients who have COVID. In contrast, a test with a low sensitivity has a high false-positive rate, which is something we try hard to avoid. Critically, this measure neglects the context of how the test is being used. Yet when it comes to the broad screening we so desperately need, context is fundamental. The key question is not how well molecules can be detected in a single sample but how effectively infections can be detected in a population by the repeated use of a given test as part of an overall testing strategy – the sensitivity of the testing regimen.

With Covid-19 cases accelerating or plateauing throughout much of the world, there's a shift from a narrow focus on the analytic sensitivity of a test (the lower limit of its ability to correctly detect small concentrations of molecules in a sample) to the more relevant measure of a testing regimen's sensitivity to detect infections (the probability that infected persons learn they're infected in time to be filtered out of the population and prevent spread to others). A point-of-care test that was inexpensive enough to use frequently would have a high sensitivity for detecting infections in time to act, without having to meet the benchmark analytic limit of detection.

The tests we need are fundamentally different from the clinical tests currently being used, and they must be evaluated differently. Clinical tests are designed for use with symptomatic people, do not need to be low cost and require high analytic sensitivity to return a definitive clinical diagnosis given a single opportunity to test. In contrast, tests used in effective surveillance regimens intended to reduce the population prevalence of a respiratory virus need to return results quickly to limit asymptomatic spread and should be sufficiently inexpensive and easy to execute to allow frequent testing – multiple times per week. Transmission of SARS-CoV-2 appears to occur days after exposure when the viral load peaks. This timing increases the importance of high-test frequency (because the test must be used at the beginning of an infection to stop onward spread) and reduces the importance of achieving the very low molecular limits of detection of the standard tests.

Educational gains among primary school students in Switzerland were cut in half with distance learning during school closures due to the Covid-19 pandemic. An analysis of educational gains during the eight weeks of school closures, compared to the prior eight weeks, found high heterogeneity in learning processes between individual primary school students during the lockdown, and that overall learning slowed down. Primary school students learned more than twice as fast in person as they did in the distance learning setting. No significant differences in the learning pace of secondary school students were found.

29.11.20

Covid has reduced our horizons, often defined by the confines of our homes. I have heard a few people talk about 'fast/slow time'. A phenomenon where each hour can seem like a day and each day feel like a week, and yet it still strangely feels like March. Time has passed achingly slowly and staggeringly quickly at the exact same time. Then there's the enforced isolation from friends and family. This has led to a near-global battle with anxiety and a concern for a future that looks unfathomable. They say that art reflects the times, and we've already had the BBC's *Staged* with David Tennant, Michael Sheen, Georgia Tennant and Anna Lundberg basically performing a drama about Covid over Zoom. The perfect encapsulation of our Covid lives of 2020. Poets are masters in expressing with words feelings that we may find difficult to define, and even during the current pandemic they have tried to give voice to the sense of unease we all feel.

As an example, in the spring of this year Italian poet Vivian Lamarque shared her thoughts and poems for one month in 'The Window on the Courtyard', a daily column in the Mondadori publishing company's Facebook poetry page. With her naive style, Lamarque looked at the world from her balcony in Milan, discovering epicurean delights in the little things like the hope of seeing a cat pass or the memory of her former vegetable garden. *The New Yorker* poetry editor Alice Quinn decided to invite 107 poets from all over the country to share their verses describing how they were feeling during the quarantine. Her initiative has resulted in the collection of poems *Together in a Sudden Strangeness: America's Poets Respond to the Pandemic.*

Quinn's book provides a unique outlook on the grief, fear and hope that those poets felt in the early months of the pandemic. The fast/slow time and the other sensations I mention above are brought into focus by these master wordsmiths. For example, in Jane Hirshfield's poem 'Today, When I Could do Nothing', she says, 'Today, when I could do nothing, I saved an ant' and concludes, 'This first day when I could do nothing, contribute nothing, beyond staying distant from my own kind, I did this.'

Susan Kinsolving equally states the need to concentrate on the menial tasks that have become so vital in our day-to-day lives. 'The mind cannot contain it all despite intent and wherewithal; it's little stuff that brings delight: a book, a drink. Keep thinking small.'

Other poets looked at the new life in quarantine, discovered different, more vital elements in their relationships. For example, in 'Ram of the Week', Linda Gregerson makes a connection between her husband Steven's past glory on the football field: 'Something about committed to the tackle and lateral pass became the skinniest guy on defence taking two men out' and his enduring commitment to take care of her because she has pulmonary problems: 'No shoulder pads, no helmet. Just the ever-unflagging-taking-care essential to him as breathing.' In 'I See on Zoom He's Growing Taller by the Day', Elizabeth J. Coleman summarises in one line the bitter choices in our expressions of love to our family that this virus has made us do: 'He didn't want to be kissed, but was all right with hugs, and squeezed me tight the next day before I ran to catch my plane.'

Some poets reflected on the meaning of the whole experience of the lockdown with an eye to the long-term ramifications. In 'In the Time of Pandemic', Kitty O'Meara wonders if being forced to reconsider what is important in their lives, people might change and build a future that is based on better respect for our planet. She concludes the poem, saying: 'In the absence of people living in ignorant, dangerous, and heartless ways, the earth began to heal. And when the danger passed, and the people joined together again, they grieved their losses, and made new choices, and dreamed new images, and created new ways to live and heal the earth fully, as they had been healed.' A bit sickly, methinks. The start is better: 'And the people stayed home. And they listened, and read books, and rested, and exercised, and made art, and played games, and learned new ways of being, and were still. And they listened more deeply.'

These poems help to show our highs and lows as a species battling this lethal infection sweeping the globe. My favourite one, mentioned above, includes ants – I did my Biology A level project on them Down Under. It's called 'Today, When I Could Do Nothing':

Today, when I could do nothing,
I saved an ant.
It must have come in with the morning paper,
still being delivered
to those who shelter in place.
A morning paper is still an essential service.
I am not an essential service.
I have coffee and books,
time,
a garden,
silence enough to fill cisterns.
It must have first walked
the morning paper, as if loosened ink
taking the shape of an ant.

Then across the laptop computer–warm–
then onto the back of a cushion.
Small black ant, alone,
crossing a navy cushion,
moving steadily because that is what it could do.
Set outside in the sun,
it could not have found again its nest.
What then did I save?
It did not move as if it was frightened,
even while walking my hand,
which moved it through swiftness and air.
Ant, alone, without companions,
whose ant-heart I could not fathom–
how is your life, I wanted to ask.
I lifted it, took it outside.
This first day when I could do nothing,
contribute nothing
beyond staying distant from my own kind,
I did this.[10]

After all this is over there will be monuments to this crisis, so what to do?

Rael San Fratello's first idea was a pragmatic one: a traditional memorial made of copper moulded into a bulbous, organic wall. The copper material would invite the touch lost to quarantine. Outdoors, it could develop a green or purple patina. 'If touched constantly,' San Fratello said, 'the patina might never occur, and the memorial will remain shiny.' Even so, a wall etched with names feels like a mismatch for Covid-19. Whom, exactly, would such a monument include? 'I feel like it's too conventional,' Rael said. It's a symptom of memorialism more broadly. Memorials and monuments have to lure visitors, draw attention, inspire photographs, structure space. Unless they don't. Perhaps, Rael San Fratello concluded, a memorial could be distributed to the people instead. A thing that you could touch all around the world, in every city or town, given that each one will have been touched by the pandemic. 'It could be something as simple as a doorknob or a balustrade – something mundane,' Rael said. 'Something anyone would touch and recall this moment.'

But Rael couldn't shake the idea of the copper penny. So personal and portable. He recalled a hundred-year-old wooden nickel his grandmother had kept, a token for a church anniversary. He had also recently started smelting down aluminum cans, and he found that friends were inexplicably drawn to the resulting ingots, many asking if they could take one home as a keepsake of nothing in particular. 'What if all we need is a copper ball?' he wondered. A keepsake that anyone – that everyone – could have. One that might act as a proxy for the touches and smells that the virus prohibits, too. But how do you distribute a copper object to everyone on Earth? The logistics seem impossible. They also correspond exactly with the coordination needed to distribute a vaccine that would successfully inoculate the planet's population. Perhaps the cure could come with the token that might preserve its own memory, like a talisman.

People have an attachment to the objects they make and use. They embed memories and carry them forward too. This one would conform to the shape of the human hand, both begging for touch and changing in response to it. 'Every memorial would become completely unique and individualised over time,' San Fratello said. 'Each memorial would be personal.' Such an expanded spirit of memorialisation would include many more people than just the dead – the families, the friends, the caregivers, and the healthy, whose persistence will, hopefully, outlive the virus. Could the vessel that delivers the vaccine itself become the memorial? Rael wondered aloud to me. 'It's the one thing that would touch everybody but not touch anyone else.'

However, when it comes to a Covid-19 monument, Sekou Cooke proposes an 'unmonument' instead, one that samples from protest movements and spreads their DNA like a different kind of virus. 'It first attacks our memorials to false leaders, then real ones, then attacks the monuments of capitalism and consumerism and industries too weak to resist,' Cooke wrote in a statement.[11]

30.11.20

It looks like we will be spoilt for choice with a plethora of vaccines coming online, all with high levels of effective immunisation. Last week, Sputnik V from Russia produced a 95% efficacy on a number on a par with Moderna's protection rates, albeit from fewer case numbers. Sputnik V's interim analysis was based on 39 confirmed cases of Covid-19, whereas Moderna's interim analysis was based on 95 cases and Pfizer-BioNTech's final analysis on 163 cases. Sputnik V's next interim readout, which is expected in December, will come at 78 cases, still shy of the other two vaccines. It's interesting that J&J has started a two-shot trial, and I wonder if the first dose, like AZN's most successful arm, will be lower than the second.

Novavax will likely be first to report Phase 3 data from a protein-based vaccine for Covid-19. A 10,000-patient UK trial of Novovax's NVX-CoV2373 is expected to read out in early 2021, and a US trial is slated to start this month.

On 7 November, CanSino announced the launch of Phase 3 testing in Mexico. According to the clinicaltrials.gov record, the Mexican sites are part of a global Phase 3 trial that started recruiting in September.

December

01.12.20

US virus cases have doubled in a month to a record 4 million, with fears that recent Thanksgiving travelling and indoor discussions across a dinner table could soon drive US daily deaths to 4,000 – or rather, with a 2–3 week lag. The number of people testing positive per day exceeded 200k for the first time on Friday, 150k yesterday, but it's hard to calibrate what's going on just now with respect to the holiday, though I note test positivity inching back towards 10%.

In Europe, infections are now falling fast, with the exception of Germany, and hospitalisations are peaking. As the lockdowns are relaxed in the run-up to Christmas, however, many see a risk of infections rising again, which could require further stringent lockdowns in late December 2020/early January 2021. In the UK, Boris Johnson headed off a rebellion in his own party ahead of today's vote on the Covid tiers coming into force tomorrow, agreeing restrictions would have a 'sunset' expiry date of 3 February and would be reviewed and potentially eased on 19 December.

The *FT* reports that the UK may become the first country to approve the Pfizer/BioNTech vaccine, expected within days. The plan is to begin delivering the first jabs by 7 December. US approval could then come as soon as 10 December, EMEA 11 December. German officials said over the weekend preparations are being made for inoculation in December once the vaccine has been approved by their own European regulators – expected in mid-December. A survey in France found that 59% of respondents said they would not get a Covid-19 vaccine once it becomes available. *The Sunday Times* reports that a specialist unit of the British army will be deployed to tackle anti-vaccine propaganda and disinformation, along with celebrities.

As a reminder, the Moderna vaccine is stable at 2–8 °C for thirty days; mRNA-1273 remains stable at -20 °C for up to six months and at room temperature for up to 12 hours. No dilution is required for mRNA-1273 at the vaccination site. mRNA-1273 has a potential wider distribution when compared to Pfizer's -80 °C vaccine stability. This has important consequences for global distribution; -80 °C freezers aren't exactly everywhere, and many locations have purchased these in advance.

The Public Health Agency of Sweden still insists that the core of their strategy was not about building natural herd immunity. Sweden's controversial pandemic policy has been both lambasted and praised around the world. The Nordic country adopted what its public health authority described as a 'soft' approach of keeping bars, restaurants and schools (for pupils up to the age of 16) open and giving only recommendations to wash hands, maintain social distance and keep gatherings to under 50 people. This is in marked contrast to neighbouring nations Denmark, Norway and Finland, which went swiftly into lockdown. In July and August, the number of infections dwindled, but much like the rest of Europe, autumn has brought an upsurge in cases and the country's highest-ever daily case numbers. According to the European Centre for Disease Prevention and Control, as of 12 November, Sweden had a fourteen-day cumulative number of 473 cases of infection per 100,000 inhabitants; in comparison, Norway had just 136. Sweden's death toll is ~7,000, surpassing all of its Scandinavian neighbours combined, though mortality remains lower than Belgium, Spain and the UK.

02.12.20

In the UK, as the tiering system comes in, Matt Hancock said, 'We have got this virus back under control.' He also said testing asymptomatic people was crucial to breaking chains of transmission, and in plans to test millions of people in the most affected areas, people will be offered £14 shopping vouchers if they agree to a test. As Welsh politicians continue to show they have control over their own policies, First Minister Mark Drakeford said hospitality businesses will not be allowed to serve alcohol from Friday and must shut at 6 p.m. This is on the back of a spike in cases after Wales emerged from its prior strict lockdowns.

In the US, Surgeon General Jerome Adams and Anthony Fauci said vaccines are likely to begin rolling out before year end, while UK Prime Minister Boris Johnson reinforced hope of a vaccine before Christmas, with approval for at least one 'in the next days and weeks'. In the UK, the military arrived in Bristol yesterday to start setting up one of the UK's first mass-vaccination centres. Still subject to regulatory approval, the centre could become operational within days. The UK's new Vaccine

Minister, Nadim Zahawi, said the government may use technology as proof of having had the vaccination as service providers such as pubs may begin to prioritise those who have been inoculated.

What can go wrong? The level to achieve herd immunity may be 70%, as per the marines on the USS *Roosevelt* and *Manaus* in Brazil. Thus, with anti-vaxxers, kids and pregnant women (or women wanting to conceive) not having vaccines, we may not reach it easily, especially if people's immunity wanes at six months and one is still reliant on a two-shot vaccine. There may be long-term toxicity too that's serious – we just don't know.

A study found that the vaccine has to have an efficacy of at least 70% to prevent an epidemic and of at least 80% to largely extinguish an epidemic without any other measures (e.g. social distancing). What about natural infection as a path forward? If asked, many scientists would probably agree with the statement, 'Natural infection gives better immunity than vaccination.' Indeed, if one survives the infection, there are certainly many pathogens for which natural infection induces stronger immune responses and more long-lived immunity than does vaccination. Measles is the prototypic of this. While there was a clear risk after infection of death, encephalitis and pneumonia before there was a vaccine, survivors gained lifelong immunity. Vaccination against measles, on the other hand, requires two shots and may not offer lifelong complete protection, but has proven to be good enough to keep the disease in check when widely implemented.

In contrast to the measles virus, there are a number of pathogens for which vaccination generates stronger immune responses and more effective protection against disease than does natural infection. In these cases, the man-made vaccine is 'superhuman'; that is, it gives humans immune responses superior to those generated in response to infection.

Overall, given the number of platforms being investigated and the huge ongoing efforts, a vaccine (or vaccines) against Covid-19 with immune responses and protection superior to that achieved through natural infection is an achievable goal.

03.12.20

The WHO does not believe there will be enough supplies of coronavirus vaccines in the next 3–6 months to prevent a surge in the number of infections, its top emergency expert said. The UK put speed before public confidence in a vaccine, says EU agency. The EMEA has suggested British regulators prioritised speed over winning public confidence to enable the UK to become the first Western country to license a coronavirus vaccine. Harsh, I think.

The MHRA (the Medicines and Healthcare products Regulatory Agency) will only become fully independent on 1 January 2021, following Brexit, but UK regulations allow it to grant authorisations on an emergency basis. Moncef Slaoui, scientific head of OWS, praised MHRA as 'an extremely high-grade agency' during a press conference. He pointed out that MHRA, alongside counterparts in other large EU nations, was EMA's 'scientific engine'. Andreas Michaelis, the German ambassador in London, criticised UK cabinet member Alok Sharma for a tweet, saying the UK had 'led humanity's charge against this disease'.

The Trump administration has invited leading vaccine manufacturers, drug distributors and government officials to convene at the White House next week for a vaccine summit. The 8 December event will feature President Trump, Vice President Mike Pence, several governors and private sector executives. Executives from Pfizer and Moderna have been invited, as have people from companies likely to be tasked with distribution and logistics, such as Walgreens and FedEx. Those familiar with the event see it as an opportunity for the administration to pressure the FDA to quickly approve the vaccines as well as to ensure that Trump receives credit for the unprecedented pace at which vaccines have been developed.

The FDA has scheduled meetings of its Vaccines and Related Biological Products Advisory Committee (VRBPAC) to discuss the emergency use authorisation from Pfizer/BioNTech and Moderna on 10 and 17 December respectively. The VRBPAC is an outside panel of independent experts that will provide advice to the FDA and vote on key topics, but the ultimate decision regarding whether to approve the EUA is made by the FDA after the VRBPAC. Background materials, including the meeting agenda and committee roster, will be published two days before the meeting is held. This is a highly anticipated meeting, and I expect additional vaccine data to be presented beyond what has been released to date. We should see detailed safety data and efficacy data in key subgroups (such as old versus young) as well as a long-term follow-up from the Phase 1 studies. I would expect vaccine approval within days of the VRBPAC. The main topics for discussion as well as how well the vaccines work will be:

1) **Full safety data:** Companies have currently only reported top-line, severe adverse events for the vaccine arm. No placebo data or data related to tolerability has been reported.
2) **Tolerability**: One can define tolerability as those side effects of the vaccine that may be uncomfortable for patients but not a safety issue that requires medical intervention. Here one can focus on placebo-adjusted rates of flu-like symptoms.
3) **Safety in older or high-risk subgroups:** Any differential safety, especially in older patients, could impact how a vaccine is used or which groups are prioritised for dosing.

4) **Key subgroups**: I expect the panel to scrutinise any differences in efficacy along with risk and demographic strata. Given both companies have already indicated the data is robust with respect to key subgroups, I do not expect any surprises.

5) **Durability**: Durability of neutralising antibody (NAb) titres is a key unanswered question and long-term follow-up from the Phase 1/2 trials could provide relevant supporting evidence. NAb titres are expected to drop somewhat after the booster dose, but it is important that titres remain within therapeutic levels for a reasonable period of time.

6) **Impact on other vaccine programmes**: The granting of EUAs will have an impact on the development of follow-on vaccine candidates in terms of recruitment as well as potential impact on the ability to maintain study blinding. I expect the VRBPAC to discuss the implications of granting an EUA. Will it even still be ethically allowable to have placebo arms and recruit people?

Meanwhile, Google's smartphone data confirm that Europe's latest restrictions have had less impact on daily life than previous lockdown restrictions. In March the average number of trips to places such as supermarkets, restaurants, transport hubs and offices fell to 35% of the level in January. After rebounding to 83% by the time of the latest lockdowns, mobility has now dropped only to 68%. This smaller effect could be caused both by more flexible rules and less enthusiasm for obeying them. Yet, these less stringent lockdowns are still working. The London School of Hygiene and Tropical Medicine's estimates of R0 are dropping. In European countries that enacted second lockdowns, R0 fell from an average of 1.1 in the week before the new restrictions to 0.9 in the week after. That small change makes a big difference. Over four weeks, it would mean new infections falling by 21% rather than rising by 36%.

04.12.20

Researchers in *Nature Communications* report a large-scale study to assess SARS-CoV-2 infection in 919 companion animals living in northern Italy, sampled at a time of frequent human infection. No animals tested PCR positive; however, 3.3% of dogs and 5.8% of cats had measurable SARS-CoV-2 neutralising antibody levels, with dogs from Covid-19 positive households being significantly more likely to test positive than those from Covid-19 negative households. Understanding risk factors associated with this and their potential to infect other species requires urgent investigation.

In the US, after appearing to stabilise in recent days, daily infections increased again to a record high of close to 209k, daily deaths increased to +2.8k – the highest since May – and the hospital census is now up at 100k. Despite these trends, US health authorities yesterday reduced the quarantine period for those coming into contact with an infected person from fourteen days to ten days if they have no symptoms and seven days if they test negative.

In further evidence of regional variations in Europe, Germany said it will extend its partial lockdown by three more weeks, with bars, gyms and cinemas remaining closed until 10 January, and Italy is set to tighten restrictions during the holiday season. Conversely, from next week, Austria will reopen schools for students under 14 years of age and most stores and services such as hairdressers. French PM Jean Castex said random border checks will stop holidaymakers going to ski in neighbouring Switzerland, where slopes have already opened. Germany has had a persistently high rate of new daily coronavirus infections despite imposing a lockdown – albeit light – at the beginning of last month. The RKI today reports >20k infections most days, continuing a trend that has lasted for weeks now. This number is something Angela Merkel and health experts would like to shrink significantly.

Among other things, RKI's head, Lothar Wieler, pointed out that outbreaks at homes for the elderly have been increasing in frequency and warned that many more will die from Covid-19 in the country. Meanwhile, here in the UK, Education Secretary Gavin Williamson sparked annoyance when he said Britain had approved the Pfizer/BioNTech coronavirus vaccine so promptly because it's a 'better' country than the US, France and Belgium. The comment was made with regard to the UK's speed, which he said was no surprise to him, continuing, '…because we're a much better country than every single one of them, aren't we?' Europe doesn't have Regulation 174 that enabled the UK's rapid approval, and in Italy, Health Minister Speranza stated they won't start till 23 January or thereabouts. 'Better?' That's debatable, but I guess he's right that we can respond quicker to decision-making over vaccines. Even Fauci was critical of UK's speed, but I have no idea why (I see he later apologised and rolled back his initial thoughts).

Pfizer now expects to ship half of the Covid-19 vaccines it originally planned for this year because of supply chain problems, but still expects to roll out more than a billion doses in 2021. 'Scaling up the raw material supply chain took longer than expected,' a company spokeswoman said. 'And it's important to highlight that the outcome of the clinical trial was somewhat later than the initial projection … Pfizer/BioNTech are now on track to roll out 1.3 billion vaccines in 2021 and the 50 million dose shortfall this year will be covered as production ramps up. The company is setting up what it has described as its biggest ever vaccination campaign through two final assembly and distribution centres in Kalamazoo, Michigan, and Puurs, Belgium, which will handle the European supply.'

Moderna announced that it plans to begin testing its vaccine in children aged 12–17. Children cannot be vaccinated against the coronavirus without data from studies testing this group. They plan to enrol 3,000 children: half of them will receive two shots of its vaccine one month apart, while the other half will receive a placebo. Pfizer/BioNTech announced back in October that it had begun dosing children in the same age group.

Interesting story on lack of tests in China at the start of all this:

In the early days in Wuhan, the first city first struck by the virus, getting a Covid-19 test was so difficult that residents compared it to winning the lottery. Throughout the Chinese city in January, thousands of people waited in hours-long lines for hospitals, sometimes next to corpses lying in hallways. But most couldn't get the test they needed to be admitted as patients. And for the few who did, the tests were often faulty, resulting in false negatives. The widespread test shortages and problems at a time when the virus could have been slowed were caused largely by secrecy and cronyism at China's top disease control agency, an Associated Press investigation has found.

Earlier in the pandemic, the same team said China had delayed releasing much Covid data:

Throughout January, the World Health Organisation publicly praised China for what it called a speedy response to the new coronavirus. It repeatedly thanked the Chinese government for sharing the genetic map of the virus 'immediately,' and said its work and commitment to transparency were 'very impressive, and beyond words'. But behind the scenes, it was a different story, one of significant delays by China and considerable frustration among WHO officials over not getting the information they needed to fight the spread of the deadly virus, the Associated Press has found.

Despite the plaudits, China in fact sat on releasing the genetic map, or genome, of the virus for more than a week after three different government labs had fully decoded the information. Tight controls on information and competition within the Chinese public health system were to blame, according to dozens of interviews and internal documents.

05.12.20

Daily reported infections rose above 700,000 globally for the first time on Wednesday. The US saw another record daily high of over

227k, with daily deaths at over 2.5k and a record hospital census of 100k. Nearly 40 million Californians are about to spend at least three weeks under a new stay-at-home order, with Los Angeles Mayor Eric Garcetti warning that the city is approaching a 'devastating tipping point'.

Let's take a step back in time – properly, not just to January 2020 – when the whole world seemed a different place. In order to comprehend ourselves and the future of humankind, it is necessary to understand where we came from. Unlike the approximately 350,000 known species of beetles on Earth, there is just one existing species of human. It is hard to imagine how our body and mind might have been constructed along different design principles or generated even a fraction of such diversity. With our recent ability to manipulate human genomes using gene editing and the emergence of technologies that enable human genomes to be rewritten in their entirety, the question of what we might become is no longer theoretical. Should humankind decide to redesign itself, the crap shot of design by Darwinian evolution may become as redundant as taxi drivers in an age of driverless cars.

Using the same body plan, evolution has fashioned four different types of ape. The techniques of molecular biology have demonstrated that we are more closely related to the African versions, chimps and gorillas, than to orangutans. DNA sequencing, furthermore, suggests that chimps are closer in kin than gorillas. This, coupled with molecular evidence indicating that modern humans shared a common ancestor with chimps and gorillas around 6 million years ago, suggested that the origin of modern humans was a recent event and that the precursor of modern humans was an as yet-to-be discovered chimp-like ancestral relative. In this pervasive 'chimp-centric' view of evolution, modern humans are made-over naked chimps. Maybe we're too modern and unevolved in fact to deal with such a new pathogen?

How has eating changed during lockdown? Researchers enrolled 1,964 voluntary participants from Bavarian universities. Their study cohort (mean age 23.3 ± 4.0 years, 28.5% male) had a mean body mass index of 22.1 ± 4.5 kg/m2. The overall food amount increased in 31.2% of participants during lockdown and decreased in 16.8%. This would explain why my trousers are tighter.

06.12.20

First, I have to note that a 102-year-old survivor of Spanish flu has survived Covid – twice, apparently.

In other areas, I note that the sheer volume of comic-based material related to Covid is immense and growing daily. Comics are particularly well-suited to visually explaining complex processes and to harnessing narratives for behavioural change. For example, in the 1990s there were *Superman* comics distributed towards the end of the Yugoslav Wars explaining the danger of landmines with accurate drawings of the most common ones, so children knew what to avoid. There are countless other examples from around the globe stretching back decades.

In the Covid-19 era, comics have once again served the purpose of explaining complex information and visually presenting public health advice. Early in the pandemic, various artists created comics that introduced the novel virus to the public, showing how it's transmitted and what people can do to protect themselves. These ranged from comics geared toward children to highly sophisticated explanations. One particularly illuminating example is Argha Manna's 'Be Aware of Droplets and Bubbles'.

Manna created this comic during strict lockdown in India, basing it on highly technical research from MIT's fluid dynamics lab. Manna's drawings are both informative and entertaining, showing what happens at the microscopic level when viral particles are discharged via a cough or sneeze and incorporated into a bursting fluid bubble. Manna scales the drawings to show the human toll the virus takes when people do not heed common-sense recommendations regarding coughing, sneezing and spitting. We are back to the simple efficacy of wearing a face covering.

Gemma Correll's 'Creativity in Captivity' comic uses split panels to contrast 'what I think I'll do during the "shelter-in-place" order vs what I'm actually doing'. It reminds me of the joke I've seen circulating on LinkedIn that states, 'so in retrospect in 2015 everybody interviewed got the answer wrong when asked "Where do you see yourself in five years" time?"'

Gemma Correll also looks at the dark reality of lockdown and points out the mental health issues occurring on top of the viral infection public health headlines in 'Save It for a Rainy Year'. Here readers are invited to use crayons with names like 'viral particulate green' to colour in images of 'unhealthy coping mechanisms'; the comic concludes with a dark circle, labelled 'the void,' into which the reader is invited to scream. All of her work around the pandemic has a dark edge that is counterbalanced by an equally dark sense of humour.

Like the best of the medium of comic books, this one transports readers into another world through visual imagery, teaching us about fluid dynamics and contagion along the way. 'The Side Eye', by Toby Morris and Siouxsie Wiles, is an online comic that uses static images and .gif animation to show how the virus replicates and spreads. This New Zealand duo (a country worth noting has done about the best in the world to stop the spread of the virus) use visual metaphors to connect viral replication on the micro level with transmission at the macro level. By scaling up and down, the authors explain the epidemiology of the pandemic. This is reinforced with a very deliberate and bold colour palate tracking how one person's infection can have a huge impact on an entire population.

I've discovered a new job: graphic journalist, a combination of journalist and comic book illustrator. This fascinating role can be highlighted in works like the series 'In/Vulnerable: Inequity in the Time of Pandemic', a collaboration between the Center for Investigative Reporting and *The Nib*, illustrated by Thi Bui. This series translates interviews with people from all walks of life, living across America, into graphic snapshots of the ways Covid-19 has affected individuals, and it reveals the fragility of our institutions. To give three quick examples, there's Martha, a nurse who is having to travel across New London, Connecticut, who is giving urgent care to the elderly and yet is hampered by all the necessary restrictions to keep them safe from the virus. Then there's Douglas Hawkins, a funeral director, whose entire career dealing with death suddenly seeing everything he knows tossed aside as funerary procedures are recreated to deal with infectious disease. Tawanda Jones, a teacher, weighs the threat of Covid-19 against the call to protest the simultaneous scourge of anti-black racism. Each comic uses a unique monochromatic hue; together, they form a multicoloured quilt that reflects the diversity of people's experiences.

Finally, there are comics as therapy. Often children who have been affected by wars in their countries are asked to draw what they saw or what they are worried about. The innocent and simple drawings of war crimes are horrific, but they help the child process the events. It is an accepted first step in coming to terms with the trauma and, hopefully, eventual rehabilitation. Right now, we are all the victims of trauma, so it should come as no surprise some are using their comic book art as a means to help them on the journey to a healthy recovery. The Graphic Medicine International Collective, for example, has hosted regular drawing together sessions in which participants are guided through live exercises that use comics as a vehicle for self-reflection, coping and community building. Moreover, *The New York Times* has featured a regular diary project in which comic artists sometimes provide prompts to readers in the form of drawing/writing exercises.

07.12.20

As the UK readies itself to roll out vaccines this week, the latest (and possibly final) Brexit impasse has raised concerns about delays at the border in January if a deal isn't reached. The solution? Military planes flying in shipments. The head of the UK's Medicines and Healthcare products Regulatory Agency (MHRA), June Raine, appeared unconcerned by the possibility of Brexit delays, telling the BBC's Andrew Marr today, 'We've rehearsed, we're ready and we know that whatever the deal, we will be able to ensure that people have access.'

A German scientist has claimed that Chinese media have misrepresented his research to assert that the coronavirus emerged in Italy, not China. Alexander Kekulé, Director of the Institute for Biosecurity Research, has featured prominently in Chinese news, with the scientist describing it as 'pure propaganda,' in *The New York Times*. There is also fear that the pandemic could significantly dampen turnout in the Romanian general elections taking place now, which ultimately could be a boost for the far right. The Serum Institute of India has sought emergency use authorisation from India's drug regulator for AZN's vaccine, and Japanese PM Suga has defended his support for GoToTravel and the Olympics.

08.12.20

This is it. After hundreds of papers, thousands of volunteers and dozens of hard-working doctors, we get to this exquisite moment: Margaret Keenan, a UK grandmother, aged 90, has become the first person in the world to be given the Pfizer Covid-19 jab as part of a mass-vaccination programme; she received it at 6.31 a.m. GMT. Margaret turns 91 next week and said the vaccination was the 'best early birthday present'.

In the UK, frontline HCWs, people over the age of 80 and care home staff will be first to receive the vaccine, with fifty hospitals in England initially chosen to serve as hubs for distributing the vaccine. Inoculations in the US could begin as early as Friday if regulators provide EUA for the Pfizer/BioNTech shot on Thursday, which they will. Russia started widespread vaccination of frontline workers and other high-risk people on Saturday. The race to develop and distribute the first effective Covid vaccine has taken on geopolitical importance. I can see a cheap and scalable Chinese vaccine distributed to BRI nations in the Global South in the 2020s having similar geopolitical effects that the US Atoms for Peace initiative had for nuclear proliferation in the 1950s. The distribution of breakthrough medicines in the past, such as quinine in the nineteenth century, seems to have diffused along non-political lines. The closest example I can think of is penicillin in the Second World War, where the Allies (and initially the US) had a monopoly, and the Axis powers were denied access. What ultimately got Reinhard Heydrich was not a Sten or even a Mills bomb, but sepsis.

09.12.20

Researchers in *Nature Communications* describe a meta-analysis of 3,111,714 reported global cases to demonstrate that while there is no difference in the proportion of males and females with confirmed Covid-19, male patients have almost three times the odds of requiring ITU admission and higher odds of death, compared to females. With few exceptions, the sex bias observed in Covid-19 is a worldwide phenomenon. An appreciation of how sex is influencing Covid-19 outcomes will have important implications for clinical management and mitigation strategies for this disease.

The Pfizer briefing docs were positive, so one can only conclude it's all a show tomorrow, with the AdCom of experts simply to reassure the public. Some details: 21% of the study population were aged over 65, but only 4% were aged over 75. I am very surprised nearly everyone (82%) recruited was white, though 46% had one or more comorbidities that are risk factors for Covid-19; 3% of the study population had baseline evidence of prior Covid-19 infection (had a positive antibody test prior to immunisation). The overall efficacy rate for this vaccine was 94.6%. This was noted to be consistent across age cohorts; over 55 years = 93.7%, under 55 years = 95.6%. In the over 75-year age group, the efficacy was effectively 100%, but note that this is based on only 4 cases of Covid-19 in this age cohort, all in the placebo group. The efficacy data were also highly consistent across sex, race, ethnicity and weight cohorts. When considering the relative risk of developing severe Covid-19, efficacy was 66% but note that this was on very small numbers (3 on placebo, 1 on vaccine).

For AZN, interim efficacy results are now available for 2/4 ongoing trials (from the UK and Brazil) based on cases occurring within approximately 4 months of follow-up in 11,636 participants, the majority of whom were aged 18–55 years (87.8%), white (82.7%) and female (60.5%). No Covid-19-related hospital admissions occurred in vaccine recipients, whereas 10 (2 of which were severe) occurred in the control groups. Vaccine efficacy for the prespecified primary analysis (combining dose groups) against the primary end point of Covid-19 occurring more than fourteen days after the second dose was 70.4%.

It looks like there will be an immediate supply shortage from Pfizer, which Moderna in the USA should be able to compensate for, and AZN, of course, only needs fridges and is cheaper. Fauci warned that Thanksgiving may have fuelled the spread of Covid-19 and 'the middle of January could be a real dark time for us'.

President-elect Biden has appointed my friend and previous colleague from Johns Hopkins, fellow resident on Longcope firm, as new CDC director. He couldn't pick a better choice. Rochelle Walensky is always her own person, a fabulous physician, not someone who runs with a crowd if it's not the right thing to do. She taught me so much about the management of drug users, 'shooters with fevers' as we affectionately called the patients involved, when I left leafy Oxford for Baltimore over two decades ago.

10.12.20

Boris Johnson urged 'discipline' as he warned London is facing a rise in Covid-19 infections amid fears that it may be moved to the more restrictive Tier 3 in a review scheduled for later this month. London had narrowly escaped with Tier 2 restrictions after the last lockdown; the decision won't happen until the end of next week. Despite shorter-term worries, the government's vaccine procurement chief has predicted Britons will be going abroad for the summer holidays. The NHS will now have 4 million doses before Christmas, and 280 GP immunisation centres will be in operation from next week.

Trump is reportedly considering taking the vaccine live on air to bolster confidence. Germany plans to vaccinate as many as 8 million people in the first quarter of 2021, including potentially 2.5 million in January, according to Health Minister Spahn. The UAE said interim analysis of China's Sinopharm vaccine showed 86% efficacy against infection. Lucky, really, since most of the population was vaccinated weeks ago using this.

I note commentary that air travellers should not be systematically tested for SARS-CoV-2 or asked to quarantine on their return home from Europe because they are generally at low risk of having the virus, according to guidance from the European Centre for Disease Prevention and Control (ECDC). Only people who have had known contact with someone with Covid-19 should be required to quarantine. The report, published jointly with the European Union Aviation Safety Agency, says that because SARS-CoV-2 is present in most European countries, imported cases are unlikely to significantly increase the rate of transmission. In the week beginning 2 November, 'imported cases accounted for less than 1% of the total number of cases, with the vast majority of cases being locally acquired,' it said.

Travel measures introduced by European countries have varied significantly during the pandemic and have resulted in considerable confusion for travellers. National criteria have been used to determine the potential need for testing or voluntary or mandatory quarantine of incoming travellers and have changed on average every one to two weeks because of the rapidly evolving situation. The UK, for example, has removed the requirement for all inbound travellers to self-isolate for fourteen days when coming from some countries, but has since reimposed it in several cases. In contrast, many high-income countries in the Asia Pacific region have introduced strict border control measures for travellers, including mandatory testing, quarantine, health declarations and thermal imaging.

With this in mind, the lateral flow devices used in the community testing pilot in Liverpool only picked up half the Covid-19 cases detected by PCR tests and missed 3 out of 10 cases with higher viral loads, according to the government's own policy paper. Given the low sensitivity of the Innova lateral flow devices when used in the field, experts are questioning how they can be used to allow care home residents to have contact with relatives over Christmas safely or for students to know for certain that they are not infected before returning home.

A questionnaire administered to 12,434 UK National Health Service users found that people who believe they had Covid-19 and recovered from it were 27% less likely to be willing to download a contract-tracing app than people who do not believe they had Covid-19. While 60% were willing to participate, the authors report this proportion is insufficient for the app to be an effective intervention.

13.12.20

I loved this, it's all from *The New Yorker*:

How dating during Covid is like being in a Jane Austen novel

- It's a long, drawn-out affair, composed of public meetings.
- The main characters lead quiet, domestic lives.
- The whole town feels invested in your behaviours.
- You regularly inquire about the health of each other's family members.
- Strict manners and customs of the day, built around a moral duty to society, dictate your interactions and lead to amusing mishaps.
- Clever planning is involved.
- It includes many brisk walks.
- Gossip helps edify listeners by determining what is and isn't acceptable, and who has violated social conventions and decorum.
- Romantic encounters are very weather-dependent.
- There's gonna be tea at some point.
- You inform your friends–who lead tranquil lives full of cooking and evenings at home–of recent romantic developments through vividly written correspondence.
- Much of the romantic relationship is epistolary, too.
- Eye contact and subtle gestures play an important role.
- You and your prospective future husband barely touch.[12]

From love to death. Unexpected circumstances require adaptation, as Harvard historian Drew Gilpin Faust observed in her acclaimed 2008 book *This Republic of Suffering: Death and the American Civil War*. The conflict, which killed 2% of the country's population – the equivalent of 6 million people today – reshaped the prevailing treatment of death, including by prompting the rapid spread of embalming so that families could safely transport their loved ones home from distant battlefields. As Faust noted, the current pandemic has once again 'made death's customary rituals impossible, overturning the forms and observances that counter the rupture of bereavement with the affirmation of community and continuity'. In her view, the challenge now is to learn 'how to reaffirm our humanity and community as we come to terms with the mortality that defines, unites and ultimately engulfs us all'.

Next, research has shown that over 80% of people in Scotland have felt awkward when trying to follow the rules, and the majority have worried about appearing rude or hurting someone's feelings. Framing what you say as an offer rather than a request will often help to reduce tension. For example, rather than saying, 'Please wear a mask,' make an offer: 'Do you need a mask? I've several spare ones.' This shows care and cooperation and is more likely to result in a positive outcome. I wonder how we'll do this with anti-vaxxers.

14.12.20

Locally, schools in Greenwich, London, will close due to a case spike. South Korea is increasing restrictions, Bahrain has approved Sinopharm's vaccine and an Australia–New Zealand travel bubble will be established. Trump tweeted, 'People working in the White House should receive the vaccine somewhat later in the programme, unless specifically necessary. I have asked that this adjustment be made. I am not scheduled to take the vaccine, but look forward to doing so at the appropriate time.'

Although not exactly the case anymore, researchers shed some light on why Germany has fared better than the United States/many European countries in handling the pandemic. The difference in mortality, morbidity and lost quality of life is difficult to attribute to medical technology, drug therapy, underlying genetics, environmental factors or virus characteristics. One contributing factor may be differences in public health messages intended to guide individual behaviours to mitigate the spread. The researchers used a national survey of German adults to test nuances in public health messaging. The nuances spanned from comprehensive messages (describing the uncertainty in both numbers and adjectives) to limited messages (leaving the uncertainty unmentioned). The results suggested that individuals tend to prefer messages with comprehensive rather than limited expressions of uncertainty (32.3% vs 21.1%). Similar findings were replicated in analyses of motivation to adopt and maintain containment efforts. Together, the findings of this thoughtful and rigorous research suggest that disclosing uncertainty can help persuade sceptics and bolster public behaviours to manage the pandemic.

This study is not the first to stress the value of expressing uncertainty to promote trust and behaviour change. In social psychology science, the strategy is termed 'correcting against self-interest' and can enhance the credibility of the messenger and increase the influence of the message. For example, a car mechanic who comments that 'you have an oil leak that is small and probably not worth correcting' seems a credible professional who merits trust when later suggesting a radiator leak repair. More generally, public health authorities might gain trust by ensuring that the public understands statistical uncertainty (such as in daily trends or replication estimates) and might lose trust by overhyping outlier anomalies (such as single-day spikes in cases or deaths). Communication requires tact when relaying information that the future is uncertain. A vague acknowledgement tends to undercut trust, such as the trite declaration 'the future is difficult to predict'. An excessive emphasis on uncertainty may be even worse, such as messages promoted by merchants of doubt who minimise public concern by capitalising on the limitations of science. A better strategy may be to acknowledge risk by explicitly providing a best-case scenario, a worst-case scenario and a likely case scenario. These communication nuances might also help clinicians to better explain uncertainty to patients and families in medical care.

15.12.20

On Friday, we learned that the US government has now purchased 200 million doses of Moderna's vaccine (mRNA-1273). The contract price for all option doses is $16.50 per dose. There are plans to deliver about 20 million doses by the end of December, its first 100 million doses in total in Q1 2021 and the additional 100 million doses in Q2 2021. I note that the US government has the option to purchase up to an additional 300 million doses.

Public comfort with vaccination continues to grow, with some brand preference even starting to evolve. In a Jefferies survey, they found 52% of Americans are now planning to get vaccinated in the next 3–6 months, compared to 47% last month. Soon there will be the question of AstraZeneca or Pfizer – a bit like, do you want vanilla or chocolate ice cream. Oh, how the world has changed in just one year.

I still see a lot of anti-vaxxing stories these days, but note celebrities are missing now from the roster, and some websites are awash with conspiracy theories involving everyone from Mossad to Princess Di. They say there are no atheists in foxholes but are there anti-vaxxers during a pandemic? Robert F. Kennedy Jr, Robert de Niro and Jim Carrey, to name but three, have argued against the vaccination of children. Even Novak Djokovic this year said his opposition to vaccines could prevent his return to the sport if a vaccine was needed. Then there was the rapper M.I.A., who tweeted, 'If I have to choose the vaccine or a chip, am gonna choose death.' Even Trump has claimed MMR links to autism. Not helpful.

There is, after all, a real history here. By the early 1950s, polio paralysed ~20k kids in the US each year. Pressure for a vaccine was overwhelming. Virologist Jonas Salk began work on a vaccine in 1953 under the assumption that if the body was presented with a vaccine containing 'killed' poliovirus, it would create antibodies protecting it from live poliovirus. The trick was to inactivate the live virus just enough so it could not cause infection, but not so much as to destroy its structure and prevent antibody production. Within two years, Salk's vaccine went from development to field testing in nearly 2 million children. On 12 April 1955, Salk's vaccine was declared effective and safe. Within 3 hours of this announcement, the federal government granted licences to five pharmaceutical companies to begin producing the vaccine. Thanks to political pressure, mass-vaccine production, dissemination and inoculation began on 13 April. Within days there were reports of post-vaccine paralysis. Even as the number of children who developed polio after getting the vaccine grew, repeated assurances of safety by the vaccine developers combined with minimal federal oversight allowed polio vaccination to continue for an additional three weeks. When the surgeon general finally stopped vaccinations on 6 May 1955, 40,000 children had developed vaccine-induced polio, 200 were paralysed and 10 had died. Salk's inactivation method had been used incorrectly by several manufacturers, and 200,000 children had received vaccines containing live poliovirus.

To be clear, if an independent monitoring programme had existed, the manufacturing flaws might have been identified before distribution or, at worst, the programme could have been halted when the first cases of vaccine-induced polio were reported. It's all very different now.

The rapid development of Covid-19 vaccines is the outcome of big pharma's R&D prowess, billions of dollars in federal investment and the dedication and ingenuity of scores of scientists. But it also illustrates the logic of the Bayh-Dole Act, passed forty years ago in the US, which governs how universities can work with industry to reap the benefits of federally funded research. The act permits universities to collaborate with private companies to license and commercialise these technologies under the rationale that the payoff for the government's investment is increased economic activity for the country. It is unlikely that the act will ever be brought back to the floor of Congress for revision, and its staying power suggests that it is a permanent fixture of the US innovation ecosystem.

Nevertheless, there are legitimate philosophical and logistical objections that the incoming administration should work to address.

Over the years, the federal government has funded most of the basic research that underlies the Covid-19 vaccines. But the government itself lacks the capacity to carry out massive clinical trials or to manufacture and distribute the vaccines on its own. The Moderna vaccine, for example, relies on patents that are licensed under Bayh-Dole to the company. The fact that vaccines could be available to HCWs as soon as this week is a testament to the effectiveness of the arrangement. When Bayh-Dole first came along, there were notable concerns among university faculties about the conflicts that would arise. Would scientists be objective about their published research if they also stood to gain financially? Would students and postdocs see their careers stalled out because results were held back while patents were filed or, even worse, results were kept secret to protect financial interests?

Universities set up ways to monitor and correct such conflicts, and though there have been problems, the system has held up well and contributed to important innovations. Still, the maintenance of technology transfer offices and conflict monitoring have introduced costs to conducting research that are not fully compensated for by the federal government, costs that have taken resources away from other important university priorities. When a faculty member holds equity in a start-up company, their interests are not completely aligned with those of the university, which can make negotiating licenses cumbersome and strained.

Some universities in the US created a boilerplate licence with standardised terms that could be automatically agreed upon when a company was formed, but this idea has not been widely adopted. The rationale against the boilerplate licence is that every deal is different and needs to be separately negotiated, but that leaves the problem of those additional administrative costs, as well as the risk of damaging the university's relationship with the faculty entrepreneur.

17.12.20

New York Mayor Bill de Blasio told residents to prepare for a shutdown of all but essential businesses soon after Christmas.

In the UK, Boris Johnson has refused to revoke Christmas freedoms. Also here, in a move to detect asymptomatic cases, from January all secondary schools will test staff each week and some pupils every day, using quick-result lateral flow tests.

In Sweden, the prime minister said that medical chiefs failed the country with its light touch, herd immunity approach. The country's second wave has been so hard that hospitals in Stockholm are now struggling to cope, but that's mainly because of staffing issues. Despite lifting its daytime lockdown, France is urging parents to take children out of school and isolate them for eight days before family gatherings. Denmark is imposing a hard lockdown over the Christmas/New Year holidays. Out in Asia, in a significant easing of travel restrictions, Singapore said it will allow a limited number of business travellers and visiting officials from other countries to enter from next month.

Dr Fauci has suggested Joe Biden and Kamala Harris should be vaccinated as soon as possible 'for security reasons'.

18.12.20

In the US, daily case growth increased to the highest on record (+242k) yesterday, daily deaths were the second highest (+3.4k) after Wednesday (3.5k), and the census continues to climb (now at 113.5k). Germany recorded the biggest increase in deaths since the start of the crisis, with Merkel hinting the latest restrictions may remain in force for longer than the planned January end date.

In the UK, Boris Johnson has encouraged the over-70s not to spend Christmas with relatives and urged people not to stay away from home unless 'absolutely unavoidable'. 'When we say 3 households can meet on 5 days, I want to stress these are maximums, not targets to aim for,' Johnson said, adding that 'of course it is always going to be safest to minimise the number of people you meet'. Quoting a popular Christmas song, Johnson wished everyone a 'merry little Christmas,' insisting that the emphasis was on 'little' this year. Wales will make it illegal for more than two households to mix. *The Times* reports that around 180k in England have been suffering from long Covid, with symptoms lasting for at least five weeks.

European authorities are said to be trying to achieve a compressed approval timeline for the Pfizer vaccine, which would allow a rollout of the vaccine pre-Christmas. This follows leaders of EU countries struggling to explain to their residents why they are still waiting for vaccines when the US and the UK have begun the rollout, despite the vaccine being pioneered in Germany. An EU official said the timing depends on the timing of the European Medicines Agency's announcement and the need for the assessment to be seen as independent from political interference.

I think it's useful to list world leaders who have caught Covid-19. The vast majority are right wing (some are, in essence, dictators), but it is not exclusive to that side of the political spectrum nor specific to one continent either. Also, while almost all are men, that's more a statement about politics than infection patterns. All have recovered from Covid (I am assuming Macron will too – he currently has it). Dates are either retrospectively when they showed symptoms or when it was reported (some news agencies are freer than others). It's a list that emphasises the truly global reach of this virus, although notable for their conspicuous absence are any leaders from Asia:

- Boris Johnson, UK Prime Minister, 27 March (nice to see Britain being first in the world)
- Mikhail Mishustin, Prime Minister of Russia, 30 April
- Nikol Pashinyan, Prime Minister of Armenia, 1 June
- Juan Orlando Hernandez, President of Honduras, 16 June
- Jair Bolsonaro, President of Brazil, 7 July
- Janine Anez, President of Bolivia, 9 July
- Alexander Lukashenko, President of Belarus, 28 July
- Alejandro Giammattei, President of Guatemala, 18 September
- Donald Trump, President of the United States of America, 2 October
- Andrzej Duda, President of Poland, 24 October
- Boyko Borissov, Prime Minister of Bulgaria, 25 October
- Abdelmadjid Tebboune, President of Algeria, 3 November
- Emmanuel Macron, President of France, 17 December

19.12.20

In London, we wake to Tier 4, and the Netherlands bans flights from the UK. The virus is likely more infectious, possibly up to 70% faster transmission now. R0 increase of ~ +0.4: 23 unique changes.

A new mutation is putting at risk all the hard-fought battles to create a vaccine. B.1.1.7, also called the Kent variant, has an unusually large number of genetic changes, particularly in the spike protein. Three of these mutations have potential biological effects that have been described previously to varying extents.

The rapid growth of this lineage indicates the need for enhanced genomic and epidemiological surveillance worldwide and laboratory investigations of antigenicity and infectivity. The B.1.1.7 lineage carries a larger than usual number of virus genetic changes. The accrual of 14 lineage-specific amino acid replacements prior to its detection is, to date, unprecedented in the global virus genomic data for the Covid-19 pandemic.

High rates of mutation accumulation over short time periods have been reported previously in studies of immunodeficient or immunosuppressed patients who are chronically infected with SARS-CoV-2. These infections exhibit detectable SARS-CoV-2 RNA for 2–4 months or longer (although there are also reports of long infections in some immunocompetent individuals). The patients are treated with convalescent plasma (sometimes more than once) and usually also with the drug remdesivir. This leads us to hypothesise that the unusual genetic divergence of lineage B.1.1.7 may have resulted, at least in part, from virus evolution with a chronically infected individual. Maybe someone who was immunosuppressed, for example they had HIV or a leukemia or were receiving chemotherapy.

The Lancet has published some of AZN's additional vaccine data: 'ChAdOx1 nCoV-19 appears to be better tolerated in older adults than in younger adults and has similar immunogenicity across all age groups after a boost dose. Further assessment of the efficacy of this vaccine is warranted in all age groups and individuals with comorbidities.'

21.12.20

B.1.1.7, the name of the new variant, has now led to the UK's isolation regardless of Brexit news. Of all the things that might happen, this set of mutations puts at risk any rapid return to normalcy/the market's euphoria; if the vaccine can't handle this it would be concerning. But, the two FDA-approved mRNA platforms are also ideally placed to rapidly adapt to it. Even their current vaccines match the 10 January Wuhan sequence, not the more recent ones with the D614G mutation in the spike that rapidly replaced the Wuhan sequence within months across the world. That means the amino acid labelled D at the 614th position in the spike protein has changed to G.

B.1.1.7 will likely be widespread in all areas of at least England and Wales fairly soon, as tiers 2 and 3 are unlikely to be enough to stop its spread. This is why the government has moved swiftly into Tier 4 this weekend, cancelling limited Christmas socialisation plans.

The case numbers yesterday were terrible, suggesting that the rate of case growth is accelerating. Some UK modelling suggests a doubling of cases within six days if the trends continue. Again, without laboratory studies, it's unclear whether the new strain is in fact less deadly than the regular strain. If there really are thousands of cases of B.1.1.7 in the UK, and the strain has been circulating since September, it seems highly implausible that it has not already arrived in Continental Europe.

European residents of the UK are currently trying to figure out how to get home for Christmas via third countries and could take the new strain with them. One scenario then is that Continental lockdowns are likely to be tightened and extended when cases of the new strain are identified in France, Germany and across Europe. Now that Johnson has made the political argument for reclosing in order to shut down the spread of B.1.1.7, most of England and Wales is likely to go into Tier 4 in fairly short order and could stay there until the vaccine rollout is advanced in late February or March. This will certainly be the case if yesterday's case numbers worsen. There is even some thought that Tier 4 will not be enough to hold the new form of the disease, which suggests there might be a Tier 5 possible for London, south Essex and north Kent at least, something akin to the very strict lockdowns in France and Italy in the spring. But the vaccine rollout in the UK has been aggressive and we have a head start. If B.1.1.7 is as transmissible as feared, here we will aim to vaccinate more of the population to reach herd immunity. Random sampling is important to capture regional coverage.

But isn't this just like the flu? After all, Covid-19 is often compared to influenza. In the middle of a pandemic with a new coronavirus transmitted from the respiratory tract, it is obvious to look at previous influenza pandemics and seasonal influenza for comparison. Yet, it is important to understand that Covid-19 is not influenza. During the Covid-19 pandemic, several countries have struggled with overburdened intensive care unit capacity, whereas during the H1N1 pandemic in 2009, intensive care unit capacity was sufficient. For example, influenza never exceeded 4.5% of the total national ICU bed capacity in Denmark. In the spring of 2020, mortality for Covid-19 in Lombardy, Italy, reached 159 per 100,000 population. By contrast, a study of influenza deaths during the 2009 pandemic estimated the all-age mortality in the USA to be 4.1 per 100,000.

22.12.20

All viruses mutate. Following weekend analysis, Peter Horby from Oxford and chair of NERVTAG (New and Emerging Respiratory Virus Threats Advisory Group) said, 'The conclusion is that there is high confidence that this variant has transmission advantage over other variants.' Data showed that the new strain had kept spreading during lockdown even when the non-variant coronavirus cases decreased.

Neil Ferguson of Imperial College said the R0 was >1.2 vs 0.8 for the normal coronavirus. While cases of the variant virus have clustered in London and the south and east of England, according to Ferguson, it is highly likely it will become the predominant strain throughout the country. But I also think we'll identify it in other countries, rendering travel bans irrelevant. The locations with the greatest propensity to lockdowns are the places most vulnerable to the new strain; one would think additional lockdowns are likely in New York and perhaps other states (the most economically valuable ones, e.g. California), but if 50 million Americans have had the virus/recovered, and 100 million Americans will be vaccinated, one would think that there will be herd immunity by the end of March.

Over the next few days I think we'll hear of the following:

- The virus is more infectious in cellular models.
- Antibodies are less effective against it.

- It isn't associated with worse illness or outcomes and, in fact, it might be better.

Even with the new strain, I think the vaccine will be protective. To me, the worst case is a small decrease in efficacy. The good news as well is that the coronavirus mutates very slowly, about half the rate of seasonal flu and a quarter of the rate of HIV.

23.12.20

Herd immunity is based on our understanding of viral pathogens as obligate intracellular parasites that require a host for replication. If enough people are immune to infection, then the virus cannot be transmitted to new susceptible hosts and will be eliminated from circulation within the population. When a sufficient proportion of the population is immune and thus thwart the pathogen's ability to circulate, that population has reached the herd immunity threshold. Throughout history, consequential human pathogens that caused debilitating disease, such as smallpox and polio, have circulated throughout the population for centuries or millennia without ever reaching this threshold. They have only been vanquished through immunisation campaigns that have required years of effort and investment. After all, the WHO has just declared Africa polio free.

Herd immunity is a relatively recent concept, and some have taken umbrage at the term as it equates human populations with animals. However, this reflects the origin of the term, which was originally coined by livestock veterinarians in the early twentieth century in reference to epidemics of 'contagious abortion,' or pathogens that caused spontaneous miscarriages in herds of cattle and sheep. By the 1950s, the term was applied to newly developed vaccines and their potential for preventing widespread viral diseases such as polio at the population scale. As herd immunity as a concept became more broadly associated with immunisation campaigns, it gained that specific meaning. Until recently, herd immunity generally referred to population immunity acquired through vaccination.

The recent reversion of the term to its original context, immunity acquired through infection or immunisation, has created a host of misconceptions about how the herd immunity threshold might be reached for SARS-CoV-2. The prospect of reaching herd immunity through natural infection is not an expeditious process, in part because of the relationship between the herd immunity threshold and the basic reproduction number (R0). R0 measures the average number of secondary infections caused by one infected person in a population of completely susceptible individuals. In the most basic terms, the herd immunity threshold is defined mathematically as $1-1/R0$. Given that estimates of R0 throughout the SARS-CoV-2 pandemic around the world have ranged from 2 to 3 in the absence of interventions to reduce transmission, the herd immunity threshold is estimated to be in the range of 50–67%.

However, R0 is not a static number, making the herd immunity threshold difficult to estimate. R0 is not solely determined by viral infectivity and virulence and rarely reflects the variables present in the real world. Interventions intended to reduce transmission can reduce R0 substantially, as can many variables that influence susceptibility, including genetic traits, receptor distribution, and immune status of the host. Furthermore, even in populations that are completely susceptible, they do not remain completely susceptible over time as a pathogen spreads through the population. I don't know if we'll reach herd immunity with this virus, or maybe we will in some places but not others, a bit of a patchwork quilt. And, am hearing of some new cases in Manaus – am worried about this as I thought Brazil or certainly Manaus was at herd immunity.

24.12.20

UK Health Secretary Matt Hancock has described the new variant of coronavirus, which came to light yesterday in South Africa as 'highly concerning'. He said the variant was 'more transmissible and appears to have mutated further than the new variant that has been discovered in the UK'. In consequence, he said the government was quarantining the two cases found in the UK, as well as their close contacts. The UK government is also placing 'immediate restrictions' on travel from South Africa. But, to me, if one looks for lots of mutations using mass genomics, or population sequences, then this is both expected and manageable. And, as concerns about the B.1.1.7 strain calm down, it will be interesting if Novavax's ongoing UK Phase 3 trial will report data on this group too and whether their vaccine protects. Hospital tensions with vaccines are high – no surprises there.

I note the American Medical Association has waded into the social media misinformation war, penning a letter to the CEOs of Facebook, Google, Twitter and TikTok to urge them to take stronger action against misinformation as Covid-19 vaccines are rolled out. 'We encourage you to continue evaluating your existing policies that are designed to combat misinformation to ensure they are as effective and comprehensive as possible. Lives – and the success of this historic effort – are on the line.'

25.12.20

Merry Christmas! As it's Christmas, let's talk about religion today. Religion has been a profound force in human history and, contrary to many assumptions, it remains so today, for better or worse. Even before humans left the cave and gave up hunter-gathering, before settled communities, in one form or another, faith shaped our destinies. Today, among other reasons to take these institutions and forces seriously, survey after survey highlights that faith leaders are often the most trusted group among leaders across many world regions.

We have fought over different gods and differ on many core values from the first inklings of civilisation. In virtually all, however, from the most primitive to the most sophisticated, the central premise has been the belief in protecting communities of believers, whether from others or from unknown or misunderstood threats. These have been fundamental principles for millennia.

Likewise, the most positive human values hold that in considering our roles and actions, we should do unto others as we would have them do unto us. Fast forward to 2020: frictions between different religions and other isms remains intense, predictably so. But Covid-19 is new, both in its qualitative and quantitative aspects. This 'new' is coupled with other factors, in particular, ease of transmission of a global virus affecting all corners of the world, science-based technological capability to limit its deadly effects, and an unprecedented ability to instantly communicate everywhere, for good or ill.

For vaccines, we know there will be individuals who will be difficult to reach, others who will be dubious about the reliability of any public health measure that comes with the backing of scientists, or who basically distrust their government in whatever form. Still, others will resist because their spiritual leaders counsel their congregants not to be vaccinated, invoking traditions, myths, customs, taboos or other reasons to oppose, however strong the case for efficacy and safety may be.

The Vatican has just said the use of Covid-19 vaccines developed using cell lines derived from aborted foetuses is 'morally acceptable' in the absence of an alternative jab: 'All vaccinations recognised as clinically safe and effective can be used in good conscience with the certain knowledge that the use of such vaccines does not constitute formal co-operation with the abortion from which the cells used in production of the vaccines derive,' the Vatican's Congregation for the Doctrine of the Faith announced in a statement. The text, which was approved by Pope Francis, also said there was 'a moral imperative' to ensure that poorer countries were able to access effective vaccines. The doctrinal orthodoxy office said that 'vaccination is not, as a rule, a moral obligation' and must be voluntary.

But from an ethical point of view, 'the morality of vaccination depends not only on the duty to protect one's own health but also on the duty to pursue the common good,' the office said.

The AstraZeneca vaccine is among those developed using cells derived from foetuses aborted decades ago, although no foetal cells will be present in the vaccine itself. It is worth a look at this, which describes the emotional relationship that led to the cells for vaccine production being isolated. As Pope Francis said, 'How sad it would be if access to a Covid-19 vaccine was made a priority for the richest. It would be sad if the vaccine became the property of such-and-such nation and not universal for everyone.' That said, religious support is not a given. Individual dioceses and bishops can and have differing opinions and have opposed Covid vaccination for various reasons. In the US, Bishop Joseph Brennan, head of the diocese of Fresno, said in a video, 'I won't be able to take a vaccine, brothers and sisters, and I encourage you not to, if it was developed with material from stem cells that were derived from a baby that was aborted, or material that was cast off from artificial insemination of a human embryo.'

In the case of Islam, the Quran obliges its followers to seek protection from illness, regardless of who is providing that protection. Respected Muslim leaders thus argue that they want a cure, or at least a vaccine, as badly as anyone else. Religious support should therefore be expected. The Prophet Muhammad said, 'There is no disease that God has created for which He has not made a cure that is known by some people and unbeknownst to others, except death.' The husband and wife BioNTech team are of Turkish Muslim heritage.

Other Islamic leaders, however, have concerns around the safety and permissibility of vaccines that are being developed, and what they say can influence millions. For the 225 million Indonesian Muslims, the supreme authority on religious affairs is the Indonesian Ulama Council or the MUI. When the central MUI issued a fatwa in 2019 that suggested that the measles and rubella vaccine was forbidden, many conservative families across the archipelago refused to vaccinate. A central problem is related to the halal status of the vaccine; in an emergency situation, halal certification in principle should not be an issue. The latest news is that the MUI, together with the Indonesian Halal Certification Agency (BPJPH), has just finished a study on the halal status of a possible Covid vaccine and is expected to soon issue a fatwa that will allow (or not) Indonesians to be vaccinated.

In other settings (Nigeria, Pakistan), Muslim leaders came to fear that polio vaccination presented dangers, though with careful dialogue most doubts were overcome. One turning point came in Nigeria when leaders vaccinated their children in public. Regarding Covid-19 and vaccine prospects, their position is still not confirmed. But, in the UAE, their highest council has recommended the use of vaccines even if they contain pork gelatine.

In Judaism, Rabbi Hershel Schachter, who is a highly respected American Orthodox rabbi, said, 'If a democratic government ultimately legislates that a Covid-19 vaccination is safe for the public or specific populations, people must comply with this ruling. Jews who refuse to abide by government-mandated vaccination endanger all of society.' He then notes that the measles outbreak in Hasidic communities in the United States with low vaccination rates and the subsequent public disgust with ultra-Orthodox Jews illustrates the potential for desecrating God's name when Jews defy normative practice and legal requirements. Remarkably, some anti-vaccination activists have begun to use the Star of David that Nazis forced Jews to wear to promote their cause.[13]

26.12.20

After a hard year (we just passed 70,000 deaths in the UK), good news related to Covid-19 is welcome. Researchers provide a reason for optimism that our healthcare system has improved in our ability to care for persons with Covid-19. Using administrative claims data from a large national health insurer, they found that a hospital's risk-standardised event rate (a composite of hospital mortality or referral to hospice) because of Covid-19 had significantly decreased from 16.56% to 9.29%.

Hong Kong scientists estimate that the SARS-CoV-2 lineage that has rapidly become the most dominant in the UK is 75% more transmissible than the previous lineage, potentially due to a mutation in the receptor-binding domain of the spike protein. Their estimates suggest that the R0 for the mutated 501Y strain is about 1.75 times that of the unmuted 501N strain. They note that this variant does not appear to have spread significantly outside of the UK at this point, although a sporadic spread of the mutation has occurred in Wales, Australia, Spain and the United States without the variant becoming as dominant in those places.

27.12.20

As we come towards the end of the dreadful year, the *BMJ* have written a darkly comic summary of the world leaders imagined as a macabre awards ceremony. This was too good not to preserve in a book, so without further ado, I give you the list of winners. All of this is from the creative geniuses from the *BMJ,* and I wish I could write something this wry and knowing. Here are the results:

- **Most likely to approve a vaccine: Vladimir Putin, President of Russia**
  Long carrying one of the biggest Covid-19 caseloads, Russia's infections have soared throughout 2020, yet deaths per capita are relatively low, despite reports of a healthcare system struggling with ageing equipment and hospitals almost constantly near capacity. Putin put restrictions in relatively swiftly but refused to lockdown and is pinning hopes on his country's own vaccine development. He has spared no opportunity to laud Russia's progress and flabbergasted the world by approving one vaccine candidate before Phase 3 trials had reported any results. He claimed it was safe because his own daughter had been administered it, though not yet himself.

- **Most likely to understand the science: Angela Merkel, Chancellor of Germany**
  One of the few world leaders with a scientific background, Merkel quickly grasped the situation when the novel coronavirus hit Europe. Germany's efficient public health system and clear communication with its state governors, as well as neighbouring countries, meant it has coped with alarming infection numbers with a robust test-and-trace system and clear effective prevention measures.

- **Most likely to impose a stringent lockdown: Xi Jinping, President of China**
  From original concern to almost full normality, China is both reprobate and role model to the world in how to handle an epidemic.

- **Most likely to eliminate the virus: Jacinda Ardern, Prime Minister of New Zealand**
  Universally lauded for being one of the few countries to achieve effective elimination of Covid-19, some may argue that New Zealand's Ardern benefited from a relatively remote and sparsely populated country, making closed borders and restrictions easier to enforce.

- **Most likely to deny everything, Jair Bolsonaro: President of Brazil**
  A man who is at least consistent. Even when he himself caught the virus, Bolsonaro maintained his dismissal of it as 'the little flu'. His blatant disregard for masks, social distancing or any kind of preventive measures led to clashes with, and the eventual dismissal

of, two health ministers in the space of three months, and it ran counter to regional governors' attempts to get the world's third largest outbreak under control.

- **Most likely to misfire, Narendra Modi: Prime Minister of India**
  Modi can't win. Not against this opponent. Imposing one of the world's largest and most severe lockdowns failed to flatten the curve, and SARS-CoV-2 infection is still running rampant throughout India, with a caseload the second highest in the world and a death toll expected to rise sharply now that the virus has reached rural areas where healthcare is severely lacking.

- **Most likely to learn from the past: Moon Jae-in, President of South Korea**
  South Korea had a scare in 2015 when MERS unexpectedly reached its shores. Never again, it declared, and Moon's response has been impressive: prompt lockdowns and restrictive measures, universal surveillance using the latest in tracking technology to warn of infected contacts, and one of the first deployments of mass (including drive-by) testing.

- **Most likely to act first: Tsai Ing-Wen, President of Taiwan**
  If there's a leader who did everything right, it's Tsai. The first to take preventive action over SARS-CoV-2, she ordered health screenings for all flights from Wuhan from 31 December 2019, and in January mobilised the Central Epidemic Command Center to coordinate the response. She introduced travel restrictions, began quarantining high risk travellers and limited the number of people allowed at gatherings.

- **Most likely to be caught between a rock and a hard place: Pedro Sanchez, Prime Minister of Spain**
  Few governments will emerge from this crisis unscathed, but Pedro Sanchez has had a particularly difficult time in territorial Spain. He has been severely criticised for his government's overly centralised and heavy-handed response to the first wave, when the country emerged alongside Italy as the centre of the European outbreak, the horrific 20,268 deaths in care homes and the imposition of one of the longest lockdowns in the world.

- **Most likely to give a clear and measured national address: Emmanuel Macron, President of France**
  Nationally broadcast addresses can be double-edged swords, but Emmanuel Macron has wielded them with some skill. They've proved crucial in communicating two strict but necessary

lockdowns and numerous curfews and restrictions on French citizens, balancing his country's teetering economy, racial tensions and the world's fifth biggest coronavirus burden. His leadership domestically as well as on the continent has earned him credit, but as France's hospitals struggle with a second wave already worse than the first, he will need to offer more than reassurance in the months ahead.

- **Most likely to refuse to wear a mask: Andrés Manuel López Obrador, President of Mexico**
'You know when I'm going to put on a mask? When there is no corruption,' said López Obrador in July. He has repeatedly broken physical distancing guidelines and continued to travel even as Mexico rocketed up the caseload rankings over the summer. With austerity foremost on his agenda, he has kept testing and tracing at a minimum and forgone any mandatory national lockdown, instead focusing on an expansion of hospital beds.

- **Most likely to stay in the background: Stefan Lofven, Prime Minister of Sweden**
For much of 2020, the public face of Sweden's pandemic response was not a government minister but Anders Tegnell, the state epidemiologist at the Public Health Agency. But Tegnell's controversial 'soft' strategy, refusing harder restrictions to spare the economy and avoid the inevitable spike that follows any lockdown, delivered a death toll of 8000, higher than all of its Scandinavian neighbours combined.

- **Most likely to misinform: Donald Trump, President of the United States**
What to say about the man who first claimed Covid-19 would 'disappear,' then blamed China, then withdrew from the World Health Organisation, then told citizens to inject bleach, repeatedly tried to discredit his own infectious diseases lead and caught the virus himself only to continue to flaunt his refusal to adopt prevention measures? Trump has made the pandemic a partisan, political issue in the US, hampering public health efforts. Soon to be former president of the United States, to the relief of many.

- **Most likely to claim to be 'world beating': Boris Johnson, UK Prime Minister**
The decision to lock down later than the rest of Europe left the UK with one of the highest death rates in the world. In November it became the first country in Europe to pass 50,000 deaths, although the NHS has coped admirably, and initial problems with PPE seem

to have been ironed out. However, confusion over constantly changing rules, a struggling 'world beating' test-and-trace system, and allegations of cronyism in key appointments and the awarding of contracts to private companies for pandemic services, not to mention overlooking the incident of Dominic Cummings' trip to Barnard Castle, have severely eroded public trust despite Johnson earning early sympathy after a serious bout of Covid-19.[14]

28.12.20

What might 2021 hold? Ten things:

1) **Climate Comeback**
   2021 looks set to be a pivotal year for the fight against climate change. US president-elect Biden has made clear that he will move to restore the country's leadership in that regard, including by rejoining the Paris Climate Agreement to fight global warming. (Donald Trump pulled the United States out of the accord, and the nation officially left the day after the 2020 election.) A key moment for climate negotiations will come at the United Nations' climate conference in Glasgow, UK, in November. Countries will make a new round of pledges on cuts to greenhouse-gas emissions, the first since they signed the Paris agreement in 2015. The European Union and China have ambitious plans to become carbon neutral by 2050–60; scientists are waiting to see whether Biden will set similar goals for the United States.

2) **Covid Detectives**
   A task force established by the WHO will head to China in January 2021 to try to identify the source of the Covid-19 pandemic. The group, which includes epidemiologists, virologists and public and animal health researchers, will begin their search in Wuhan. The initial stages of the project will look at meat and animals sold at the Huanan market.

3) **Vaccines and the Pandemic**
   The effectiveness of several new vaccines will become clearer in early 2021. Of particular interest will be the results of Phase 3 clinical trials from Novovax and J&J, which are one shot. The roles of all these vaccines in preventing asymptomatic transmission will be of interest.

4) **Open-access Drive**
   Many eyes will be on science publishing in 2021 as a two-year open-access project organised by some of the world's

largest research funders comes to fruition. More than twenty organisations, including Wellcome in London, the Bill & Melinda Gates Foundation and Dutch national funder NWO, will from January start stipulating that scholarly papers published from the work they fund must be immediately free to read.

5) **Stem-cell Revamp**
Stem-cell scientists will be eagerly awaiting updated guidelines for research from the International Society for Stem Cell Research (ISSCR). The ISSCR last issued guidelines four years ago.

6) **Crunch Time for Alzheimer's Drug**
Regulators are slated to decide whether the first drug reported to slow down the progression of Alzheimer's disease (or not) can be used as a treatment.

7) **China's Ambitious Agenda for Space Science**
A Chinese probe destined for Mars should touch down there in February. The Tianwen-1 mission will look for water and signs of life using thirteen instruments, including cameras, radar and particle analysers. If successful, it will be the country's first exploration of the red planet and the only time a probe carrying an orbiter, lander and rover has touched down there. Craft from the UAE and the United States should also arrive at the red planet around the same time.

8) **Launch of the James Webb Space Telescope**
October will see the long-awaited launch of the James Webb Space Telescope, which NASA calls the 'largest, most powerful and complex space telescope ever built'. This will seek to repeat the success of the Hubble Telescope, which revolutionised astronomy when it launched in 1990 and has made more than 1.3 million observations since.

9) **Ripple Effect**
Radio astronomers could be on the verge of demonstrating a new way of detecting gravitational waves by harnessing pulsating neutron stars as beacons.

10) **Brexit**
Here we will see what it really means for science (and plenty of other things) in general.

29.12.20

As the UK reported >40k daily cases for the first time yesterday, all 200 million doses of the EU's order of Pfizer's vaccine are scheduled to be distributed by September 2021, the European Commission said. On the second official day of the bloc's coronavirus immunisation campaign, countries are comparing notes about how many doses each received in their initial shipments and finding cause for concern. Italy, for example, is slated to distribute some half a million doses per week, starting yesterday. However, the Italian media noted that Italy's first allotment of 9,750 doses was similar to tiny Malta's, even though countries are set to be allocated vaccines based on their populations. The commission insisted the allocations will ultimately reflect the formula by the end of the month.

The commission and capitals are also working to secure an additional 100 million doses.

Two weeks after Switzerland ordered all British travellers to quarantine with immediate effect, hundreds have fled 'under cover'.

In China, journalist Zhang Zhan, one of the first people to document what was happening in the streets and hospitals of Wuhan during the early days of the coronavirus outbreak, has been sentenced to four years in prison for 'picking quarrels and provoking trouble', a broad offence used to stifle dissidents. Zhan's reports criticised China's response to the outbreak, accusing authorities of silencing dissenting voices and downplaying the severity of it; she has been detained since May.

The UK government's plans for community testing for Covid-19 received a further blow last week when early results from students testing at the University of Birmingham and universities in Scotland showed that tests had a sensitivity of just 3% and that 58% of positive test results were false. Birmingham University used the Innova SARS-CoV-2 Antigen Rapid Qualitative Test, the only officially approved lateral flow C-19 antigen test. It was sent by the government to those universities that volunteered to test students.

The same test will be rolled out to test for the virus in asymptomatic students and staff in schools and universities around the country from January. Birmingham spent six days testing 7,500 students in a process overseen by Alan McNally, director of the university's Institute of Microbiology and Infection, who in March was seconded to set up the government's first flagship Covid-19 testing facility in Milton Keynes. They found 2 positives in 7,189 students, which scales up to 30 per 100,000 and was shocking in itself, as Birmingham has a rate of 250 cases per 100,000. Using PCR testing, the team retested 10% of the samples that had been negative with the Innova test and found 6 false-negative cases, raising the rate to 60 per 100,000.

The findings present a fresh challenge to the government's decision to purchase 20 million of the £15 tests in October, with plans to perform regular tests in the hope of picking up asymptomatic cases 'across hospitals and care homes, to test patients and residents yet more regularly to help keep people safe, and for schools and universities so we can keep education open safely through the winter,' as Matt Hancock said at the time.

30.12.20

Nearly 5 million vaccines given thus far, climbing every day, as the new variant reaches the US. Yesterday, Arcturus released disappointing vaccine data for its self-amplifying RNA technology. With approximately 200 vaccines in the works, not everyone is going to be a winner.

Particles ejected when an infectious person sneezes, coughs, sings or breathes form a spectrum of respiratory droplets and aerosols. Respiratory droplets are large droplets (>5 µm in diameter) that settle more quickly on surrounding surfaces. They are responsible for droplet transmission, which occurs when a person in close contact (within about 6 feet) inhales these droplets. Aerosols (<5 µm in diameter) are smaller, lighter particles, which can remain airborne for much longer and can be carried farther by airflow and wind currents. They are responsible for airborne transmission, which occurs when a person inhales these particles.

The SARS-CoV-2 virus, which is around 0.1µm, generally does not travel through the air by itself. For Covid, there is no substantial evidence on classic, long-range airborne transmission as there is for other pathogens such as TB, measles or varicella (chickenpox). Though aerosolised SARS-CoV-2 virus has been shown to be stable in aerosols for 3–16 hours in laboratory settings, real-world factors such as temperature and relative humidity affect the stability of the virus, while ventilation and exhaled viral load affect the concentration necessary to infect others.

Several instances of 'short-range' airborne transmission beyond what could be attributed to droplet transmission alone have been documented. These events are associated with enclosed, indoor settings with poor or improper ventilation, prolonged exposure to infectious persons and activities that increase the rate of droplet and aerosol generation. For example, an outbreak occurred in a restaurant in which directional airflow from an air conditioner is suspected to have transmitted infected aerosols from the table of the index patient to adjacent tables. And there was an outbreak during a 2.5-hour choir practice when an attack rate of 53–87% occurred, with indoor transmission likely augmented by singing.

31.12.20

As the world heads into a new year, it's the story of the coronavirus that has dominated the whole of 2020.

Italian Prime Minister Giuseppe Conte has announced the country will inoculate between 10 million and 15 million people by April 2021. The vaccine will not be mandatory. French Health Minister Olivier Véran has announced the French national curfew will be brought forward by 2 hours to 6 p.m. Regeneron announced initial Phase 1/2 data from an ongoing trial of the company's antibody cocktail (casirivimab and imdevimab) in hospitalised Covid-19 patients requiring low-flow oxygen, which showed the treatment passed a futility analysis by demonstrating a lower risk of death or mechanical ventilation in a subgroup of patients, and the Phase 3 portion of the trial will continue.

There have already been thousands of mutations of SARS-CoV-2 since the start of the pandemic, leading to hundreds of variants of the virus (lineages defined by distinct mutations that replicate and come into dominance), though essentially all of these have been relatively inconsequential to the epidemiology of the virus and for the outlook of the pandemic, except for potentially the UK variant (B.1.1.7) and a similar one reported in South Africa (501.V2). The UK variant contains seventeen unique mutations. Most tracking of the UK variant has occurred through sequencing, which is done regularly in the UK (5–10% of new cases are sequenced), but much less elsewhere (e.g. around 0.3% of new cases in the US sequenced) given lack of a national screening programme.

A new Covid-19 vaccine may be needed every year, or every two to three years, but there's uncertainty here as this will depend on the amount of antigenic variability developed in the virus, which varies according to the evolutionary rate of the virus and the amount of viral transmission occurring. As we have already seen, two important mutations in 2020 (and remembering it first entered human infections more than a year ago), I anticipate one or two more important variants causing scientists headaches in 2021. Will the vaccines remain effective? Who knows, but I doubt the virus will mutate so far (at least in the short term) as to make them useless. Saying that, as this dreadful year closes, the pandemic has claimed 1.9 million lives. When the dust has settled it is likely to be far higher.

Right, I think it's time to crack open some champagne, remember those we have lost and celebrate simply surviving 2020.

Endnotes

1 'Weekly Threat Report 17th July 2020', nsc.gov.uk.
2 Thompson, Derek, 'Hygiene Theater is a Huge Waste of Time, *The Atlantic* (27 July 2020).
3 Laborde, David, Will Martin, Johan Swinnen and Rob Vos, 'Covid-19 Risks to Global Food Security', *Science*, Vol. 369, Issue 6503 (31 July 2020), pp. 500–502.
4 Virreall, Luis P., 'Are Viruses Alive?', *Scientific American* (8 August 2008).
5 'Viruses Have Big Impacts on Ecology and Evolution as well as Human Health', economist.com (22 August 2020).
6 Garner, Paul, 'Covid-19 at 14 Weeks – Phantom Speed Cameras, Unknown Limits, and Harsh Penalties', thebmjopinion (23 June 2020).
7 Khazan, Olga, 'The Most American Covid-19 Failure Yet', *The Atlantic* (31 August 2020).
8 Thorp, H. Holden, 'Trump Lied About Science', *Science*, Vol. 369, No. 6510, p. 1409.
9 'AZD1222 Vaccine Met Primary Efficacy Endpoint in Preventing COVID-19', astrazeneca.com (23 November 2020).
10 De Ambrogi, Marco, 'I Send You A Poem From My Window', *The Lancet Infectious Diseases* (1 January 2021).
11 Bogost, Ian, 'How Will the Future Remember Covid-19? Three Visions for a Hypothetical Pandemic Memorial', *The Atlantic*, (24 November 2020).
12 Marshall, Katherine and Richard Seifman, 'Covid-19 Vaccines: Bridging Religious Divides, Engaging Religious Support', Impakter (10 December 2020).
13 Collier, Amy, 'How Dating During a Pandemic is Like Being in a Jane Austen Novel', *The New Yorker* (4 December 2020).

14 'The Covid-19 Yearbook: World Leaders Edition, bmj.com, (16 December 2020).

These are just a small handful of the sources used and referred to in the writing of this book. Apologies if we have used any publicly available sources without due acknowledgement. If this has happened please do not hesitate to contact the publisher and the neccessary adjustments will be made as soon as possible.